Industrial Arts Woodworking

# Industrial Arts

# WOODWORKING

### Revised

### By John L. Feirer

Head, Industrial Education Department
Western Michigan University
Kalamazoo, Michigan

Chas. A. Bennett Co., Inc. *PUBLISHERS*
PEORIA, ILLINOIS

# Preface

Woodworking has always been the most popular industrial arts activity. In spite of the many new courses that have been added to the industrial arts curriculum in recent years, woodworking has increased rather than decreased in popular favor. The reasons are plain, for wood is one of man's most abundant materials and is one of the easiest materials for students to work with. Articles made of wood have general usefulness, and tools and machines especially suited to school workshops are readily available.

It is with this in mind that INDUSTRIAL ARTS WOODWORKING has been written. The content has been organized to meet the needs of students at all levels of the junior and senior high school. The book has been divided into four major parts:

*Sections I-X* give instruction on how to do the fundamental processes in hand woodworking, with particular stress on student participation in shop activities. The units have been written in the informal style and have been well illustrated to utilize the visual approach. They are complete as to information about tools, materials, and the ways

to use them. They have been organized in the approximate order in which they would be needed to make larger projects. Tools, materials, and processes have been carefully evaluated to include only those which are considered important and significant as based upon recent research. The student is given an opportunity to *preview* the content in each section and to check his understanding at the end of each unit.

*Section XI* describes the use of the fundamental machine tools in woodworking. Each tool has been completely treated but without an unnecessary quantity of detail, since the book is intended for beginning students. This is done so that the instructor may determine which machines are desirable and in what order the students will be allowed to use them. The smaller types of woodworking machines have been used to illustrate the instruction, since these are most desirable for both school and home workshops.

*Section XII* deals with the related information about woods, wood products, and opportunities in woodworking. Only the most significant information has been in-

5

cluded, since there is a wealth of reference material available on these subjects and since any industrial arts course should be limited in the amount of related information presented to make sure that the program will remain an activity one.

*Section XIII* is a group of carefully selected wood projects. An effort has been made to display a variety of well-designed projects and to show how woods can be combined with other materials. Also, they have been constructed in a good range of difficulty and with emphasis on student motivation based on likes and interests. No specific directions on making each project have been included, but rather an opportunity for student selection and planning under carefully guided conditions has been given. See *Section XIV*.

*Section XV* introduces the reader to the simple upholstery processes.

As in any other book, many individuals and concerns have coöperated. These are:

# Acknowledgments

## Companies

American Forest Products Industries, Inc.
American Hardwood Company
American Screw Company
E. C. Atkins Manufacturing Company
Atlas Press Company
Behr-Manning Corp.
Berry Brothers, Inc.
Carborundum Company
Cincinnati Tool Company, The
Douglas Fir Plywood Association
Henry Disston & Sons, Inc.
Imperial Furniture Co.
North Brothers Manufacturing Company
Russell Electric Company
Reynolds Metals Co.
Sprague and Carleton Furniture Co.

Stanley Tools Div., The Stanley Works
Jam Handy Organization, The
United States Plywood Corp.
Western Pine Association

## Acknowledgments for Section XIV

Allan Gould Designs
Atlas Press Company
Brandt Cabinet Works, Inc.
Consider H. Willett, Inc.
Douglas Fir Plywood Association
Dunbar Furniture Corporation
Herman Miller Furniture Co.

## Acknowledgments for Section XV

The Rubber Manufacturer's Association
No-Sag Spring Company

# Contents

# From Wood to Product Through Processes

WHEN YOU look at a piece of woodwork such as the table illustrated in Fig. 1, you no doubt have an immense appreciation for the fine workmanship, the finish, and the beautiful lines of the piece. However, you may say to yourself, "That is too complicated for me ever to consider building."

Yet, *if you consider just the essential elements of this table, it is as fundamental in its construction as the little trays in Fig. 2.* Each is a product that resulted from

1. HERE IS AN EXAMPLE OF WHAT AN ADVANCED CRAFTSMAN can make in woodworking. This beautiful butternut table was made by an advanced woodworking student.

2. IN CONTRAST TO THE TABLE, THESE SIMPLE SERVING TRAYS are typical of what you might attempt as a first project. They involve many of the same processes needed to do all kinds of woodworking.

selecting a piece of wood and applying it to certain basic processes to shape, form, assemble, and finish it. The table, of course, involves many more pieces of wood and much more time and effort, but fundamentally it has only a few more applications of basic processes.

All products are the result of applying certain basic woodworking processes to wood. If you want to build attractive projects, you must first start with a good, raw material. A fine piece of furniture or a good project cannot be made from poor wood.

Wood is the most fundamental of all materials used by man. This raw material, used to make the finished product, is supplied in its natural form. Also, many other manufactured articles, whether they are of metal, plastic, or other substances, are first made of wood. For example, automobiles, refrigerators, airplanes, and even the telephone were first made from wood in the designing rooms of factories.

## What you can do with wood

Wood is interesting in its characteristics. It is made up of fibers or grain that cut more easily with the grain than across it. Wood itself is only the raw material. From the same piece of wood you could build a beautiful tray with a very fine finish——or a platform for your garbage can!

The only difference in the products is the difference in the basic processes applied to this raw material. These fundamentals are described in the 54 units in this book. Here is described how to do these processes by using hand tools and simple machines. By these same methods you can construct such different projects as the tray or the table.

## Three basic elements in construction

Whether or not you end up with an attractive project will depend on the following three elements: the kind of wood you select, the design of the project, and how well you execute the basic processes. Remember that, if you learn to do these basic processes correctly, you can apply them to any product successfully with desirable results. In the latter section of this book, you will find many projects, some very simple and others that require much more time to complete; but, regardless of size, each one includes these same three elements.

If you are beginning your work in wood, select your project wisely and learn to do the processes accurately and correctly; for, once they are learned, greater enjoyment in what you do will be yours and greater success will be attained through the kind of project you will be able to make.

## FOUR AREAS OF WOODWORK YOU'LL FIND DESCRIBED IN THIS BOOK

Bench or Hand

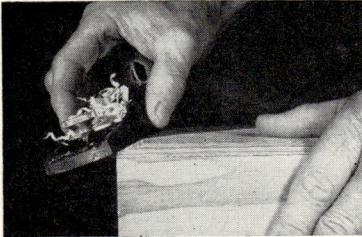

Machine

Finishing

Upholstery

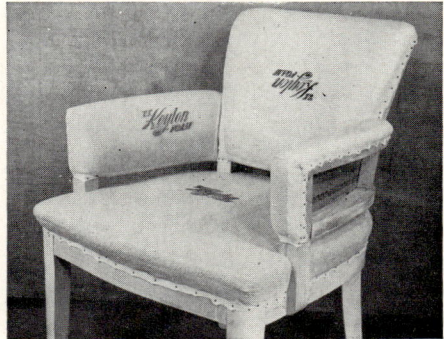

# Section I

# Getting Started in Woodworking

The first 5 steps in hand woodworking—what you must know and be able to do.

1. How to select a project: the size, difficulty, kind of wood; design and finish.

2. The difference between pictorial and working drawings: what they mean and how to read, use, and understand working drawings.

3. The importance of a bill of materials: size and number of pieces, description, amount of lumber; the grade, quality, finish, and how it is dried.

4. Being efficient: first plan, then carry out the steps needed for building with wood.

5. Taking care of the shop: how to keep the shop running well, how to keep oneself neat, orderly, and free from accident; and how to treat an accident if it occurs.

DURING your first few days in the woodshop, you won't be able to get right to the work of building a project. As in everything worth while, there are things to be learned first. For instance, a man who decides to build a house can't just start putting up the frame immediately. He has a lot of planning to do first on what kind of house he wants, what materials to use and how much of them, how to go about using these materials and a great many other questions to decide. In the school shop, we need, in addition, to become acquainted with the working conditions before we can begin. These are listed in the "box" above. Further steps are on pp. 37, 53, 84, 97, 111, 119, 148, 174, and 187.

SELECTING THE PROJECT

Since the project is the visible result of all of your efforts, it is very important that you spend considerable time in choosing a good one. There are many things to consider, among them your needs, the size of project you are qualified to make, the kind and cost of the wood, the finish, and the design.

## Do you have a need and use for the project?

The most important thing is to determine whether or not you can use the article after it is finished. Too much of what is made in the school and home workshops finds its way into a storage room, attic, or basement. There are so many practical and useful things that can be made of wood that it is a shame to waste your time and effort on some needless object.

Before deciding on one particular project, ask yourself what you need for your house, yard, for sports, or for some other activity in which you are interested. This should give you a good clue to the type of project you will find most satisfying.

You will notice that in the project section in this book the articles have been organized around different areas of interest.

## Can you build it?

The next thing to think about is the size of the project and the difficulty of building it. There is a tendency for beginners to want to make something too big, too complicated, or too difficult. While you need not "fear" any project, you must have the time and experience for it. If you choose too big a project at first, you will face so many problems that you may lose interest, never finish the project, and thus become discouraged with

woodworking. So begin by making some small article that involves few tools and processes until you have gained some experience and know how long it takes for one step; for example, building one single joint or squaring up a piece of stock.

The size of the project shouldn't be the measure of its appeal.

## Is the kind and cost of the wood satisfactory?

Another decision is the kind of wood to use and how much you want to spend. Of course, ideal cabinetmakers' woods for fine pieces of furniture are the better woods such as walnut, mahogany, oak, cherry, and maple. But the kind of wood you choose will naturally affect the cost of the project. One made of oak or walnut will cost twice as much as the same one of fir, spruce, poplar, or red gum.

Selection of woods for beginners is important also because of the difference in the working qualities of woods. When learning the first procedures, it is much easier to work with soft woods like poplar, pine, or bass. It takes a good deal more skill to do planing and chiseling on birch, for example, than on a soft wood, because birch and other hard woods tend to resist tools.

## What kind of finish will you apply?

Still another problem to think through is the color or kind of finish. If you are planning to use some opaque finish such as lacquer or paint, it is just as well to use some relatively inexpensive wood like pine, basswood, or poplar. If you plan to have a transparent finish, it will be important to decide on the color and kind of that finish before you begin. Of course, all woods can be bleached to give them a light appearance, but, generally speaking, we think of oak or maple as being lighter than walnut, mahogany, or cherry. The kind of finish you apply should bring out the best qualities in the wood.

## Have you considered the design of the project?

Regardless of the size or the kind of article you choose, the style or design should fit your needs and the kind of home in which you live. Too frequently small projects such as bookends, end tables, and similar pieces are made with no regard to the kind of room in which they will be used. Even such a project as a small watch stand can be varied considerably between traditional and modern style to fit your tastes.

## Where can you find good project designs?

After you have decided on what you want to make, you come to the question of its size, shape, and design. This requires a working drawing or sketch. There are many places to look for suggestions. In the last section of this book, there are representative groups of projects for your room and home, and for sports and other activities. If none of these satisfy, you can turn to popular magazines dealing with woodwork. Many of you may have seen some finished article in a store that you would like to copy to some degree. In other cases, you may want to design and make a finished drawing of one of your own ideas. This, however, ought not be attempted until you have had a little experience with the drawings already available.

When all of these questions have been answered and exactly the right project selected, you are ready for the fascinating job of building it. From now on you will need lots of patience and attention to detail, but the results will be well worth it.

## Can You Answer These Questions on Selecting the Project?

1. Name the most important thing to consider when selecting a project.
2. Why isn't it a good idea to start with a large project?
3. Do all woods work about the same? Explain your answer.
4. If oak is chosen for the project, a paste filler may be selected for finishing. Give several other examples of how the wood chosen determines the kind of finish that is to be applied.
5. Give several sources for good projects.

## READING THE WORKING DRAWING OR SKETCH

The working drawing or sketch is your map to follow in making the project. It will tell you the exact size of the article, the number and sizes of the pieces, the design of each part, the way in which the project fits together, and every other detail of construction and finish. Without it you would be lost, especially if you were just beginning to learn woodworking.

The importance of understanding your working drawing *before beginning to build the project* cannot be too strongly emphasized. In the woodworking industry, everything produced must be first drawn to correct dimensions in the drafting room. If you lack experience in drawing and blueprint reading, you should give special attention and study to the drawing or it will be very easy to make mistakes.

### Pictorial drawings

The pictorial or picture drawing is the kind with which you are best acquainted, since it shows the project exactly the way it looks in use. Fig. 3. This drawing, however, usually is not used for construction purposes, as it does not give true measurements or dimensions of the pieces. A pictorial drawing is used most frequently when a photograph is not available to give the builder an idea of how the completed project will look.

3. PICTORIAL DRAWING OF A MODERN TABLE. While this drawing shows what the table will look like, it would not be used for constructing the project.

### Working drawing

Drawings used for construction are called working drawings and have one, two, three, or more views that show the article from different positions. Most projects require two or three views. In the three-view drawing, the lower left-hand view is the way the project looks from the *front*, the view above that how the project looks from the *top*, and the view to the right is the *right side or end view* of the project. Fig. 4. These views give the correct dimensions of each piece. These dimensions are placed on the views to be read from the bottom or right side. If there are only two views, most frequently the front and top views are shown. Fig. 5.

TRINKET BOX
THREE VIEW DRAWING

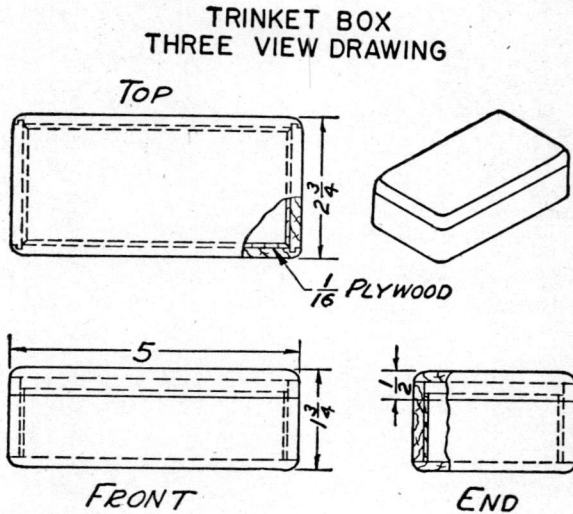

4. A TYPICAL THREE-VIEW DRAWING OF A BOX. This is the type of drawing needed for construction. (A pictorial drawing of the box is also shown with the working drawing.)

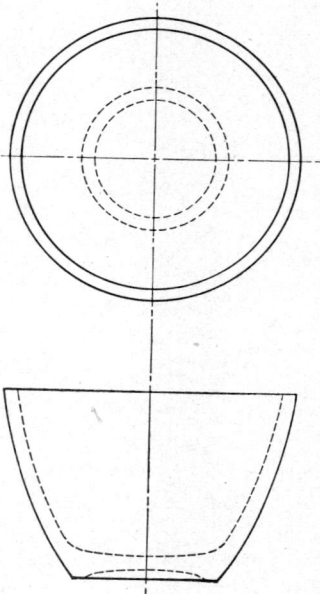

## Meaning of lines

In making a working drawing or sketch, different kinds of lines are drawn, each indicating some certain thing. An incorrect line on a working drawing is a much worse error than an incorrect direction for its construction, since a mistake on the drawing gives the user a great deal of trouble in construction. Fig. 6 shows a drawing of a lamp. In reading this drawing, these lines will indicate the following:

*Visible outline.* Indicates the major outline of the article.

5. MANY PROJECTS SUCH AS THIS TURNED BOWL need only two views.

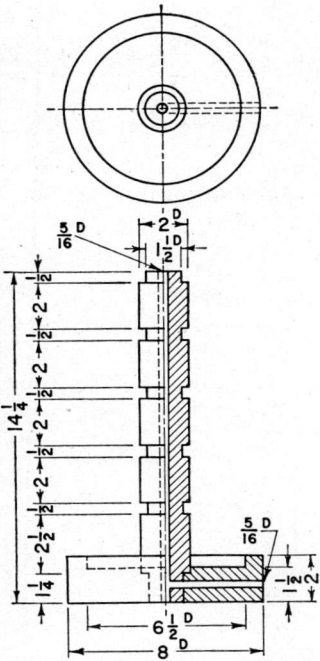

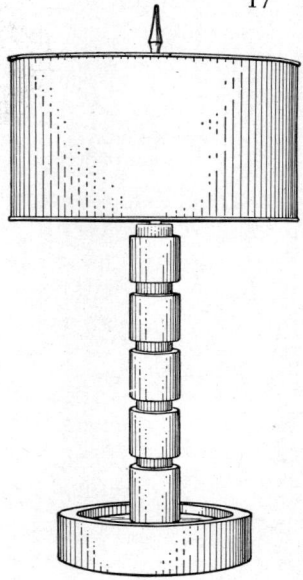

6. SKETCH AND DRAWING OF A LAMP. The drawing shows the meaning of lines. Note the different lines in this drawing and then refer to the meaning of these lines as described below.

OUTLINE ————————

INVISIBLE OUTLINE — — — — — — —

CENTER LINE ———— - - ————

EXTENSION LINE ————————

DIMENSION LINE ◄——— 4″ ———►

*Invisible outline.* Indicates invisible outline that cannot be seen from the surface.

*Center line.* Shows the center or divides the drawing into equal or symmetrical parts.

*Extension line.* Extends out from the solid lines to provide two lines between which measurements or dimensions can be shown.

*Dimension line.* Has arrowheads at either end and is broken in the center. These lines run between the extension lines and give the measurements or dimensions.

## Scale of the drawing

When large projects must be drawn, it is necessary to reduce the size of the drawing so that all of it can be put on one page. In this case, the drawing is made to scale. Frequently, for example, a drawing is made half size (6″ = 1′) and is so stated in the drawing. (If even larger projects must be drawn, a scale such as ¼″ to the foot (¼″ = 1′0″) may be followed, as in house plans.)

## Reading the working drawing

In reading a working drawing, the important thing is to be careful to observe all dimensions. When you are making out the bill of materials, you must be sure to read these dimensions correctly. Then, after the materials are purchased and you are ready to begin, equal care must be taken in transferring these measurements to the pieces of wood.

Even if a drawing is made full size, never attempt to measure it. Always use the dimensions as stated on the drawing, since the paper on which the drawing is printed may have shrunk. More mistakes are made in woodworking through carelessness in reading the drawings and in transferring these measurements to the wood than in any other place in construction.

## Can You Answer These Questions on Reading the Working Drawing or Sketch?

1. Why must you be able to understand your working drawing?
2. Name the kind of drawing that is similar to a photograph.
3. Does a working drawing always have three views?
4. How are invisible parts shown on a working drawing?
5. If the working drawing is full size, can you trace it to make the layout?

## MAKING A BILL OF MATERIALS

After selecting the project you plan to build, you will determine what materials you need in the way of lumber, hardware, and finishing supplies. This should be put down in an organized form just what and how much to secure.

## Finished bill of materials

Use a form similar to the one in Fig. 8, and, from the information obtained from the working drawing, write out a complete description of each different item. For lumber items, include the number of each piece needed, the size of the piece, a description of the item, and the kind of lumber. In Fig. 8 you will see a bill of materials for the beverage cart, Fig. 9.

Notice that in each case the information about the size of each piece is given with the thickness, width, and length indicated in that order. The thickness and width of the project are always shown in inches (") and the length is indicated either in inches (") or feet ('). For small pieces, the length is shown in inches. In listing these items, the width is always measured across the grain and the length with the grain. Therefore you may have some pieces that are wider than they are long. If you will need different kinds of wood, organize the list with pieces to be made of one kind of wood listed together. In some cases, the dimensions given on the drawing will not include material enough for the joints and this will necessitate adding to the length as needed.

## Making a rough bill of materials or stock-cutting list

The finished bill of materials must now be changed or converted into what may be called a rough bill of materials or stock-cutting list. Fig. 8. In this list you must add to the thickness, width, and length of the stock to allow material for cutting, planing, chiseling, and other operations. Usually $\frac{1}{16}$ to $\frac{1}{8}$ inch is added to the thickness, $\frac{1}{8}$ to $\frac{1}{4}$ inch to the width, and about $\frac{1}{2}$ inch to the length.

## Determining the board feet of lumber

After you have made a rough bill of materials or stock-cutting list, then figure the number of board feet in each piece or group of identical pieces. A board foot of lumber is a piece 1 inch thick, 12 inches, wide, and 12 inches long. Fig. 7. Stock less than 1 inch in thickness is figured as 1 inch. Stock more than 1 inch is figured by actual measurement. For example, a piece of stock $\frac{1}{4}$" x 6" x 4' would have 2 board feet of lumber in it, while a piece $1\frac{1}{4}$" x 6" x 4' would have $2\frac{1}{2}$ board feet of lumber.

The formula to use for board feet is:

$$BF = \frac{T \times W \times L \text{ (all in inches)}}{144}$$

Board feet equals thickness in inches times width in inches times length in inches divided by 144; or, if length is in feet, divide by 12.

## Determining cost of lumber

When you buy lumber, the price

7. NOTE THE TERMS INCLUDED IN THESE DRAWINGS. Each piece is one board foot of lumber. The length of a board is always given *with* the grain and the width of the board is given *across* the grain.

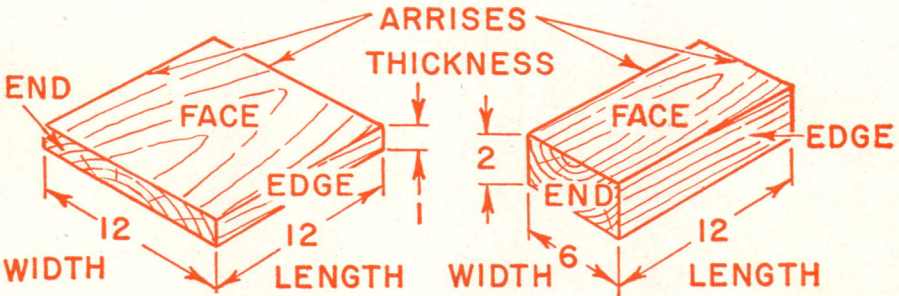

# BILL OF MATERIALS

Name_____ Date Started_____
      Last           First         Middle

Project_____ Beverage Cart _____ Date Completed_____

### FINISHED BILL OF MATERIALS

| No. of Pieces | SIZE | | | Description | Kind of Wood |
|---|---|---|---|---|---|
| | T | W | L | | |
| 2 | 1⅝ | 3⅝ | 32 | Frame Sides | Pine |
| 2 | 1⅝ | 3⅝ | 18¼ | Frame Ends | Pine |
| 2 | ¾ | 6 | 24 | Front Legs | Pine |
| 2 | ¾ | 3 | 24 | Back Legs | Pine |
| 2 | ¾ | 6 | 36 | Exterior Sides | Pine |
| 2 | ¾ | 6 | 24 | Exterior Ends | Pine |
| 2 | ¾ | 2 | 17 | Handles | Pine |
| 1 | ¾ | 22½ | 34½ | Top | Fir Plywood |
| 4 | ¾ | 8 | 8 | Wheels | Fir Plywood |
| | (Two thicknesses must be nailed together for wheels) | | | | |
| 1 | 1¼ dia. | | 30½ | Axle | Birch dowel |
| 2 | ¼ dia. | | 3¼ | Axle Pin | Birch dowel |

### STOCK CUTTING LIST

| No. of Pieces | SIZE | | | Description | Bd. Ft. or Sq. Ft. | Cost per Bd. Ft. or Sq. Ft. | Total Cost |
|---|---|---|---|---|---|---|---|
| | T | W | L | | | | |
| 2 | 1¾ | 3¾ | 32½ | Frame Sides ⎫ | | | |
| 2 | 1¾ | 3¾ | 18¾ | Frame Ends ⎬ 6* | | | |
| 2 | ⅞ | 6¼ | 24½ | Front Legs ⎫ | | | |
| 2 | ⅞ | 3¼ | 24½ | Back Legs | | | |
| 2 | ⅞ | 6¼ | 36½ | Exterior Sides ⎬ 9¼* | | | |
| 2 | ⅞ | 6¼ | 24½ | Exterior Ends | | | |
| 2 | ⅞ | 2¼ | 17½ | Handles ⎭ | | | |
| 1 | ¾ | 22¾ | 35 | Top ⎫ | | | |
| 4 | ¾ | 8¼ | 8¼ | Wheels ⎬ 7½* | | | |
| 1 | 1¼ dia. | | 31 | Axle | | | |
| 2 | ¼ dia. | | 3½ | Axle Pins | | | |

Other items: nails, paint.
* Approximately

8. THE BILL OF MATERIALS AND STOCK CUTTING LIST for the beverage cart. This project was selected as a sample because it illustrates a variety of materials and shows the need for planning both the finished bill of materials and the rough-cutting list before beginning to work.

# BEVERAGE CART

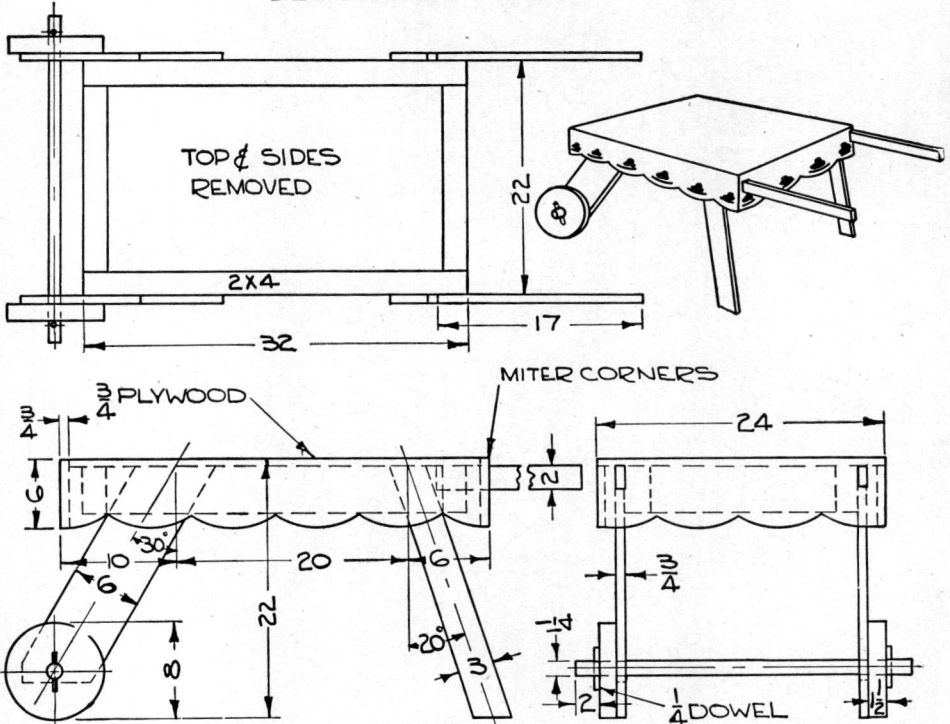

TOP & SIDES REMOVED

2X4

22

32

17

¾ PLYWOOD

MITER CORNERS

24

6

10

30°

20

6

2

22

8

6

20°

3

¾

1¼

2

¼ DOWEL

1½

**9. BEVERAGE CART.** Here is a working drawing of the project from which the sample bill of materials, p. 20, was made. Note how the dimensions of each piece are clearly indicated. This is the type of drawing that you will find for each of the projects in Section XIII. You will need to prepare your own bill of materials for any project you plan to make.

is quoted as so much per board foot, per hundred board feet, or per thousand board feet (M). To find the cost of each item on the rough bill of materials, multiply the number of board feet in each piece or group of identical pieces by the cost per board foot. When the cost of hardware items and finishing materials is listed, all items can be totaled to find the total cost of the materials for the project. Plywood is sold as so much per square foot and molding and special pieces as so much per linear foot. Prices vary according to quality.

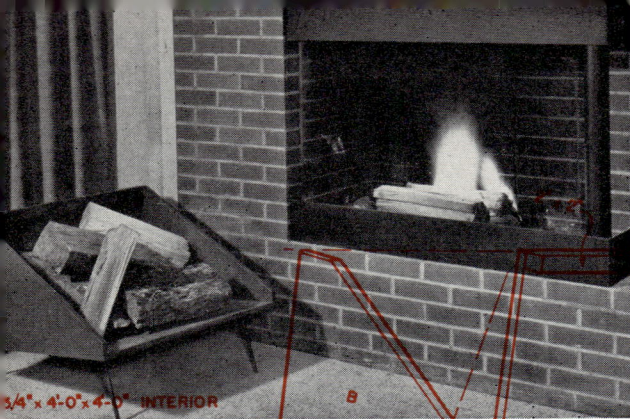

3/4"x 4'-0"x 4'-0" INTERIOR

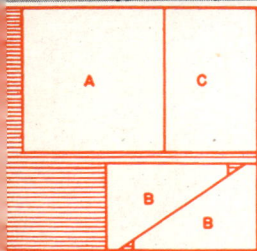

## CUTTING DIAGRAM

| NO. REQ'D | SIZE | PART IDENTIFICATION |
|---|---|---|
| 1 | 26¼"x28½" | Bottom |
| 2 | 18"x27" | Side |
| 1 | 18"x28½" | Back |
| 2½ Lin. Ft. | 2"x2" | Stiffener |
| 1 Only | ½" Diameter | Wrought Iron Frame |

Miscellaneous—6d Finish Nails and Glue
1" No. 8 R. H. Screws as required

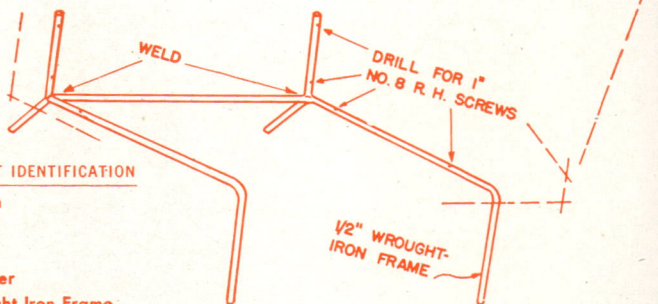

WELD

DRILL FOR 1"
NO. 8 R. H. SCREWS

½" WROUGHT-
IRON FRAME

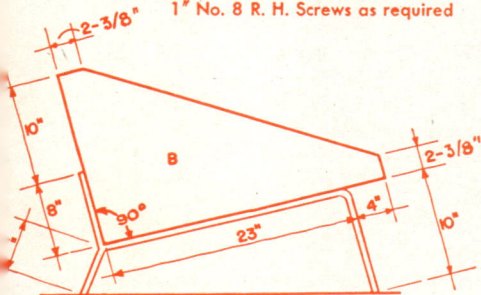

SIDE

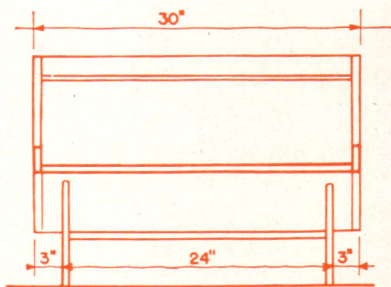

FRONT

10. **PHOTOGRAPH AND DRAWING OF WOOD BIN FOR A FIREPLACE.** The cutting diagram shows how, by efficient layout, you will use a minimum of materials. Remember that wood products are expensive and waste adds to the cost of the project without adding to its value.

22

## Lumber defects

In selecting lumber, check for these common defects:

1. A *knot* is the base of a branch that forms a mass of woody fiber running at an angle to the grain.

2. A *check* is a lengthwise separation of the wood, like a small crack or split. It often appears at the end of a board. *Honeycombing* is an area of checks that is not visible at the surface.

3. A *split* is a lengthwise break or a big crack in the board.

4. *Decay* is rotting of wood.

5. A stain is discoloration of the wood surface.

Sometimes defects such as knots add interest. For example, knotty pine is used for interior paneling.

## Figuring the standard pieces of lumber needed

After you have made out the rough bill of materials or stock-cutting list and have figured out the number of board feet required, it is a good idea to determine how many pieces of standard size lumber you will need. You may do this by grouping all of the pieces that are made from the same thickness of lumber and then making an imaginary layout of these pieces on larger standard pieces of stock, as in Fig. 10.

Softwood lumber comes in standard widths from 2 to 12 inches, increasing by 2 inch intervals, and in standard lengths from 8 to 20 feet, increasing at intervals of 2 feet. Hardwood lumber is available in standard thicknesses, but, because of the high cost of this stock, it is cut in whatever widths and lengths are most economical and convenient. If you are selecting lumber from a rack, see if you can use shorter pieces first, and, if not, cut lumber as economically as possible.

Remember, don't waste lumber.

## Points to consider when purchasing lumber and plywood

When you are ready to select or purchase lumber or plywood, remember these points (Fig. 11):

### LUMBER

1. Rough or finished. You can purchase lumber in rough (specified "Rough") or finished (specified S2S or S4S—surfaced on two sides or surfaced on four sides). Rough lumber is the type that comes just as it was cut at the sawmill. Finished or dressed lumber has been put through a planer. Of course, finished or dressed lumber is somewhat more expensive than rough lumber, but it is wise to buy this kind if you do not have a planer in your shop. When you buy finished or surfaced lumber, the actual dimensions will be less than the size indicated. For example, one inch hardwood will be about $^{13}/_{16}$ inch thick and standard construction 2" x 4" will actually measure $1\frac{5}{8}$" x $3\frac{5}{8}$". (Fig. 11)

# YOUR GUIDE IN SELECTING LUMBER AND PLYWOOD

## LUMBER

| SURFACE | GRADE | | METHOD OF DRYING | METHOD OF CUTTING |
|---|---|---|---|---|
| | SOFTWOOD | HARDWOOD | | |
| Rgh. or Rough—as it comes from the saw mill. | 1. Yard Lumber<br>*Select*—Good appearance and finishing quality.<br>Grade A—Clear. | FAS—First and seconds. Highest Grade. | A.D.—Air dried.<br><br>K.D.—Kiln dried. | Plain Sawed or Flat Grain<br>Quarter Sawed or Edge Grained |
| S2S—surfaced on two sides. | Grade B—High Quality<br>Grade C—For best paint finishes. | No. 1 Common and Select. Some Defects. | | |
| S4S—surfaced all four sides. | Grade D—Lowest select. | No. 2 Common. For small cuttings. | | |

| | | | Standard Thickness of Hardwoods | |
|---|---|---|---|---|
| *Common*—General utility. Not of finishing quality. | Standard Sizes of Softwoods | | | |
| Construction or No. 1—Best Grade.<br>Standard or No. 2—Good Grade.<br>Utility or No. 3—Fair Grade.<br>Economy or No. 4—Poor.<br>No. 5—Lowest. | Stock Size | Actual Size | Rough | S2S |
| | 1" x 2" | $\frac{3}{4}$" x $1\frac{5}{8}$" | $\frac{3}{8}$" | $\frac{3}{16}$" |
| | 1" x 3" | $\frac{3}{4}$" x $2\frac{5}{8}$" | $\frac{1}{2}$" | $\frac{5}{16}$" |
| | 1" x 4" | $\frac{3}{4}$" x $3\frac{5}{8}$" | $\frac{5}{8}$" | $\frac{7}{16}$" |
| 2. Shop Lumber—For manu- | 1" x 8" | $\frac{3}{4}$" x $7\frac{1}{2}$" | $\frac{3}{4}$" | $\frac{9}{16}$" |
| facturing purposes. Equal | 1" x 10" | $\frac{3}{4}$" x $9\frac{1}{2}$" | 1" | $\frac{13}{16}$" |
| to Grade B Select or better | 2" x 2" | $1\frac{5}{8}$" x $1\frac{5}{8}$" | $1\frac{1}{4}$" | $1\frac{1}{16}$" |
| of Yard Lumber.<br>No. 1—Average 8" wide. | 2" x 4" | $1\frac{5}{8}$" x $3\frac{5}{8}$" | | |
| No. 2—Average 7" wide. | 2" x 6" | $1\frac{5}{8}$" x $5\frac{5}{8}$" | | |
| | 2" x 10" | $1\frac{5}{8}$" x $9\frac{1}{2}$" | | |
| 3. Structural Lumber. | 4" x 4" | $3\frac{5}{8}$" x $3\frac{5}{8}$" | | |

## PLYWOODS

| HARDWOODS | | FIR (SOFTWOOD) | |
|---|---|---|---|
| Grade | Uses | Grade | Uses |
| Custom Grade | Best quality for very high-grade natural finish. Too expensive except for best cabinet work or paneling | A-A | Best grade for all uses where both sides will show. Exterior or interior. |
| | | A-B | An alternate for A-A grade for high-quality uses where only one side will show. Exterior or interior. The back side is less important. |
| Good Grade (1) | For good natural finish. Excellent for cabinets, built-ins, paneling and furniture. | Plypanel | A good all-purpose "good-one-side" panel for lesser quality interior work. |
| Sound Grade (2) | For simple natural finishes and high-grade painted surfaces. | Plyshield | A "good-one-side" grade for exterior uses where the back won't show. Used for such things as fences and siding. |
| Utility Grade (3) | Not used for project work. | | |
| Reject Grade (4) | Not used for project work. | | |

Widths from 24" to 48" in 6" multiples.
Lengths from 36" to 96".
Veneer-core panels in plies of 3, 5, 7 and 9 are available as follows:
   3 ply—$\frac{1}{8}$", 3/16", $\frac{1}{4}$"; 5 ply—5/16", $\frac{3}{8}$", $\frac{1}{2}$";
   5 and 7 ply—$\frac{5}{8}$"; 7 and 9 ply—$\frac{3}{4}$".
There are three types: Type I is fully waterproof, Type II is water resistant, and Type III is dry bond.

Many other grades for special uses in home construction are available in thicknesses of $\frac{1}{2}$", $\frac{3}{8}$", $\frac{5}{8}$" and $\frac{3}{4}$"; both exterior and interior; 1" is also available in exterior grades. Common widths 3', 4', or 4'; common length is 8'. Be sure to specify exterior grade for outside work (including boats) and interior grade for interior construction.

## 11. LUMBER AND PLYWOOD CHART.

2a. Grade of Lumber — Softwoods.

It is important to indicate the grade of lumber you want. The grading of softwoods (pine, fir, redwood, etc.) is not difficult to understand, although it is somewhat more involved than hardwood grading. Softwood is classified first according to use: yard lumber, factory or shop lumber, and structural lumber.

Yard lumber is that which is cut for a wide variety of uses, is handled by all lumberyards and is divided into two main classes, namely: select and common. The select grade is lumber of good appearance and suitable for various kinds of finishes (stain, paint, enamel, etc.). It is the kind that you would select for projects.

The select lumber is available in four grades as follows:

Grade A: practically clear and suitable for natural finishes.

Grade B: High quality, generally clear, and also suitable for natural finishes.

Grade C: Quality suitable for a good paint finish.

Grade D: Lowest select grade; can be painted.

Common lumber is the type suitable for rough carpentry. It is not of finishing quality. It is graded Nos. 1, 2, 3, 4, and 5. Only Nos. 1, 2 and 3 are suitable for good, rough construction.

Factory or shop lumber is that which is intended to be cut up for manufacturing purposes. It is usually handled only by lumberyards that do millwork or sell to manufacturing concerns and school shops. It is the grade that you would order for projects in place of one of the select grades listed above. There are two grades of shop lumber, Nos. 1 and 2 as said above. Both compare in quality to B select or better of yard lumber and differ only in the average width of the pieces. No. 1 averages 8 inches wide and No. 2 averages 7 inches wide.

Structural lumber grading is based upon the strength of the pieces and is not of particular concern to the average woodworker.

2b. Grade of Lumber—Hardwoods.

The top grade is indicated by the letters FAS, meaning firsts and seconds. This is not perfect lumber, but it will produce about 90 per cent clear stand cuttings. The next grade is called No. 1 common and select. It contains more knots and defects. The poorest grade is No. 2 common, which contains many defects and is suitable for small cuttings.

3. Methods of drying. Another thing to know about the lumber you buy is whether it is air dried (AD) or kiln dried (KD). Air-dried lumber has been dried over a long period of time by exposure to the weather. It contains a moisture content of from 12 to 15 per cent. Kiln-dried, on the other hand, has

been scientifically dried to a moisture content of about 6 per cent or less in a controlled-temperature building. Projects that are to be glued must have a moisture content of not more than 9 per cent. Therefore specify kiln-dried lumber.

4. Method of cutting. Most lumber is cut in such a way that the annular rings form an angle of less than 45 degrees with the surfaces of the piece. This is called *plain-sawed* (when it is hardwood) or flat grained (when it is softwood).

When lumber is cut with the annular rings making an angle of more than 45 degrees with the surface of the piece, it is called *quarter sawed* or edge grained or vertical grain. Quarter-sawed lumber is usually more expensive because it is less economically cut and because it is considered more beautiful.

## Plywood and Hardboard

The use of plywood is so common that you should become acquainted with the various types. Plywood is made either of *veneer core* or *lumber core*. In *veneer-core plywood*, from three to nine layers of thin veneer make up the panel. *Lumber-core plywood* has a thick middle layer of solid wood. This is commonly used for fine furniture.

The grade of plywood is determined by the quality of its two faces. The exact grading of soft and hard plywoods is shown on page 24. When you go to the lumber yard, you can usually get the grade of plywood you want by indicating "good two sides" (G2S) for the most expensive grade or "good one side" (G1S), which is good only on one side. Specify whether it is for interior or exterior use. See Pages 238-241.

*Hardboard* is closely related to plywood. It is made of wood fibers held together with a strong glue bond. There are two types—the standard, or untreated, and the tempered, or treated. In the tempering, the board is dipped in drying oils and baked. One face of the hardboard is smooth while the other is rough and looks like screening. Tempered hardboard can be purchased with evenly spaced holes drilled all over the surface. This is used for hanger boards for tools, displays, and many other purposes. The standard sizes of hardboard are ⅛" thick by 4' by 6' and ¼" thick by 2' by 12'.

## Can You Answer These Questions on Making a Bill of Materials?

1. Describe a bill of materials.
2. How is the width of stock measured?
3. Is the longest measurement of a piece of stock always the length? Explain.
4. How many board feet of lumber are there in a piece 1½" thick, 8" wide, and 10' (feet) long?
5. Suppose one kind of lumber cost $200.00 per M. What would be the cost of five board feet?
6. How is plywood sold?
7. How is hardwood lumber cut?

8. What does the term "S2S" mean?

9. Indicate how you would describe the best grade of walnut. Of pine.

10. Describe the two methods of drying lumber.

## PLANNING YOUR WORK

Before you begin to work with your tools, it is wise to plan carefully the steps you will follow in making the project. This procedure is just good sense and protects you from making unnecessary mistakes. It is followed in all industries. Like good business, you should "Plan your work; then work your plan."

### Planning a project

The idea in planning a project is to think through exactly (1) what materials you need, (2) what tools and equipment are necessary, (3) what steps you will follow, and (4) in what order they will be done to complete the project in the best way possible.

If you haven't planned your work, you may, for example, begin to sand parts of the project before all of the cutting-tool operations are completed, with the result that you will dull some of your tools. Or you may forget to make the proper allowance for the kind of joints needed, resulting in a waste of the pieces. Many such mistakes can creep into your work.

12. THE PIPE RACK THAT IS DESCRIBED IN THE PLAN OF PROCEDURE. Note the various parts of the project as you read through the plan of procedure.

## Method of procedure

In planning your job, you should decide on the order in which the parts are to be made and then list all of the things you will need to do to complete each particular part.

For example, suppose you are making a pipe rack as shown in Fig. 12. You first decide on all of the rough lumber that is required. Then you think through all of the steps in cutting, shaping, fitting, and finishing the project. In written form, this project might be as follows:

## Plan for Making Pipe Rack

Tools and materials:

Crosscut saw, ripsaw, backsaw, plane, chisel, gouge, coping saw, twist drill, hand drill, countersink, brace, rasp, sandpaper, walnut stain, wax, ruler, try square, pencil, spokeshave.

Project materials:

1 piece ¾″ x 2¾″ x 9½″ walnut for base.
2 pieces ½″ x ¾″ x 5¼″ walnut for uprights.
1 piece ½″ x 1″ x 8″ walnut for crossbar.
4 No. 5—¾″ F. H. screws.

Procedure:

1. Make a rough cutting list.
2. Lay out and cut out all pieces to rough size.
3. Complete the base.
   a. Square up stock to the finished size.
   b. Lay out the location of the recesses for the pipe bowls.
   c. Form the recesses with a gouge.
   d. Round the edges of the base with a plane, spokeshave, and rasp.
   e. Sand the base.
4. Complete the crossbar.
   a. Square up stock to the finished size.
   b. Lay out the location of the opening for the pipe stems.
   c. Cut out the openings with a coping saw or jigsaw.
   d. Round the front edge with a plane and rasp.
   e. Sand the crossbar.
5. Complete the two uprights.
   a. Square up the pieces to finished size.
   b. Lay out the rabbet at the bottom of each upright.
   c. Cut and fit the rabbets of the uprights to the base.
   d. Lay out the dadoes to receive the crossbar.
   e. Cut and fit the dadoes of the uprights to the crossbar.
   f. Round the front edges with a plane and rasp.
   g. Sand the surfaces.
6. Assemble the pipe rack.
   a. Fit the rack together to see that all joints are correct.
   b. Drill the clearance holes and countersink the uprights.
   c. Drill the pilot holes in the base and crossbar.
   d. Assemble the rack with screws.
7. Finish the pipe rack.
   a. Sand the surface with fine sandpaper.
   b. Apply a coat of walnut stain. Dry.
   c. Apply a coat of wax.

This written plan, though not always absolutely necessary, is an excellent idea. At least, you should always think carefully through each step you will take before you begin to work. You will avoid a great deal of trouble. Remember again, "Plan your work, then work your plan."

## Can You Answer These Questions on Planning Your Work?

1. What is a good motto to adopt in starting a project?

2. List the important parts of a plan sheet.

### YOU, YOUR FELLOW STUDENT, AND YOUR SHOP

We all want to do things in this life that will make us proud and happy. Many times, however, we are not willing to make the effort that is necessary to do good and satisfying work, with the result that we are miserable and discontent. There are many wonderful things that can be made of wood. We can see these things everywhere — in people's homes, in store windows, in magazines, and in exhibitions. It is possible to build these wood things; all that is required is a willingness to start right and to keep that way.

The woodshop has the tools and machines which will make it possible to possess these fine wood projects. If we are capable of taking good care of the shop and the things in it and are men enough to persevere in good working habits, we will find that, besides the possession of wood projects, we will derive a great deal of satisfaction and pleasure from woodworking and will find it a source of great interest and enjoyment.

The tools are designed in such a way as to help us with our work, and the machines also are built for certain jobs. When we treat the tools and machines with the proper

13. HERE IS THE CORRECT WAY TO KEEP YOUR TOOLS. Never pile them one on top of the other. The results you achieve in woodworking depend largely on the way in which you take care of your tools. An additional reward will be found in your health and safety. COURTESY THE JAM HANDY ORGANIZATION.

**14.** HERE'S A BOY WHO IS DRESSED PROPERLY for work in the woodshop. He is wearing a shop apron, his sleeves are rolled up, his tie is tucked in, his hair is not too long, and he has no loose articles dangling from his clothing. COURTESY THE JAM HANDY ORGANIZATION.

Horseplay, running, or playing practical jokes is not only bad but downright dangerous. After you have begun your work in the wood-shop, you will find that you resent anyone's mistreating the shop, the tools, or the machines.

## Start right, work right, be right

First, let's think of the place in which we work as *your* shop. Everyone of you has an equal responsibility for taking care of it and seeing that the tools and machines are used correctly. If *you* don't, the others won't either and the shop will become anything but a shop for work. Everything you learn in the shop should be done accurately and correctly. The best way to get your project done and to develop the ability to do things well in woodworking is to try to do everything the correct way. When you come in the shop, treat it as your own.

When you are given an instruction on how to do a thing properly, don't attempt to do it differently just this once. It's learning the hard way if you have to let a piece of wood kick back from a circular saw to strike you in the stomach with the force of a baseball bat swung by a major leaguer before you learn to respect the saw. It's no joke to see a fellow student lose several fingers because he has tried to plane too small a piece on the jointer. In the shop, we learn by doing, but that means by doing correctly.

respect and use them and care for them as they deserve to be, they will give us better service and will add greatly to our enjoyment of shopwork. Use the tools exactly as they should be used, keep them sharp and in their proper places, and they will reward you with the ease with which they can be handled. Fig. 13. When you are qualified, use the machines as they are meant to be used, keep them in good shape, and they too will increase your ability to do woodworking.

## Act the part

If you are getting ready to play in a football game, you don't dress up in a basketball outfit.

For everything that you **do**, whether it's ice skating, playing football, or working, there are correct clothes that should be worn. In the shop, all outer clothing, such as coats, sweaters, and jackets, is removed. Make sure your tie is tucked into your shirt. Roll up your sleeves and put on a shop apron. Fig. 14. This kind of clothing will protect your other clothes from dust, paint, and other shop dirt. It will also help to prevent accidents, since nothing is more apt to cause trouble than a loose tie or sleeves hanging over a lathe, saw, or other such machine. Also, if you don't have a short haircut, make sure that your hair does not fall loosely over your forehead to be caught in some revolving machine. That could scalp you faster than an Indian of 1849.

## Doing your part

Keeping up a shop requires coöperative effort, and everyone must learn to do his part in maintaining a safe and well-kept shop. Here are some of the things you can do:

1. Pick up small pieces of wood on the floor and throw them in the waste box. Some student may turn his ankle on them.

2. Keep the aisles clear by keeping projects in their proper places.

15. KEEP FINISHING RAGS IN A METAL CONTAINER. One of the more common causes of fire is the combustion of rags that have been soaked in oil or paint and allowed to lie piled together in an open place. COURTESY THE JAM HANDY ORGANIZATION.

3. Keep your tools properly arranged on your bench. Don't allow sharp-pointed tools to protrude.

4. Keep oil wiped up from the floor. Oil may cause a bad fall.

5. Don't come up behind a student when he is working on a machine. He may be startled and make a false move. If someone is using a machine, wait until he is finished. Things usually happen at this time.

6. Be ready and willing to sign a safety pledge card. Your instruc-

tor is having you do this to protect
you, himself, and your fellow students.

7. Know the fire regulations in
your shop. The shop is one of the
places most likely to have a blaze.
Fig. 15.

## It can happen here

This is a true story. Two boys
were working on a project of turning a large table top on a lathe.
They came down to the shop to
work extra time. One boy stood
by the lathe and the other turned
on the master switch. By mistake
the lathe was set at high speed. The
lathe started with terrific force, the
table top flew off, and struck and
killed the boy standing there. This
actually happened and it can happen
in your shop. Not many major
accidents occur in shops, but each
year several students are killed. Every one of these accidents could
have been prevented. They all occur
because someone does something he
is not supposed to do.

Do you plan to play baseball or
to play some musical instrument?
If so, you will need all of your
fingers. Much more frequently
than you realize, some boy cuts one
or more fingers off on the circular
saw or the jointer. You can do your
part to prevent this by:

1. Carefully watching your
teacher's demonstrations on how to
use each tool and machine.

2. Obtaining your instructor's

16. USE A TWEEZERS TO LIFT OUT
THE SLIVER CAREFULLY. Be sure
that the wound bleeds and then dress it
properly. COURTESY THE JAM HANDY
ORGANIZATION.

permission before operating a power
machine. You may not be qualified
or ready to use power machinery;
so don't attempt it until you are.
The machines may look harmless,
but they are far from it.

## An ounce of prevention

Even when working correctly
with tools and machines, minor accidents do occur. Three of the most
common things are slight cuts and
bruises, including getting a sliver in
your finger, small burns, and getting
something in your eye. None of
these is serious, but they all *can* be.
A sliver, for example, can cause
blood poisoning. Fig. 16. Your eyes
can be permanently damaged if they
are not treated immediately. Give
immediate first aid to these small
mishaps.

If it is a slight cut, allow it to
bleed freely for a short time and
then bandage it properly. Fig. 17.
Remove slivers immediately with a

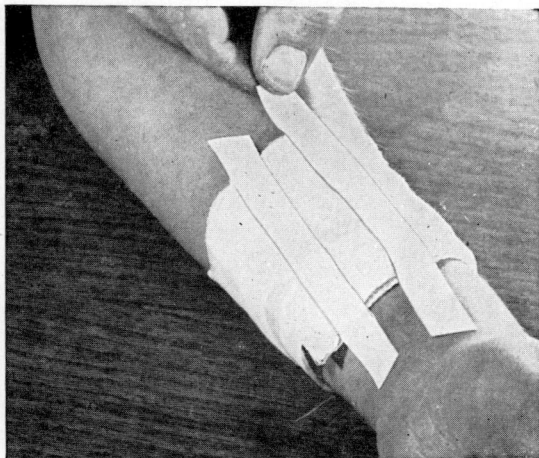

**17. THE PROPER WAY OF DRESSING A BURN, CUT, OR WOUND.** Wrap a gauze bandage around the dressing to hold it in place. Put adhesive tape across to secure the bandage. COURTESY THE JAM HANDY ORGANIZATION.

clean knife or tweezers and then sterilize the wound. If it is a slight burn, apply baking soda and water or carbolated vaseline. If a more serious burn, it should be treated by a physician. If you get something in your eye, hold your handkerchief over it lightly without rubbing, to allow your eye to water. If the particle does not come out by itself,

have a physician or nurse remove it. Fig. 18. Don't let a fellow student use such a thing as a match or toothpick to remove a particle from your eye.

## Is it worth it?

In the shop, you will be handling many different kinds of materials, including lumber, nails, screws, and

**18. EYE INJURIES ARE A SERIOUS MATTER.** See a doctor or nurse immediately to care for this type of injury. COURTESY THE JAM HANDY ORGANIZATION.

**19. WHEN LUMBER MUST BE CARRIED,** ask someone to give you a hand. Make sure that the way is clear, and then carry it as it is done here. COURTESY THE JAM HANDY ORGANIZATION.

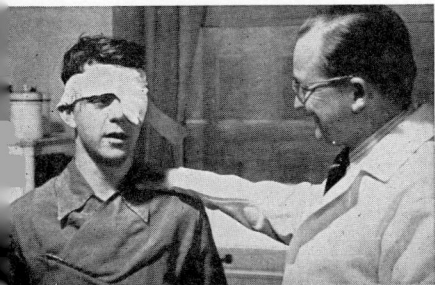

unfinished projects. You should learn to handle them all correctly. Fig. 19 shows the proper way of carrying lumber when you are taking it off a storage rack. Be careful that you lift it properly so that you do not squeeze your fingers or your fellow worker's in the process. Always make sure that the lumber is kept in a neat pile, because a poorly stacked lumber pile is a danger spot.

Screws and nails are fine for fastening work together, but they don't digest; so don't carry them

21. HERE IS EVERYTHING THAT SHOULD NOT BE DONE. This poor woodworker isn't looking where he's going, is carrying sharp-pointed tools incorrectly, and has his arms too full. COURTESY THE JAM HANDY ORGANIZATION.

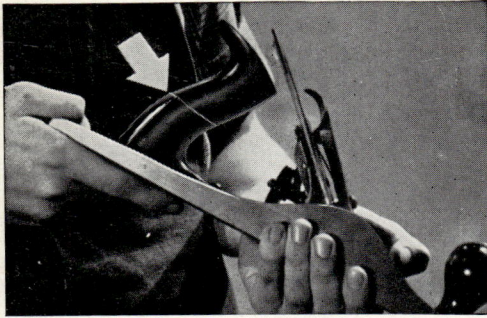

**22. CHECK YOUR TOOLS TO SEE IF THE HANDLES ARE IN GOOD CONDITION.** Cracked or splintered handles on saws, chisels, planes and gouges can cause blisters which may become infected. Then, too, it is irritating to work with a tool that has a rough handle and you cannot do a good job with it. COURTESY THE JAM HANDY ORGANIZATION.

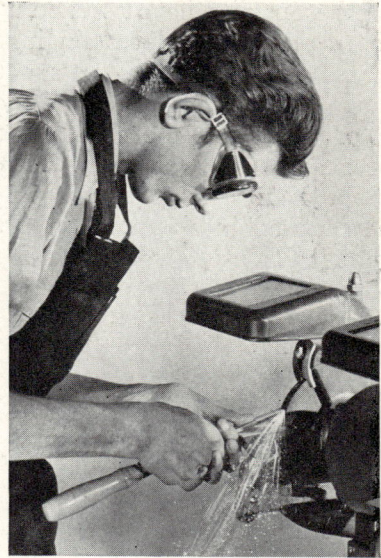

**23. HERE IS A PICTURE YOU SHOULD STUDY,** for it shows every good practice, especially protection of your eyes. You have only two eyes and money can't buy a new pair. COURTESY THE JAM HANDY ORGANIZATION.

around in your mouth. There is also a danger of infection from this practice. When storing your project, do it neatly and never place it high on a locker or window ledge where it can fall off on someone. If you have a large finished project or a machine that should be moved, lift it correctly. Fig. 20. There is a danger of rupture from improper lifting.

## It's the little things that count

Many of the tools in the woodshop have sharp cutting edges that are used for marking, shaping, and cutting stock. These tools can cause many minor accidents. Some of the practices to observe are (1) never to carry pointed tools in your pockets (Fig. 21); (2) always grind off a mushroom head; (3) always cut and chisel away from yourself; (4) never use tools with loose handles (Fig. 22); (5) always carry cutting tools with the sharp edge down; and (6) use tools for the proper purpose. Fig. 23.

The best way of working with hand tools is to follow the instructions given in the units that follow. Remember, always, the correct way is the safe way.

## Can you qualify?

Before you are allowed to drive

a car you must have reached a certain age, have had certain instructions, and be able to pass certain performance tests. This is required to protect you and others. The same precautions are observed in your shop. You cannot expect to use power machinery until you are old enough to use it safely, until you have been given proper instructions, and until you have demonstrated the ability to do so by passing a performance test. As in everything else, you must qualify before you can use power machinery.

You will find certain specific suggestions for correctly and safely using each machine in this book.

## Can You Answer These Questions on You, Your Fellow Student, and Your Shop?

1. Who is responsible for taking care of the tools and machines?
2. Why is the right attitude important before beginning to work?
3. Describe the proper clothes for the woodshop.
4. Why is long hair dangerous?
5. List five things you can do to keep the shop in order.
6. Can you tell what causes most accidents?
7. How would you treat a slight burn?
8. If you get something in your eye in the shop, should you ask a fellow student to remove it? Explain your answer.
9. There is a correct way of carrying lumber in the shop. Can you tell how it should be done?
10. List three good ways for taking care of sharp cutting tools.
11. When can you expect to use the power machinery in the shop?

# Section II

## Getting Out the Rough Stock

The second 2 steps in hand woodworking—what you must know and be able to do.

6. Getting acquainted with measuring and marking tools: kinds of rules, other layout and measuring tools and how to use them, marking tools, holding devices, how to measure and mark stock for cutting.

7. Learning about the saws: set, point, and size. The difference between ripsaw and crosscut saw and what they are used for, how to saw and do it right.

ARE YOU ready to get out the rough stock you will need for your project? You will be if you have carefully made your plans, following the suggestions in the first five units. Now comes the actual work with the wood and with the tools in the shop. You may be asked to take the wood directly from the lumber pile. However, if this is your first project, your instructor may have already rough-cut the lumber to size to help the class in getting started and to save time for other things.

Measuring, marking, and cutting are the important things to learn and do now. These things will be done over and over again as long as you do any kind of woodworking, so it is wise to learn them well in order to make all future work easier and more enjoyable. Learn these skills well enough to make them almost automatic. See "box" above. Further steps are on pp. 12, 53, 84, 97, 111, 119, 148, 174, and 187.

### MEASURING AND MARKING OUT THE ROUGH STOCK

After you have chosen the lumber for your project, it is necessary to measure and mark out the amount of stock needed for each piece listed in the rough bill of materials or found on the drawing. This requires several types of measuring tools. Using measuring tools seems very simple, but accuracy is impossible unless you take enough time and care to use them properly.

SIXTEENTH INCH GRADUATIONS

EIGHTH INCH GRADUATIONS

QUARTER INCH GRADUATIONS

HALF INCH GRADUATIONS

INCH GRADUATIONS

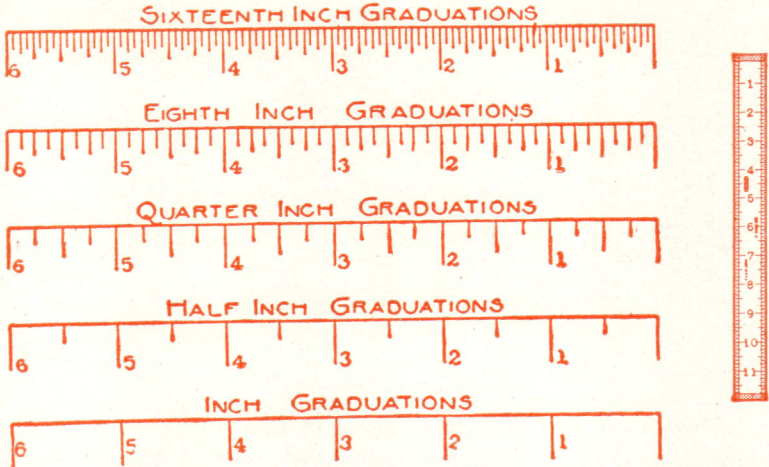

24. THE BENCH RULE IS 12 INCHES LONG and has vertical figures that are easy to read in any position. It is graduated on one side in eighths of an inch from left to right and on the other side in sixteenths of an inch from right to left.

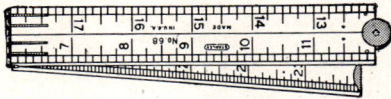

25

27

25. A 2-FOOT, FOUR-FOLD RULE that is very satisfactory for average shop use. 26. A 6-FOOT, ZIGZAG, EXTENSION RULE. It is especially useful in measuring longer lengths and is used mostly by carpenters. 27. A "PULL-PUSH," STEEL-TAPE RULER. It is particularly adaptable as a shop rule, since it will accurately take inside and outside measurements. It is flexible and can be used for many special jobs such as measuring cylindrical objects.

## Rules for measuring short lengths

There are several kinds of rules in common use for woodworking. The best one for measuring small pieces and marking short distances is the bench rule. Fig. 24. This is a wooden rule 1 or 2 feet long with

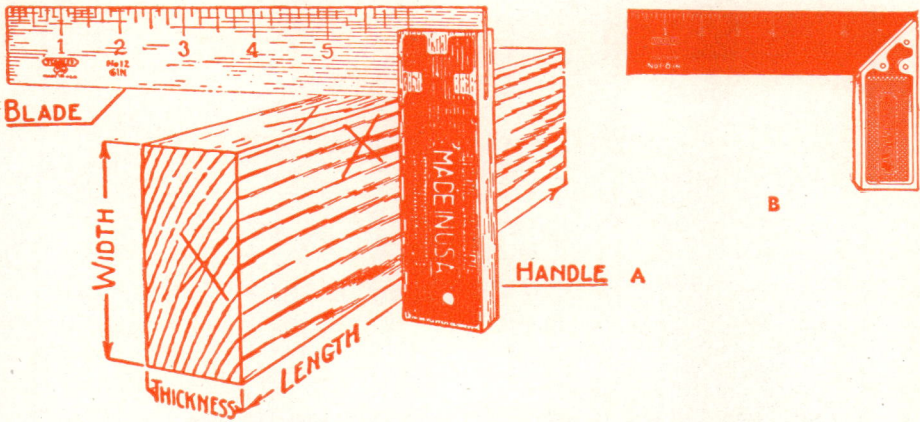

**28.** **A.** A 6-INCH TRY SQUARE with both metal blade and metal handle. This tool is accurately machined so that the handle and blade will be at right angles to each other. Therefore, never use this tool as a pounding device. **B.** A TRY AND MITER SQUARE with one edge of the handle shaped at an angle of 45 degrees. For many layout jobs, this kind of try square is better and more convenient to use.

a brass cap at either end to protect it. One side of the rule is divided in halves, quarters, and eighths and the other up to sixteenths of an inch. The folding rule is a 2-foot rule which can be folded to make it more compact. Fig. 25.

## Rules for measuring longer pieces

The zigzag rule for measuring long pieces of stock or for marking greater distances (Fig. 26) is about 8 inches long when folded and can be extended to its full length of 6 or 8 feet. This rule is the standby of most carpenters. Another rule for measuring long distances is the steel tape. Fig. 27. This tool has a small catch at its end that slips over the side of a board, making it easier

to pull out the tape. The steel tape has a standard length of 6 feet.

## Squares

The *try square*, which consists of a metal blade marked in eighths of an inch along its top and a handle of either wood or metal, should be your constant aid for all woodworking. Fig. 28a and b. The try square is used for many things, the most common being to lay out a line square with an edge, to check the squareness of two surfaces, and to test 90-degree angles. Make sure that you never use this tool for hammering or pounding because it must be accurate to do its job.

The carpenter's square (framing square) is used by the carpenter. See Fig. 29.

**29. CARPENTER'S FRAMING SQUARE.** Among all the carpenter's tools, none is so nearly indispensable as this steel square. It has a table stamped on the body of the square for figuring rafters. Many squares also contain other tables for figuring board measurements.

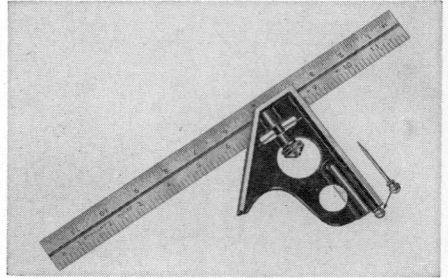

**30. A COMBINATION SQUARE** is a valuable tool for all kinds of measuring and marking.

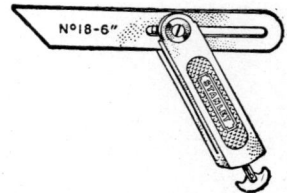

The *combination square* is a very useful measuring and marking tool. Fig. 30. This tool is called a combination tool because it is a try square, a miter square, a level, a plumb, a depth gauge, and a scriber. The combination blade has a groove cut along its length. The head slides along and can be tightened at any position.

The *sliding T bevel* is for laying out all angles other than 90-degrees. Fig. 31. It has an adjustable blade in a handle. To lay out a 45-degree angle, for instance, the adjustable T bevel can be set with the framing square as shown in Fig. 32. To set the tool to such angles as 30 degrees and 60 degrees, the bevel can be checked with the

**31. THIS TOOL IS CALLED A SLIDING T BEVEL.** It gets its name from the fact that it can be adjusted at any angle desired. The blade slides back and forth in the handle and is locked in position with a little thumbscrew.

**32. A METHOD OF SETTING THE SLIDING T BEVEL** by using a steel square. This shows the bevel being set at an angle of 45 degrees.

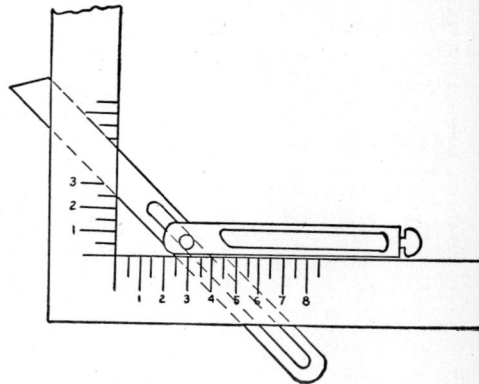

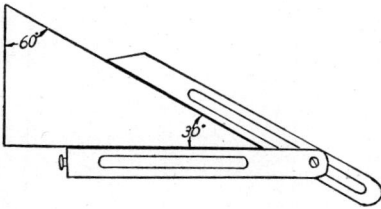

**33. USING A RIGHT TRIANGLE TO SET A SLIDING T BEVEL.** By drawing a triangle with a hypotenuse two units long and one leg one unit long, you will have a right triangle with 60- and 30-degree angles.

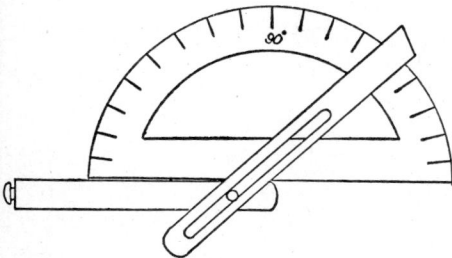

**34. SETTING A SLIDING T BEVEL BY USING A PROTRACTOR.** By this means, any angle can be quickly and accurately established.

triangles used in drawing, or it can be set by laying out a right triangle with the hypotenuse two units long and one leg one unit long. Fig. 33. For other angles, the sliding T bevel can best be set with a protractor as shown in Fig. 34.

## Marking tools

An ordinary *lead pencil* is the most commonly used marking tool because it can be easily seen on both rough and finished lumber, it can

be easily removed, and it does not scratch or mar the surface of the wood. Use a pencil with a rather hard lead for laying out fine, accurate lines. Keep the pencil sharpened in the shape of a chisel so the point can be held directly against the edge of the rule or square.

A *knife* is used for very accurate marking. Be careful, however, not to use it except when you know that the mark will disappear as the wood is cut, formed, or shaped. A *sloyd knife* (Fig. 35) is used for marking and is a very handy tool, since it can also be used for trimming a fine edge, slicing a piece of thin veneer, whittling a small peg, etc.

A *scratch awl*, which is a thin metal-pointed tool with a wooden handle, is good for marking and for punching the locations of holes that are to be drilled or bored. Fig. 36.

**35. THE SLOYD KNIFE IS A HIGHLY DESIRABLE TOOL** for layout work and also for many odd jobs such as cutting, trimming, and whittling. This knife is so named because it was used in the old Sloyd system of teaching.

**36. THE SCRATCH AWL IS ANOTHER LAYOUT TOOL** that will be very handy to have in the shop. It is used to lay out the position for drilling or boring holes.

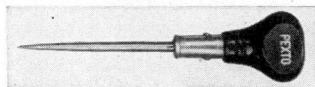

**37.** A STURDY WOODWORKING BENCH IS A PRIME REQUIREMENT for doing good work. A woodworking vise in which the jaws are lined with wood should be attached to the left front side of the bench.

**38.** THE PROPER METHOD OF LOCKING STOCK ON A BENCH TOP for doing planing, cutting, forming, and shaping. As you can see, the vise dog is in a raised position so that the wood can be clamped between it and the metal stop on the other end, which cannot be seen in this picture. The metal stop fits into one of the holes, which are drilled along the top of the bench.

## Holding devices

A necessity to doing good work is a solid workbench with a sturdy bench vise. Fig. 37. The bench vise holds work to be cut, formed, or shaped. Most woodworkers line the metal jaws with wood inserts to protect the pieces to be clamped. The movable jaw of the vise has a small, sliding section called a vise dog which, in conjunction with a metal stop, can be placed in various holes across the top of the bench for holding long, flat pieces of stock when planing, cutting, forming, or shaping. Fig. 38.

When handling larger pieces for layout, sawing, and assembling, one or two wood sawhorses are required. They should be about 20 inches high, and the best type is like the one shown in Fig. 39, which is open down the center.

**39.** THE TYPE OF SAWHORSE WHICH IS MOST PRACTICAL for layout and cutting because it is open down the center, thus permitting the sawing to be done with the blade free to move down the center of the opening.

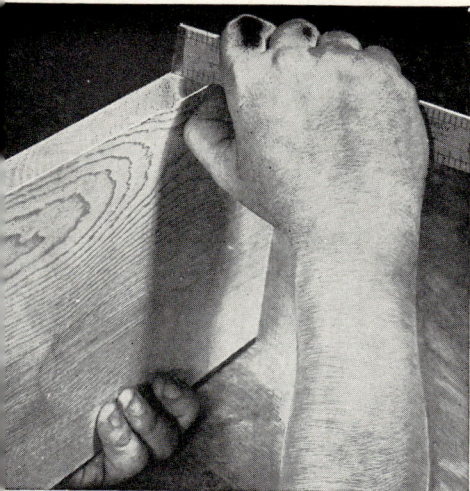

**40. MEASURING THE THICKNESS OF STOCK.** Notice that a bench rule is being used, one end of which is held directly over one arris of the wood and the thumb slid along until it indicates the thickness of the stock.

**41. MEASURING THE WIDTH OF STOCK.** The rule is held on edge for more accurate measurement. The left end of the rule is held flush with the left side of the board, using the forefinger of the left hand. The thumb is slid along the rule until the correct width is indicated.

## Measuring stock

1. Measuring thickness. The lumber selected should be checked for thickness, width, and length. Measure the thickness of the lumber

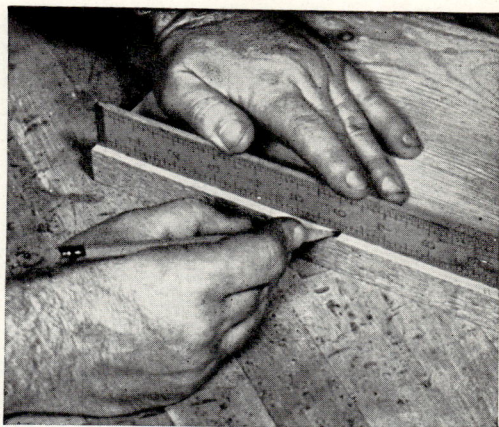

**42. MEASURING SHORT LENGTHS.** For measuring short lengths, as you can see here, the end of the rule is placed directly over the end of the stock with the rule on edge. Then a pencil is used to mark the correct length of stock required.

by holding the rule over the edge. The thickness is found by reading the two lines on the rule that just enclose the stock. Fig. 40.

2. Measuring width. Measure the width by holding the left end of the rule (or the inch mark) on one edge of the stock and sliding your thumb from the right to the left along the rule until the width is indicated. Fig. 41.

3. Measuring short lengths. Select the end of the stock from which the measurement is to be taken and check its squareness by holding a try square against the truest edge. Also, make sure that the end is not split or checked. If it is, the end of the wood should be squared off and cut and the measurement taken from the sawed end. If a short length of stock is needed, hold the rule on edge and mark the length with a pencil or knife. Fig. 42.

4. Measuring longer lengths. For measuring longer distances use a zigzag rule or a steel tape, as they will eliminate the measuring error that often results from moving a short rule several times. Fig. 43. Make a small mark at the point to be squared.

## Marking stock for cutting to length

1. Marking lengths on narrow lumber. If rather narrow lumber is being marked for cutting, hold the handle of the try square firmly

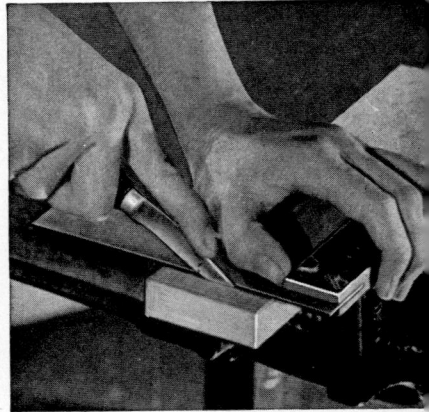

against the truest edge of the stock. Square off a line. Figs. 44, 45, 46.

**46. ANOTHER WAY TO MARK ACROSS THE FACE OF THE STOCK.** This time a pencil is the marking tool. Make sure that if you do use a pencil, it is hard and sharpened to a point that will make a thin, clean line on the surface of the wood.

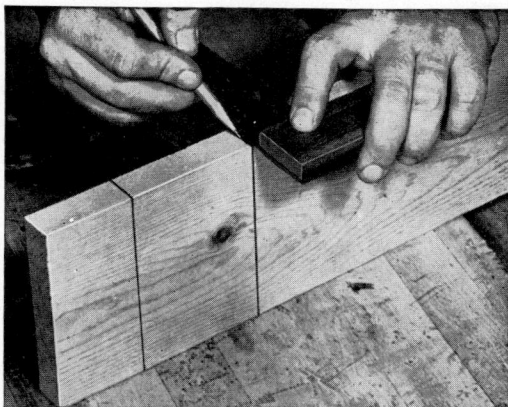

**47. ON WIDE STOCK, THE FRAMING SQUARE IS USED TO MARK THE LINE.** The blade has been tipped slightly and is being held firmly against the edge of the stock while a knife is used to mark across the face of the work.

**2. Marking lengths on wider lumber.** Use a framing square on wider stock. Since the framing square is uniform in thickness, the blade should be tipped slightly and then held firmly against the truest edge while the mark is made across

**48. SQUARING THE LINES ACROSS THE EDGES OF THE STOCK.** It is a good idea to mark a line down the edge of the stock, as shown, since it will help you to make an accurate saw cut.

**49. FREQUENTLY IN WOODWORKING,** several pieces of the same length are required. It is easier and more convenient to mark them all at the same time, as shown here. Make sure that you hold the try square over the ends to align them before marking the correct length.

the stock. Fig. 47. Sometimes it is a good idea to square a line across the edges with the face line. This can be done with a try square as shown in Fig. 48.

3. Marking duplicate parts. If a group of pieces must be measured and marked out to equal lengths, place them side by side. Make sure that the ends are aligned by holding a try square over the ends, and then move the try square to correct length to mark the pieces. Fig. 49.

## Measuring and marking stock for cutting to width

Determine the width of stock required. Hold the rule at right

50. MEASURING THE CORRECT WIDTH OF STOCK, using a zigzag rule. On narrower widths, a try square is the marking tool. Place the thumb of your left hand on the correct width and hold this firmly against one edge of the stock while you mark the width with a sharp pencil.

51. AFTER SEVERAL POINTS HAVE BEEN LOCATED, a straightedge is held over these points and a knife or pencil used to mark the correct width. In doing this, be careful that the straightedge does not slip. COURTESY THE JAM HANDY ORGANIZATION.

52. LAYING OUT THE WIDTH OF STOCK by holding a rule in your left hand and a pencil held against the end of the rule, sliding both along at the same time.

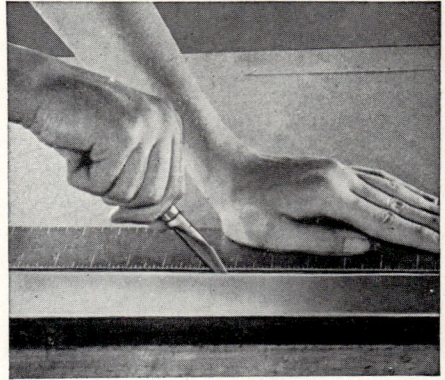

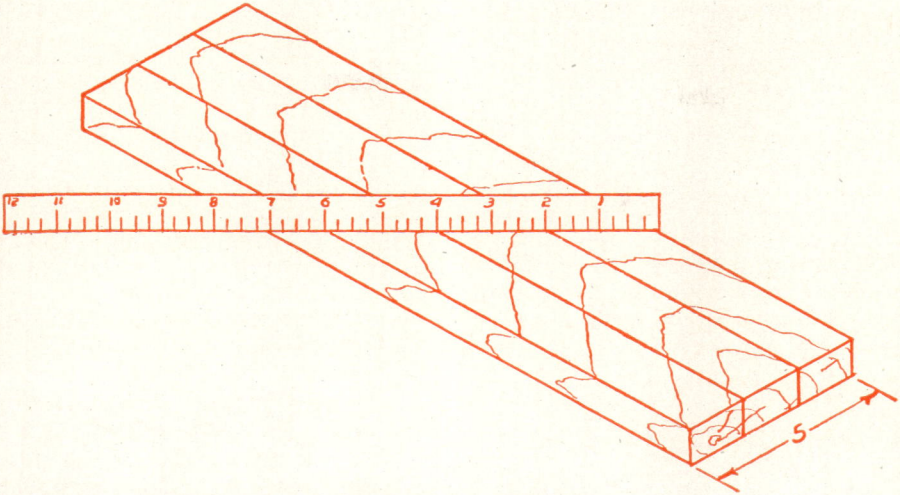

**53.** THE PROPER METHOD OF DIVIDING BOARDS into several equal parts. This piece is 5-inches wide and is to be divided into three equal parts. The end of the rule is held over one edge of the board and the rule shifted at an angle until the 6-inch mark is over the other edge. Then, by placing a mark at the 2- and 4-inch points, the board is divided equally into three parts.

angles to the truest edge of the stock and measure the correct width. Fig. 50. This can also be done by using a try square. Do this at several points along the stock; then hold a straightedge over these points and connect them. Fig. 51. Sometimes a framing square is used to measure the width of stock needed. Another method of marking the width of rough stock is to hold a rule to the correct width between the thumb and forefinger as it is guided along the truest edge of the stock with a pencil held against the end of the rule. Fig. 52.

## Dividing a board into equal parts

To divide a board into two or more equal parts, hold a rule at an angle across the face of the stock until the inch marks evenly divide the space. Fig. 53. The board must be true along both sides for this to work.

## Can You Answer These Questions on Measuring and Marking Out the Rough Stock?

1. Name two rules used for measuring short distances.

2. The carpenter usually depends on what rule?

3. Give the parts of a try square. List three uses.

4. When is a framing square used in the woodshop?

5. The sliding T bevel can be used in a way that no other layout tool can. What is this use?

6. Why is the lead pencil the most commonly used tool for marking on wood?

7. What kind of knife is best for marking wood before making a fine cut?

8. How many sixteenths in 1¼ inches?

9. The scratch awl is a marking tool but is also used for what other job?

10. Why is the bench vise frequently lined with wood inserts?

11. To secure the most accurate measurement, should the rule be held flat or on edge?

12. For measuring longer lengths, why is it better practice to measure with a zigzag rule or steel tape than with a bench rule?

13. Why do you square a line across a board with a try square or framing square rather than with a rule?

14. Describe the method for dividing a board into equal parts.

54. A HIGH-QUALITY HANDSAW. It is always wise practice to buy a good grade, and, with proper maintenance, it will give years of service.

## CUTTING OUT ROUGH STOCK

For cutting stock into unfinished pieces you will need either a ripsaw or crosscut saw and sometimes both. Fig. 54. If a circular saw is available, much time can, of course, be saved by using it to cut out rough stock. (See Machine Woodworking.)

55. AN ENLARGED VIEW OF A CROSSCUT SAW-BLADE SECTION, showing the knifelike shape of the teeth. Looking at the blade from the top, the teeth are bent alternately to left and right.

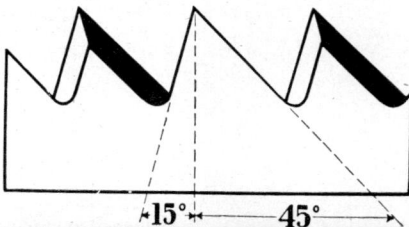

## Saws

There are several things that you should know about saws. The saw used for cutting across grain is the crosscut and the one for cutting with the grain is the ripsaw.

The *crosscut* saw. The teeth of the crosscut saw are shaped like little knife blades. The teeth are bent alternately to right and left. Fig. 55. This is called the "set" of the saw. When you use a crosscut saw with the proper set, the outside edges of the teeth cut the small fibers on either side and the center of the saw removes these fibers to form the saw kerf. Fig. 56. The teeth are

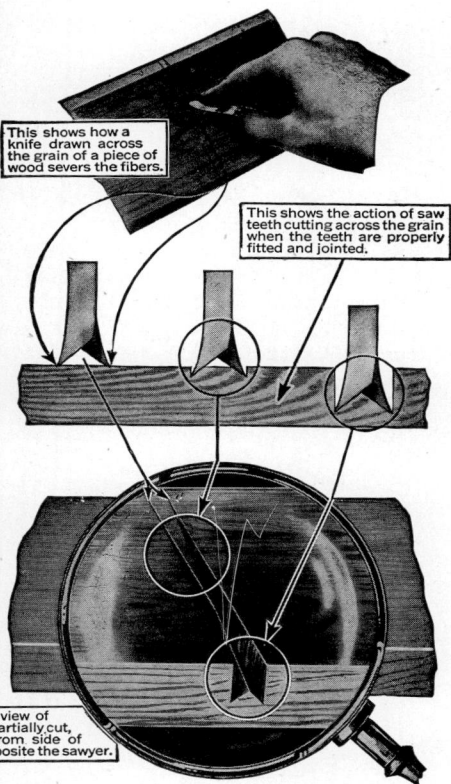

This shows how a knife drawn across the grain of a piece of wood severs the fibers.

This shows the action of saw teeth cutting across the grain when the teeth are properly fitted and jointed.

view of partially cut, from side of opposite the sawyer.

56. HOW A CROSSCUT SAW PER-FORMS ITS CUTTING OPERA-TION.

bent this way to make them wider than the saw itself, thus preventing buckling or scraping.

Crosscut saws come in many different lengths, but the easiest size to handle is one about 20 to 26 inches long. If you are cutting rather wet, green wood, use a saw with about five or six points to the inch. There is always one more point to the inch than there are

teeth, as you can see in Fig. 57. For hard, dry wood, a finer saw with perhaps seven, eight, or nine points to the inch is best.

The *ripsaw*. The ripsaw, for cutting with the grain, has chisel-like teeth that form the saw kerf by cutting the ends of the fibers. Fig. 58. A ripsaw used for ordinary woodworking ought to be 24 to 26 inches long with 5½ points per inch.

Sawing long stock to length

1. Laying out the cutting line. If the stock must be cut from stock

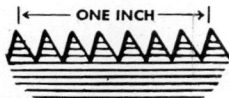

ONE INCH

57. THERE IS ALWAYS ONE MORE POINT TO THE INCH than there are teeth. The fewer the number of points to the inch, the rougher the cut.

58. A. RIPSAW TEETH ARE DE-SIGNED TO CUT WITH THE GRAIN. The teeth appear as a series of chisel edges. B. When you look at the top of a ripsaw the teeth appear to form rows of chisel edges. Note that the teeth are filed straight across.

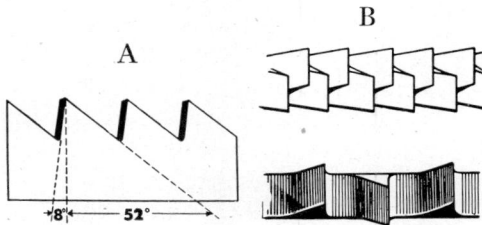

A          B

8°   52°

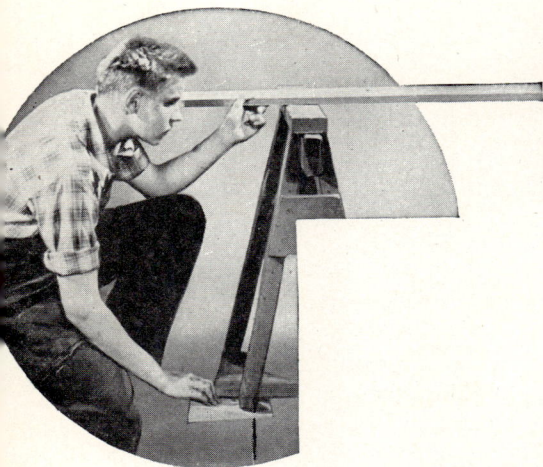

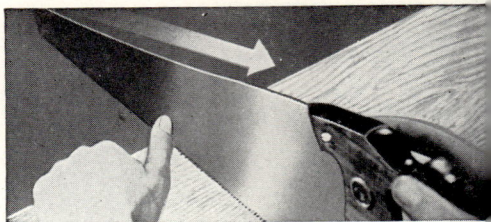

59. **IF LONG STOCK IS BEING CUT,** place it over two sawhorses with the cutting line extending just beyond one of the sawhorses. Never try to make a cut in between the supports. COURTESY THE JAM HANDY ORGANIZATION.

8 to 16 feet long, the board should be laid across two sawhorses. Mark the cutting line and place this point beyond the top of one of the sawhorses. Fig. 59.

2. Beginning the cut. Place your left knee over the board to hold it secure. Then grasp the handle of the saw with the forefinger straight out on one side of the handle and the thumb and other fingers clamped tightly around the handle opening. Hold the saw at an angle of about 45 degrees to the stock. Put your left thumb against the smooth surface of the blade to guide the saw in starting. Fig. 60. Start the saw near the handle and draw up on it to begin the kerf. Make sure the cut is started just outside the measuring line, to keep the kerf in the waste stock.

3. Precautions to take in begin-

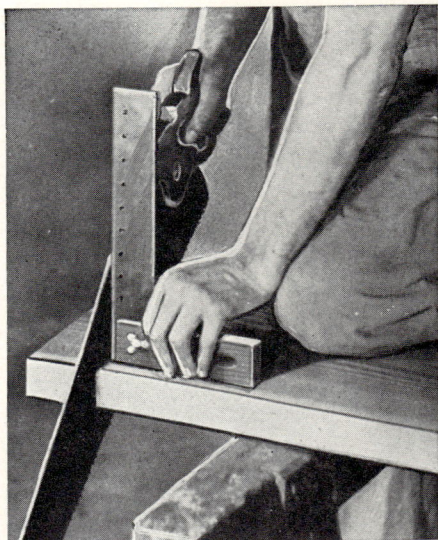

61. **A WAY OF KEEPING THE SAW CUT SQUARE** with the face of the board. The operator places the handle of the try square firmly on the face of the wood and then slides it along until the blade of the try square comes in contact with the blade of the saw, to check it for squareness.

ning the cut. If you try to begin the cut on the downward stroke immediately, you may find that the saw jumps out of place to cut your hand or nick the wood. Therefore draw up on the saw once or twice before

50

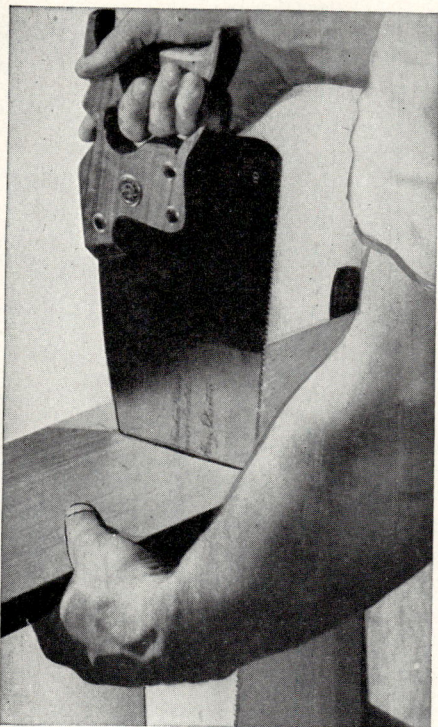

**62. TAKING THE LAST FEW CUTS IN SAWING OFF A BOARD.** Notice that you should hold the stock to be cut off in your left hand while sawing with your right hand. In this way, the wood will not crack off before the saw kerf is completed. COURTESY THE JAM HANDY ORGANIZATION.

you begin the cutting. When cutting, establish a steady, even, rhythmic movement. Do not force the saw. If it is sharpened properly, its weight is enough to make it cut correctly.

4. Making the cut. Make sure that you are cutting square with the surface of the board. If you are a beginner, you should hold a try square against the side of the saw blade to check it. Fig. 61. As you saw, watch the line and not the saw itself. Once in awhile, blow the sawdust away from the line so you can see it. If the saw starts to go askew, twist the handle slightly to get it back on the line. When you have cut almost through the board, take hold of the end of the board to be cut off while you make the last few cuts. This will prevent the board from splitting off before the saw kerf is complete. Fig. 62.

## Cutting short pieces of stock to length

If you are working with short lengths of stock, you will be cutting them to length with the work held in a vise. Place the stock in the vise in a flat position with the cutting line protruding just a little bit from the left side of the vise. Hold and start the saw in the same way as before. You will find that you do a good job if you follow the same directions given above.

## Cutting long pieces of stock to width

Sometimes the lumber selected is too wide for your purposes and it is necessary to cut it to width. For cutting along the grain of the wood you will use a ripsaw. If the stock is long, place it over two sawhorses. Because the teeth are different from the crosscut saw, the saw should be held at an angle of about 60 degrees.

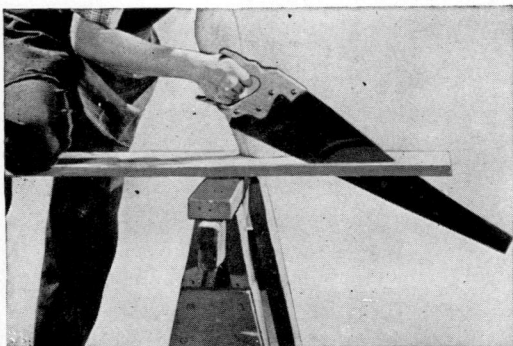

**63. RIPPING A BOARD WITH THE WORK HELD OVER SAW-HORSES.** As the cut progresses, place a little wedge at the beginning of the saw kerf to hold it open. COURTESY THE JAM HANDY ORGANIZATION.

As you cut a long piece of stock to width, the saw kerf may close in behind the saw and cause binding. Fig. 63. Placing a little wedge at the beginning of the saw kerf will keep it open.

## Cutting short lengths to width

If a short length is to be ripped, place it in the vise as in Fig. 64. The sawing should not be done too

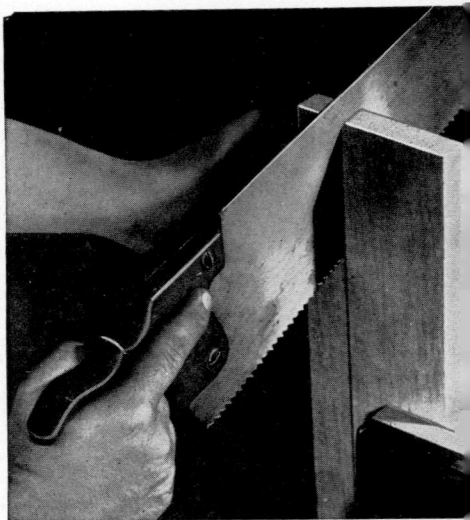

**64. RIPPING WITH THE WORK HELD IN A VISE.** Notice that the saw is held at an angle of about 60 degrees to the work. Always do the sawing close to the vise jaws, so that the board will not vibrate.

far above the surface of the vise, because this causes too much vibration. Begin with the board near the top of the vise and move it up a little at a time as you continue your work.

## Can You Answer These Questions on Cutting Out Rough Stock?

1. There are two kinds of handsaws. Name them and tell what the parts of a handsaw are.
2. Why must a saw have the proper set in order to cut correctly?
3. A saw with five points to the inch would be best for cutting wet, green wood. Why?
4. What does a ripsaw tooth resemble?
5. If you could have only one saw for your shop, which one would you choose?
6. Why shouldn't the cutting line on a long board be placed between the saw-horses?

7. To start a cut, should you push down or draw up on the saw? Why?
8. At what angle to the stock should you hold the crosscut saw?
9. Which should you watch, the action of the saw or the cutting line?
10. What is a saw kerf?
11. Why does the crosscut saw have knifelike teeth?
12. When a saw binds or sticks, what is the most likely cause?
13. Tell how you can prevent the board from splitting off just before the saw cut is completed.

# Section III

# Completing the Squaring Operations

The third 7 steps in hand woodworking—what you must know and be able to do.

8. Everything about a plane: its parts, the many kinds and how they differ, why we keep the iron sharp, how to put a plane together so it is ready to work.

9. The first surface: how to tell if it has warp or wind and how to remove it, locking the board in place, how to plane the surface true and smooth, and how to check it.

10. Working to width and thickness: which edge to choose first, what plane to choose, holding the stock, using a marking gauge, how to hold the plane correctly, how to do planing, and planing the stock to thickness and width.

11. Learning to cut end grain: why it is more difficult to cut, cutting with the block plane, how to plane end grain, how to check.

12. Making a very fine saw cut: how to use the backsaw, the dovetail saw, the handy bench hook; how to do crosscutting and ripping with a backsaw.

13. Gluing up stock: how wood is prepared for gluing, how to know what glue to select, clamps, different ways of joining wood with glue, and how to do the gluing.

14. Correct procedure for squaring up stock: the three different methods that can be followed.

$Y$ou won't find planing wood the easiest or pleasantest part of woodworking, but it is something that must be done well, since every piece of wood you use must be true, smooth, and square on two or more surfaces before further work such as decorating, drilling, or making joints can be done.

Lumber sometimes comes to the shop exactly as it is cut in the saw-mill, with all surfaces rough. More often, however, stock has been run through a planer and the sides are surfaced or dressed. Even these surfaces must be planed a little by hand to make sure that they are true and smooth.

Often, stock will not be large enough in either thickness or width

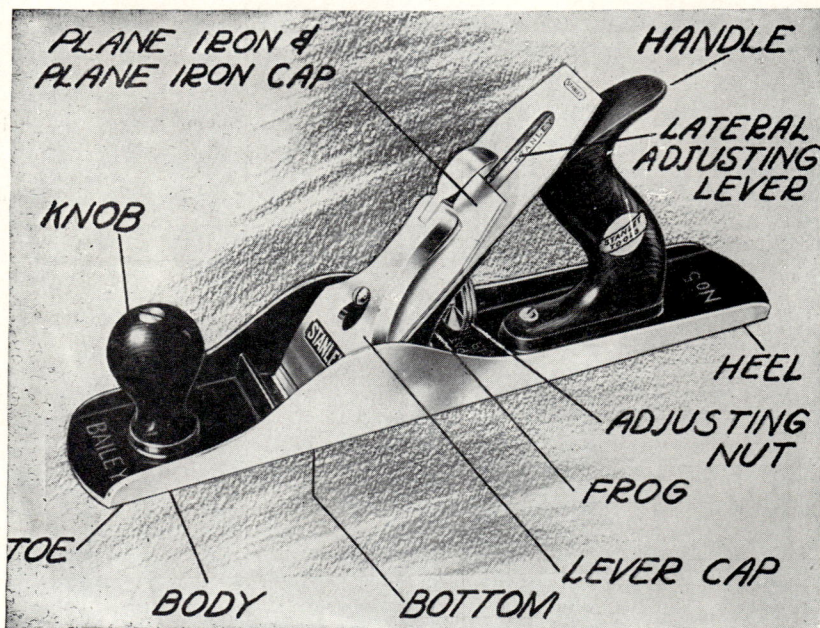

65. STUDY THE PARTS OF THIS PLANE, as you will need to know them when learning to use it.

to make parts needed, and then you will need to glue up the stock to form these larger pieces before completing the squaring operations. See "box" above. Further woodworking steps are on pp. 12, 37, 84, 97, 111, 119, 148, 174, and 187.

## ASSEMBLING AND ADJUSTING A PLANE

After the pieces are sawed out, they are rough and need to be planed smooth. Even if the lumber is S2S (surfaced two sides), the sides must be dressed with a plane. You will need to develop consider-

able skill in using a plane before you can turn out satisfactory work.

## Parts of a plane

The plane is perhaps the most complicated hand woodworking tool you will use and requires more care, attention, and adjustment than any other tool. Therefore it is well to get acquainted with some of the common names of the parts so that you can identify them. Fig. 65 is an illustration of the major parts.

The body of the plane is made of cast steel. The *base* or *bottom*, as it is sometimes called, is either

smooth or ribbed. There is no difference between these two planes,
except that some woodworkers feel
that the plane with the ribbed base
works a little better.

Right behind the opening in the
plane there is a *frog* that provides
the support for the plane iron. This
frog contains two adjustments, a
*brass knurled nut*, which adjusts
the depth of cut or regulates the
thickness of the shavings, and a long,
slender lever called the *lateral adjusting lever*, which provides for
the sidewise adjustment of the
cutter.

The *double plane* iron consists
of the plane iron itself, sometimes
called the cutter, and the plane iron
cap. The plane iron fits over the
frog, held firmly with a *lever cap*.

## Kinds of bench planes

There are three common types
of bench planes, all of which are
very similar. The primary difference
is in their length. Fig. 66a, b, and c.
The jack plane, which is used most
commonly, is from 11½ to 15 inches
long. This tool is for all types of
general planing. The smooth plane
is the same, except that it ranges
from 7 to 9 inches in length. The
fore and jointer planes are much
longer, from 18 to 24 inches in
length, and are especially useful for
planing a long edge straight, as
when fitting large doors. They are
used frequently for jointing long
pieces of stock before gluing them up.

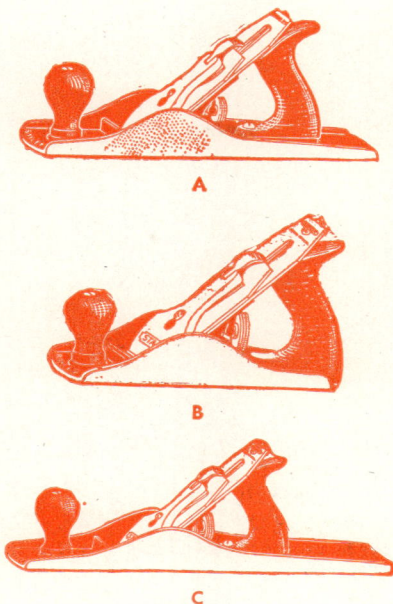

66.  **THREE TYPES OF HAND PLANES.**
A. This is a jack plane, which has a
bed 14 or 15 inches long. It can be used
to true the edges of boards and for
general planing. B. This is a smooth
plane and can be purchased in lengths
from 7 to 9 inches. It is good for
smoothing and finishing work for which
a light plane is desired. C. These are
the fore and jointer planes and are the
type used to obtain a true surface on
long edges for gluing up stock.

## Testing a plane iron for sharpness

Check the plane iron or cutter
to make sure that it is sharp. One
way to do this is to sight along the
edge. A properly sharpened blade
will not reflect any light. Another
method is to cut a piece of paper
with it. Fig. 67. It can also be

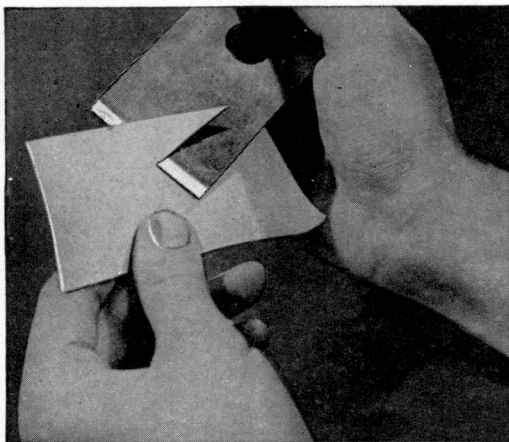

**67.** ONE METHOD OF CHECKING A PLANE FOR SHARPNESS. The plane iron blade will cut paper when it is the proper sharpness. COURTESY THE JAM HANDY ORGANIZATION.

tested by allowing the cutting edge to rest on the thumbnail and then pushing it lightly. If the blade tends to cling to the nail, it is sharp; but if it slides easily it needs sharpening

or whetting. You should never use a dull plane iron. Sharpen it before you assemble the plane. (See the unit on sharpening hand tools.)

## Assembling the double plane iron

Hold the iron in your left hand in a vertical position with the bevel away from you. Place the plane iron cap at right angles to the plane iron and drop the setscrew into the plane iron through the large opening. With the plane iron cap still at right angles, slide it back and away from the cutting edge. Turn the plane iron cap parallel to the plane iron and slip it forward until it is about $\frac{1}{16}$ inch away from the cutting edge for rough work and up to $\frac{1}{32}$ inch for finished work. Fig. 68. Make sure that you do not injure the cutting edge of the plane iron by shoving the cap too far forward. Tighten the setscrew firmly.

**68.** THE CORRECT METHOD OF ASSEMBLING A DOUBLE PLANE IRON: a. Hold the plane iron in your left hand, with the bevel side down. Place the plane iron cap at right angles to it and drop the set screw through the large opening. b. Slide the plane iron cap back as far as it will go and then, c, turn it so it is parallel to the plane iron. d. Move the plane iron cap to within about $\frac{1}{16}$ inch of the cutting edge. Then tighten the set screw with a screw driver or the lever cap.

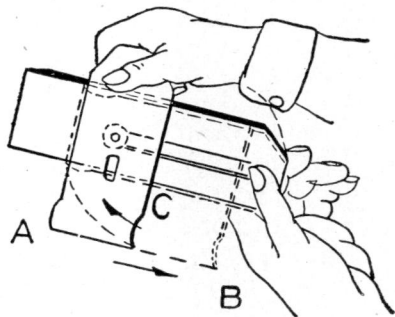

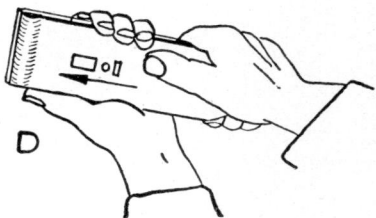

The plane iron cap serves two purposes. It helps to stiffen or strengthen the plane iron and serves as a chip breaker.

## Inserting the plane iron in the plane

Insert the double plane iron in the plane with the bevel side down. There are several things that you must watch when doing this. Fig. 69. First, don't hit the cutting edge on the body of the plane as you insert it over the frog; second, make sure that the slot in the plane iron cap fits over the little Y adjustment; and third, check to see that the roller on the lateral adjustment slips into the slot of the plane iron.

Next pull the little thumb adjusting cam on the lever cap up at right angles (Fig. 65) and then slip

70. ADJUSTING THE PLANE. Hold the plane with the bed or bottom at eye level. Turn the knurled brass screw until the plane iron just appears. Move the lateral adjustment from left to right until the plane iron is parallel to the bed. COURTESY THE JAM HANDY ORGANIZATION.

the lever cap over the lever cap screw on the frog. Push the thumb-adjusting cam down to fasten the plane iron securely in the plane. If you find it must be forced, it is probably necessary to unscrew the lever cap screw just a little bit or, if it is too loose, to tighten it a little.

## Adjusting the plane

The plane should be adjusted before beginning the cutting and again several times while the planing is being done. To make the first adjustment, turn the plane upside down with the bottom about eye level. Turn the brass knurled nut until the plane iron appears just beyond the bottom of the plane. Then, with the lateral adjustment lever, move the blade to one side or the other until it is parallel to the bottom. Fig. 70.

69. INSERTING THE DOUBLE PLANE IRON IN THE PLANE. Be extremely careful in doing this to keep the cutting edge from becoming nicked.

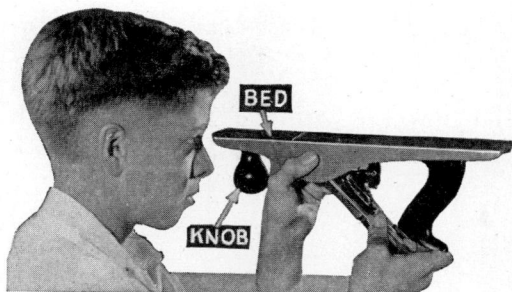

The experienced woodworker then tries the plane on a piece of scrap stock to see how it cuts, adjusting it to the chip he wants. For rough planing and when much stock is to be removed, set the plane deeper. When you are truing up a surface and making it smooth, a light cut that forms a feathery shaving is most desirable.

## Can You Answer These Questions on Assembling and Adjusting a Plane?

1. Name the important parts of a plane. Why is it necessary to know these parts?
2. Name the three common types of bench planes. What is the major use of each?
3. Why do you suppose the jack plane is best for the school shop?
4. Tell three ways of testing the sharpness of the plane iron.

5. What is the purpose of the plane iron cap?
6. To do finished planing, how far should the cap be set from the cutting edge? How far for rough work?
7. Describe in detail the steps to follow in fastening a plane iron in a plane.
8. Tell how to make the depth adjustment on a plane.

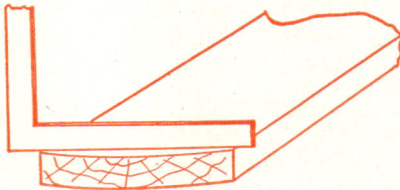

71. WARP is a bow or cup in the wood.

## PLANING A SURFACE

The first surface that you choose to plane should be the best flat surface of the piece. It should be free of imperfections and should be the side with the most interesting grain, since it will be an exposed surface.

### Inspecting the surface for warp and wind

A woodworker with experience can tell if a board is warped by sighting along it. A beginner

can check warpage with a straight-edge or the blade of a try or framing square. Fig. 71.

Wind in a board indicates that the board is twisted throughout its length. One way to check this is to lay the board on a level surface to see if it rocks on two corners. An-

72. CHECKING A BOARD FOR WIND. Place a parallel board at either end of the stock. Then sight along the top edge of the first board. If any part of the second board is visible, you can tell about how much wind there is and which way it goes.

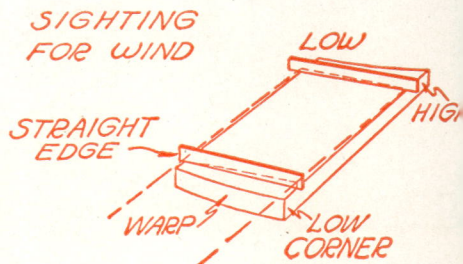

SIGHTING FOR WIND
LOW
HIGH
STRAIGHT EDGE
WARP
LOW CORNER

other method is to place two parallel pieces of wood across the grain, one on either end of the board. Then sight along the top of the first parallel. If you can see one end of the second parallel, you know that the board has a wind. Fig. 72. With a pencil, mark the high points of the board if it is warped or has a wind, because more stock must be removed at these points.

## Fastening a board in the vise

If the wood is rough, you may need to take a few cuts with the plane before the direction of the grain becomes apparent. Planing against the grain roughens the surface. Lock the board between the dog of the vise and the bench stop, or lay the board on top of the bench with one end supported against the bench stop. Never lock a board cross-grain, as this tends to warp it.

## Planing the surface true and smooth

Grasp the knob of the plane in your left hand and the handle in your right hand. Fig. 73. Take a position just back of the work with your left foot forward, so you can swing your body like a pendulum as you plane and at the same time use a forward motion with your arms.

Place the toe or front of the plane on the board. Apply pressure to the knob at the start of the stroke. As the whole base comes in con-

73. PLANING THE FACE OF A BOARD. Note that the work is locked securely between the bench stop and the dog of the vise. You can tell when the plane is cutting properly by the kind of shaving that is being formed. The shaving should be uniform in thickness and width. The thickness of the shaving depends on the setting of the plane. For rough cutting, a heavy shaving should be taken; for finished work, the shaving should be light and silky. Always plane *with* the grain of the wood.

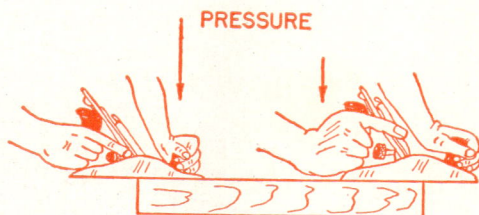

74. PROPER METHOD OF APPLYING PRESSURE WHEN PLANING. More pressure is applied to the knob at the start of the stroke and to the handle at the end of the stroke, so that you don't cut a convex curve.

tact with the wood, apply even pressure to the knob and handle. Then,

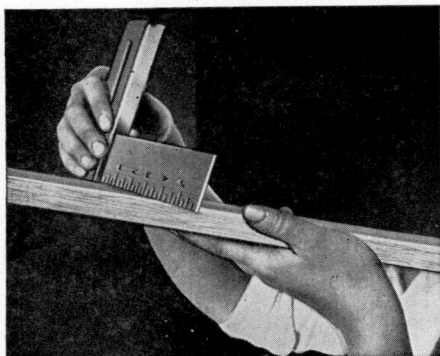

75. CHECKING A BOARD BY HOLD-
ING A STRAIGHTEDGE ACROSS
IT. Hold the board at about eye level
and place a straightedge across it. If
any light shows through, you will know
that it is a low spot. Mark the high
spots on the board with a pencil and
then plane lightly over these areas.

as the plane begins to leave the surface, apply more pressure to the
handle. Fig. 74. This way, you won't
cut a convex curve in the board.

Lift the plane off the board on
the return stroke. Don't drag the
plane back to the starting position.
Sometimes the plane will cut more
easily if you take a shearing cut
rather than a straight cut.

Work across the board gradually. If you have marked any high
points, these will take more planing
than other areas.

## Removing wind from a board

If there is a wind in the board
which requires taking a partial cut
at either the beginning or end of the
board, it can be done as follows:

To take a partial cut at the beginning of the board, begin the
stroke as before. Then, as you plane
along the board as far as you think
necessary, slowly lift the handle to
finish the cut.

To take the wind out of the end
of the board, start the partial cut at
some point in the center of the
board. Begin with the handle held
away from the surface and gradually lower it as you begin the forward motion.

## Checking the surface

After the surface begins to
appear smooth, check it with a
straightedge to make sure that it is
true. Light will show through
where there are low spots on the
board or the straightedge will
touch the high points. Fig. 75. It is
well to check the total length every

76. CORRECT METHOD OF CHECK-
ING THE FACE SURFACE OF THE
BOARD. It should be checked along
its lengths every few inches and diagonally across both corners.

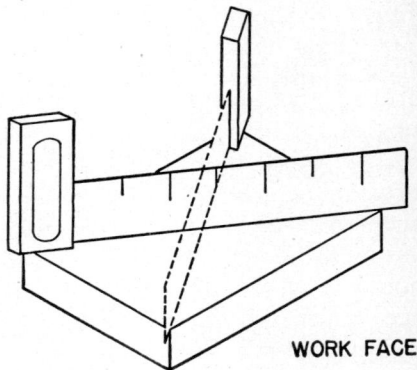

**WORK FACE**

few inches and diagonally across the corners, using a pencil to mark the high points. Fig. 76. Sometimes one plane stroke will remove these.

This first surface which has been planed true and smooth is called the *face surface* or *face side* and is the basis for squaring up stock.

## Can You Answer These Questions on Planing a Surface?

1. Which surface of the board is the first to be planed?
2. Can you see if a board is warped? How is this checked?
3. What are the two ways of checking wind in a board?
4. Planing against grain will roughen the board. Why?

5. What is likely to happen if the plane is dragged rather than lifted back to the starting position?
6. Tell how you would go about removing wind from a board.
7. What is the surface called that is planed first?

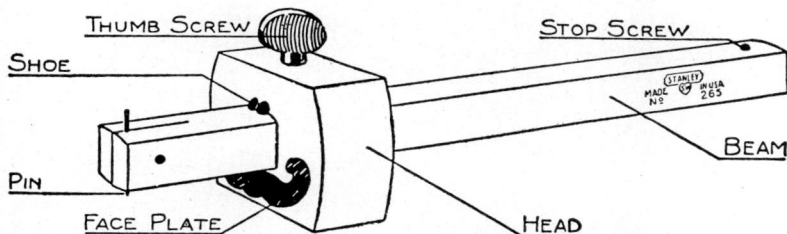

THUMB SCREW    STOP SCREW
SHOE
STANLEY
MADE IN U.S.A.
N9    265
BEAM
PIN
FACE PLATE    HEAD

77. A MARKING GAUGE. This tool is a necessity in laying out and marking the thicknesses and width of stock. NOTE: GAUGE is preferred spelling, but some handbooks and technical magazines spell it GAGE.

## PLANING STOCK TO WIDTH AND THICKNESS

Most of the pieces for a project must be planed to width and thickness to make the surfaces smooth and true and to bring the stock down to the finished size. In performing these steps, you will have constant use for a *marking gauge*. Fig. 77. This tool is used for marking thickness and width on small pieces of stock. In planing to thickness and width, all measurements should be taken from the face surface or side which you will already have planed true and smooth. This

surface should be marked with the number "1," or some small mark near the first edge that you are going to plane.

## Selecting and checking the face or joint edge

Select the edge that is truest and freest from irregularities. With the try square held against the face surface, test the edge at several points along the stock for squareness. Also check with a straightedge along the length. Mark with a pencil the high points where you must do most of the planing.

**78. HERE IS THE REASON FOR USING A PLANE WITH A LONGER BED** to plane the edge of long stock. The jointer plane tends to straighten out any irregularities, while the shorter plane tends to follow curves.

## Selecting the proper plane

For shorter pieces, the jack plane will be very satisfactory. In planing an edge, however, especially a long one, it is better to use a plane with a longer base such as the fore or jointer plane. As you see in Fig. 78, the jointer plane tends to straighten the edge while the shorter plane will follow any curve that may be in the edge.

## Fastening the work in the vise

Lock the stock in the vise with the edge protruding above the surface. Fig. 79. If it is a long piece of stock, the front end should be supported by the vise and the back held in place with a hand screw as shown in Fig. 80. Sometimes the work is held against a V block on top of the bench. Fig. 81.

## Holding the plane

Adjust the plane to take a very fine cut. In planing an edge you may hold the handle of the plane the same way as you did for surface planing. Fig. 82. Sometimes, to use the second method, place the thumb around the back of the knob with the other fingers curled under the bottom of the plane. In this way you can use your fingers to guide the plane along the face side to help in keeping the plane at right angles. Fig. 81.

## Planing the edge

Plane with the grain. First remove any high spots that you have marked. Then take long, continuous strokes to remove a thin chip all along the edge. Be sure to apply pressure on the knob in starting the stroke and on the handle when finishing it. Fig. 83. The idea in planing this first edge is not to remove stock but to get this edge square with the face surface and straight along its entire length as rapidly and with as little effort as possible. Check with the try square and straightedge frequently as shown in Figs. 84 and 85. Mark this edge with two light pencil lines to indicate that it is the face or joint edge.

## Setting the marking gauge

Check on the drawing the width

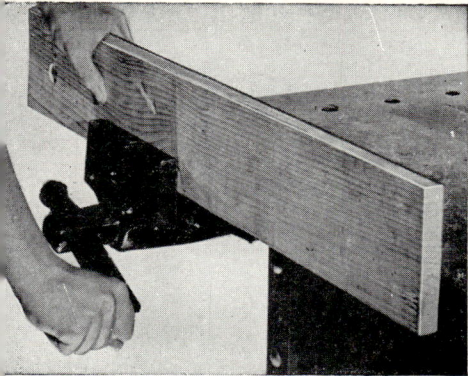

**79. LOCKING STOCK IN A VISE.**
Make sure that the stock is held firmly
in the vise jaws so that there will be
no movement when using the plane.
COURTESY THE JAM HANDY ORGANIZATION.

**80. SUPPORTING LONG PIECES OF
STOCK WHEN PLANING AN
EDGE.** The hand screw is fastened to
support the end of the stock while
the front is locked in the vise.

**81. HOLDING STOCK AGAINST A V
BLOCK TO DO EDGE PLANING.**
This is especially satisfactory for planing long stock and for planing whenever a vise is not available. Note how
the thumb is held around the back of
the knob and the fingers curled under
the bottom of the plane to guide it.

**82. PLANING THE EDGE OF A
BOARD BY HOLDING THE KNOB**
firmly in your left hand. When using
this method, you must be extremely
careful not to rock the plane. COURTESY
THE JAM HANDY ORGANIZATION.

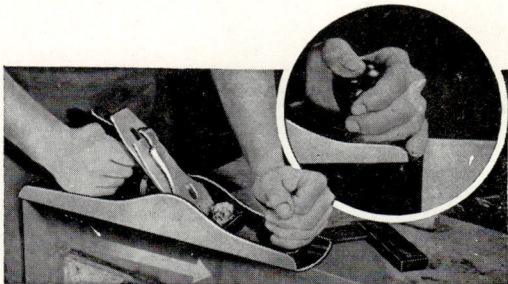

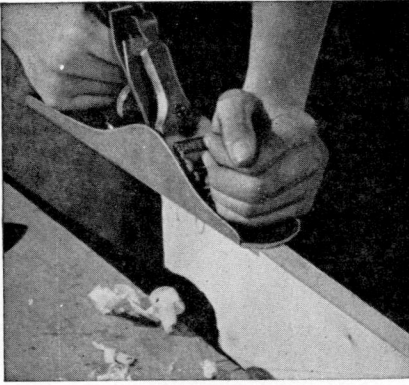

**83.** STARTING THE CUTTING STROKE IN PLANING AN EDGE. Pressure is being applied to the knob.
COURTESY THE JAM HANDY ORGANIZATION.

**84.** CHECKING THE JOINT EDGE by holding the handle of a try square firmly against the face side or surface. Move the try square along to make certain that the edge is square along its total length.

of the stock needed and then set the marking gauge to this width. To mark stock which is too wide for the marking gauge, see Fig. 50. As you have noticed, the marking gauge has a scale along one surface. This scale, however, will usually be inaccurate, since, in sharpening the small spur to wedge shape by filing, the starting point of the scale becomes incorrect. However, set the head of the scale to the correct distance as shown on the beam and then lightly turn the thumbscrew. Then hold the marking gauge upside down in your left hand and use the rule to check the distance

**85.** CHECKING AN EDGE FOR STRAIGHTNESS. This is especially important on long stock. The edge must be square with the face surface and not be a convex or concave curve. Hold the straightedge against the planed edge and sight at eye level to see if any light shows through.

from the head to the point of the spur. Fig. 86. If the measurement is slightly incorrect, tap the head a bit one way or the other to correct it and then tighten the thumbscrew. Always recheck the measurement before using the marking gauge.

## Marking the stock to width

Hold the stock to be marked with the face surface up and the face or joint edge to your right. Place the head of the marking gauge firmly against this joint edge, and then tip the marking gauge forward with a slight twist of your wrist until the spur just touches the surface of the wood. Beginning at the end toward you, push the marking gauge forward, applying pressure as shown in Fig. 87.

Sometimes when widths greater than the capacity of the gauge must be marked, it will be necessary to mark the width at several points and then hold a straightedge along these points, marking a fine line with a knife.

## Planing the second edge

If there is considerable excess stock to be removed, the board should be ripped to within ⅛ to 3/16 of an inch of the finished line.

Lock the stock in the vise as described above and begin to plane the second edge. As the plane approaches the layout line, use the try square frequently to check the

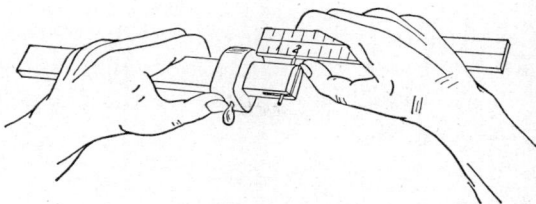

86. SETTING A MARKING GAUGE. Note that the gauge is held upside down in the left hand and a rule held in the right hand to check the distance from the point or spur to the head of the marking gauge.

87. USING A MARKING GAUGE. Notice that the marking gauge is tilted slightly and that the worker is pushing it away from himself. In doing the marking, pressure should be applied to hold the head of the gauge firmly against the edge while forward pressure is also applied.

edge for squareness with the face surface and a straightedge to check the length. Take special care as you approach the finished line to take light, even shavings that are the total width and length of the edge. The last cut you take should just split the indentation made by the marking gauge.

## Marking the stock to thickness

Check the thickness of the stock needed and then set the marking gauge to this measurement. Hold the head of the marking gauge against the face surface and mark a line on both edges to indicate the proper thickness.

## Planing to thickness

Observe the lines that indicate thickness and see if there are any areas that are higher than the re-

mainder of the board and require extra planing. Lock the stock between the dog of the vise and the bench stop and plane these areas first. Then begin to plane the total length of the stock, working from one side to the other to bring it down to its proper thickness. The actual procedure of planing to thickness will be the same as that for planing the first surface, except that you must constantly observe the two lines indicating thickness. When the stock is planed to thickness you should be able to hold the handle of the try square against this second surface and find that the edges are square, as they were with the face surface.

## Can You Answer These Questions on Planing Stock to Width and Thickness?

1. When is a fore or jointer plane used?
2. The first planing should be done on which edge?
3. How can a piece of long stock be supported for planing along one edge?
4. Describe the two ways of holding the knob of the plane in planing an edge.
5. What should be accomplished by planing this first edge? Should a large amount of stock be removed? Explain.
6. Describe a marking gauge and name its parts.
7. Should you depend on the marking

gauge scale for setting the tool to width? Why?
8. Should the mark made by the marking gauge be heavy and deep?
9. Suppose that considerable stock must be removed to bring the stock to width. Can you tell how this should be done?
10. Would you completely remove the marking gauge line when you planed the second edge?
11. A piece of stock that has been squared to thickness and width has certain characteristics. What are these?

## PLANING END GRAIN

Planing end grain is more difficult than planing the face or edge with the grain because, in planing the end, you will actually be cut-

ting off the ends of the fibers. This necessitates an extremely sharp plane iron.

When the stock to be planed can be locked in a vise, a jack plane is used. For other jobs, the block plane is satisfactory.

## The block plane

The block plane (Fig. 88) is much smaller than the others you have used so far. It has a single plane iron which is placed in the plane with the beveled side up. The plane iron also rests in the plane at a much lower angle than the iron in a regular plane. This makes it possible to cut end grain more efficiently. As you can see, this particular plane has no lateral adjustment, but only an adjusting screw to regulate the depth of cut. However, some block planes do have a lateral adjustment.

## Adjusting the block plane

The block plane is adjusted in the same manner as other planes, except when there is no lateral adjusting lever. To make this adjust-

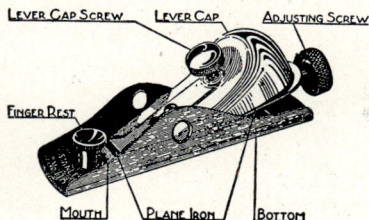

89. PLANING END GRAIN WITH A BLOCK PLANE. Note how the plane is held in the right hand. Because of its size, the block plane is most convenient when work cannot be locked in a vise.

ment, loosen the plane iron cap and sight along the bottom of the plane. Then, with your fingers, press the plane iron to the right or left until it is parallel to the bottom of the plane. Tighten the lever cap screw. The depth adjustment is made in the same way as for the other types of planes.

## Using the block plane

Hold the block plane in your right hand with the thumb on one side, the forefinger over the finger rest, and the other three fingers on the other side. Begin from one edge to work toward the center. Fig. 89. Begin from the other edge, doing the same. Take pains to hold the block plane square with the work. You will find that it takes considerable pressure to cut the end grain. It is best to take a shallow cut to

88. HERE IS A BLOCK PLANE that can be used for planing end grain and for doing small forming and shaping work. The cutter rests at a much lower angle than other types of planes, which makes it ideal for planing across grain.

LEVER CAP SCREW    LEVER CAP    ADJUSTING SCREW
FINGER REST
MOUTH    PLANE IRON    BOTTOM

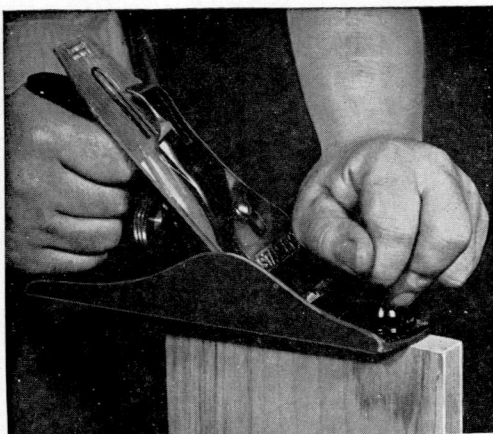

A

B

90. A. PLANING END GRAIN WITH A HAND PLANE by planing halfway across and then reversing the plane to finish the cut. B. The block plane is excellent for end grain because of the low angle of the blade.

cap is set very close to the cutting edge, not over $\frac{1}{32}$ inch. Lock the stock firmly in the vise with the end protruding slightly. In planing end grain, it is not possible to go completely across the end, as this will split out the wood. Therefore one of the following three methods should be followed:

1. Plane about halfway across the stock; then lift the handle of the plane slowly. Begin at the other end to do the same thing. Fig. 90. Check the end for squareness with the working face and working edge. Fig. 91.

2. Plane a short bevel on the waste edge of the stock and then begin from the other side to plane all the way across. Fig. 92.

3. Secure a piece of scrap stock exactly the same thickness as the piece you are working on and lock it in the vise just ahead of the fin-

91. CHECKING THE END OF THE STOCK. Hold the try square against the face side and also the joint edge to make sure that the end is square both ways.

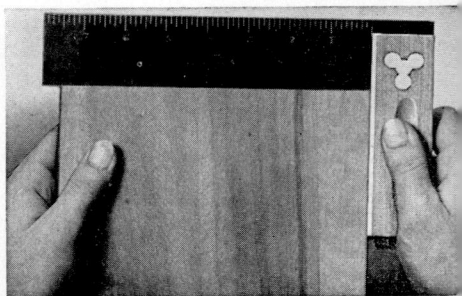

keep the plane from jumping instead of cutting smoothly.

The block plane is also used for planing with the grain, especially in model work.

## Planing end grain with a jack plane

Make sure that the plane iron is very sharp and that the plane iron

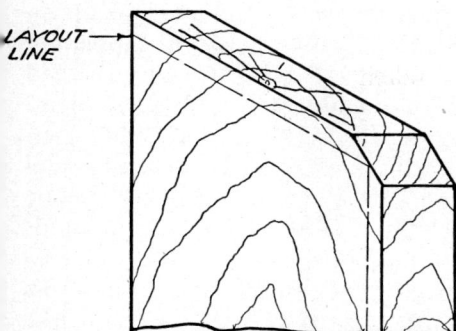

92. A SECOND METHOD OF PLAN-
ING END GRAIN. Note that a bevel
is cut. This tends to prevent the wood
from splitting out, and you can therefore plane completely across the end.

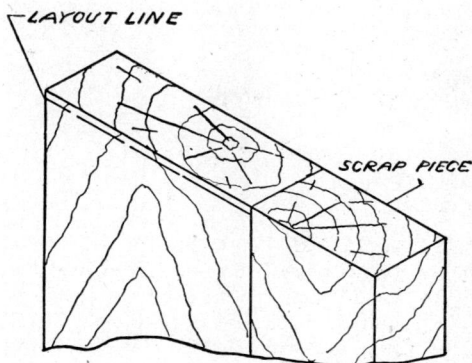

93. A THIRD METHOD OF PLANING
END GRAIN. A scrap piece of the
same thickness is placed against one
edge of the piece to be planed. Thus
you actually extend the end grain.

ished piece so that you actually have
extended the end grain. Then you
can plane all of the way across the
end grain without fear of splitting
out the piece. Fig. 93.

Whichever method is used, frequently check the end grain from
both the working face and working
edge to make sure that it is square.

## Can You Answer These Questions on Planing End Grain?

1. What is there about end grain that
makes it difficult to plane?
2. How is a block plane different from
other planes?

3. When would you choose a block
plane to plane with the grain?
4. Describe the three ways of planing
end grain.

### CUTTING STOCK WITH A BACKSAW

Whenever you need to make a
very fine saw cut, as in squaring up
stock or in making joints, you will
use a backsaw or dovetail saw.

### The backsaw and dovetail saws

The backsaw (Fig. 94) has a
very thin blade with fine teeth
which enable it to make a very accurate cut. This saw is used to cut
both across grain and with the
grain. It gets its name because it is
so thin that an extra band of metal
must be put across the back to make
the saw rigid. The dovetail saw is
very similar to the backsaw, except
that it has a narrower blade and
finer teeth. Fig. 95.

### The bench hook

A device that you will use with
the backsaw is a bench hook. Fig.

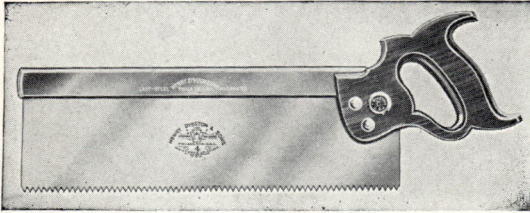

**94. A BACKSAW.** In hand woodworking, this is one of the most frequently used tools whenever an accurate cut is required. Because the blade is relatively thin, it is strengthened on the back with a strip of metal, from which it gets its name.

**95. A DOVETAIL SAW.** This is very similar to the backsaw except that it is smaller and has a thinner blade and therefore is used for extremely accurate work.

**96.** This is a piece of wood with a hook or stop on either end, one of which is shorter than the width of the board itself. When in use, the wide stop goes over the edge of the bench and the piece to be sawed is held against the shorter stop. This hook protects the top of the bench from injury by the backsaw.

## Laying out the cut-off line

Accurately lay out the location of the cut to be made, using a try square and pencil. For very accurate layout, mark a line with a knife; then cut a groove on waste stock with a knife or chisel. Fig. 97. If the stock is to be cut to length, lay out a line across the face side of the

board as well as both edges. If no planing is to be done, the cut should be taken just outside the layout line, with the saw kerf in the waste stock. However, if the edge is to be planed or chiseled, allow about $\frac{1}{16}$ inch.

## Crosscutting

Place the bench hook over the edge of the bench. Hold your work with one hand firmly against the stop as shown in Fig. 98. Use the thumb of your left hand to guide the blade of the saw. Hold the saw in a slanting position across the work and draw it back once or twice to start the saw kerf. As the cut begins, gradually lower the saw until it is parallel to the wood. Fig. 99.

Make sure that you are holding the saw at right angles to the face of the work. Be extremely careful to take light, easy cuts as the saw goes through the opposite side of the wood, to prevent splintering.

**96. A BENCH HOOK,** which is simply a piece of wood with a wood cleat on either end, is used constantly to protect the top of the bench when sawing, cutting, and doing other forming operations.

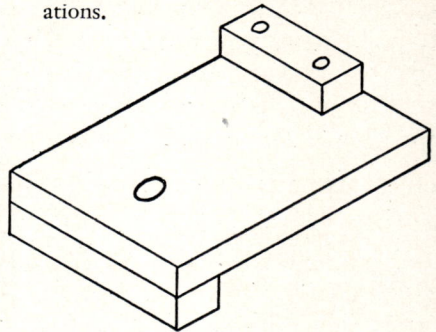

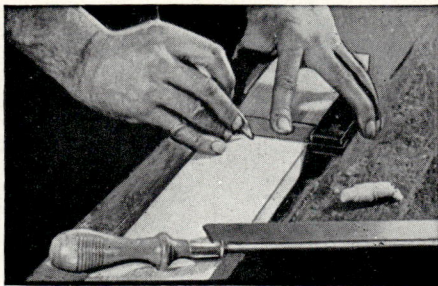

a

b

c

**97. HOW TO MAKE AN ACCURATE CUT.** a. To make a very accurate cut, a line is laid out across the stock with a try square and knife. b. A slight groove is cut along the layout line with a knife. c. The cut is made with a dovetail saw or backsaw.

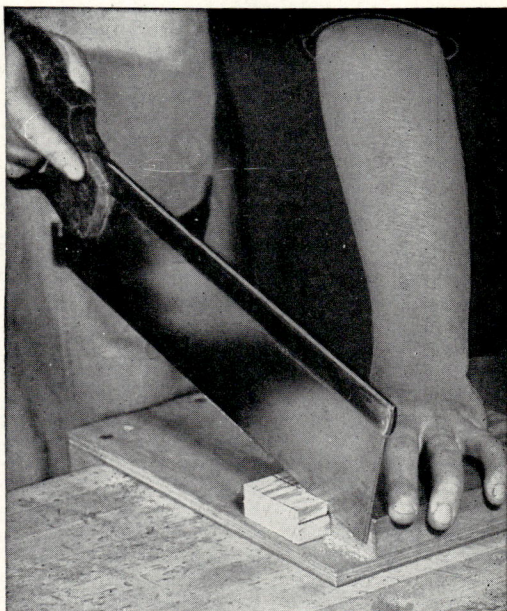

**98. STARTING A CUT WITH A BACK-SAW.** Note that the stock is held firmly against a bench hook and the handle of the saw held high until the first two or three strokes are taken.

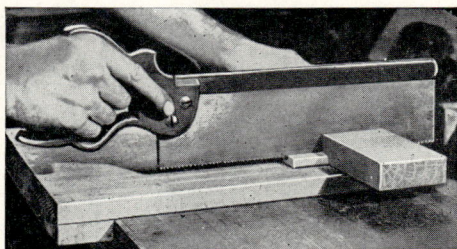

**99. CONTINUING THE CUT WITH THE BACKSAW.** As the saw kerf is formed, the handle is lowered until it is parallel with the top of the bench.

71

**100. RIPPING WITH A BACKSAW.** The proper method of cutting with the grain with a backsaw to form a tenon for a mortise-and-tenon joint.

## Ripping

The backsaw is also used for cutting with the grain of stock, especially in making joints and in doing other fine cabinetwork. Lock the stock in a vise, with the end to be cut protruding slightly above the vise jaws. Begin the cut in the same manner as you did in crosscutting and continue to lower the handle until it is cutting the total width of the wood. Fig. 100. In cutting with the grain, be very careful not to allow the saw to creep in at an angle, as this will make a crooked cut.

You will find many uses for the backsaw in making all types of joints, as you will see later.

## Can You Answer These Questions on Cutting Stock With a Backsaw?

1. How did the backsaw get its name?
2. In what ways does the dovetail saw differ from the backsaw?
3. What is a bench hook and how is it used?

When using the backsaw, some stock must remain for planing. How much?
5. Which saw resembles the backsaw the most—the crosscut or the ripsaw?
6. Can the backsaw crosscut and rip?
7. Why must care be taken when sawing with the grain?

### GLUING UP STOCK TO FORM LARGER SURFACES

When you begin to make larger articles, one of the first things you are confronted with is the necessity for gluing up several pieces of stock to form a larger area. Sometimes this will mean gluing stock edge to edge to form a large surface, for making anything from a cutting board to a table top or ends of a desk. At other times, you will need to glue stock face to face to form a larger rectangular area, for making a lamp base or perhaps the legs of a table or stool. Later you will need to clamp and glue up stock when you begin to assemble your project.

### Kinds of glue

There are five common kinds of glue that may be used in the school shop. These may be purchased under a variety of trade names. A study of the description of the glue will tell you which type it is.

1. Animal glue. This is made from hoofs, hides, bones, and other refuse of animals which have been refined and purified and then made into sticks or ground into powder. There are many grades, depending on the quality and kind of wood for which it is intended. Animal glue makes a stronger-than-wood joint but is not waterproof. If it is used in the dry form, it is necessary to have a glue pot or double boiler for preparing it. For many years, it has been used as an all-purpose furniture glue. It is also available in liquid form, which eliminates the necessity for heating and mixing. If stick or powder glue is used, it must first be soaked in cold water from six to twelve hours. While there are strict manufacturer's specifications as to the amounts of glue and water, a satisfactory mixture can be made by soaking the glue in just enough water to cover. The glue will absorb this water and then, when the heating is done, a small amount of water can be added as needed. After animal glue is soaked, place it in the top of a double boiler or a regular gluepot and heat it to steam temperature. The glue will dry out too much if heated directly over a flame. Animal glue is ready to use when it runs off the brush in a light stream.

101. USING WHITE LIQUID RESIN GLUE from a squeeze bottle is a good way to apply glue.

Before applying hot animal glue, the wood must be brought to a temperature of about 80 to 90 degrees. This type of glue must be applied rapidly, as it sets very quickly after cooling. Cold liquid animal glue, which can be purchased, eliminates these disadvantages.

2. Casein glue, made from milk curd, is available in powdered form. It is mixed with cold water to the consistency of cream and applied to the wood cold. It is easy to mix and makes a stronger-than-wood joint. It is not completely waterproof. Some types stain oak, mahogany, and other acid woods and must be bleached off. It is excellent for all indoor and outdoor gluing with the exception of things which require complete waterproofing.

Do not mix more than you need at one time, as it loses its strength in a few hours after mixing. To mix it, pour the powder in a container and add a small amount of water, stirring until it becomes a heavy

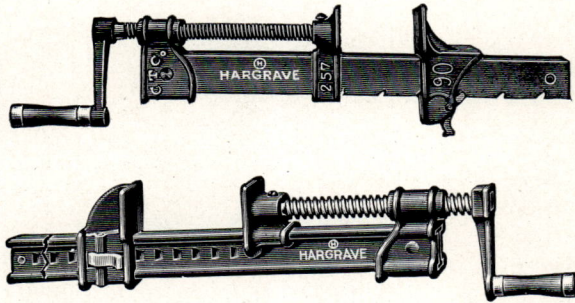

**102. THIS BAR CLAMP CAN BE USED FOR GENERAL-PURPOSE WORK. It is** particularly useful in all wide clamping for furniture construction.

paste. Add more water until the mixture is about the consistency of thick cream. Allow the glue to age about fifteen minutes before applying it with a stick or brush.

3. Plastic resin glue is made from urea resin and formaldehyde. It comes in powder form and is mixed with water to the consistency of cream. It does not stain woods, is waterproof, and dries to a light color. It is used in the same general manner as casein glue, but the manufacturer's directions must always be followed for mixing and drying. It is used for cabinetwork and is a type of glue commonly employed in bonding plywood.

4. Resorcinol resin glue is made by mixing liquid resin with a powder catalyst. It comes in a can divided into two compartments and should be mixed only as needed, according to the manufacturer's directions. It does not require much pressure and will fill gaps and can be chosen for gluing poorly fitting joints. It provides complete protection from both fresh and salt water and is therefore ideal for all outdoor sports equipment.

5. Liquid resin glue (white in color) is excellent for furniture making and repair. It is always ready for use, is non-staining, economical and odorless. It cannot be exposed to weather and is not so strong or lasting as liquid hide glue, which is recommended for fine furniture. Fig. 101.

## Ten hints for successful gluing

1. Make sure the surfaces are clean and dry.
2. Prepare well-fitted joints.
3. Select the correct glue.
4. Mix the glue to the proper consistency.
5. Mark the pieces to be glued for correct assembly.
6. Have the proper clamps ready.
7. Apply the glue to both surfaces of the joint.

103. GLUING UP A FRAME, USING BAR CLAMPS. This type is adjusted with catches.

8. Clamp parts together properly.

9. Remove excessive glue from the joint before it dries.

10. Allow the assembly to dry properly.

## Kinds of clamps

1. The cabinet or bar clamp. Fig. 102. This clamp is used for gluing up larger surfaces edge to edge and for clamping parts together when assembling projects. Made in various lengths of from 2 to 8 feet and in several styles. One end is adjusted to length by friction or by catches, while the other is moved in and out by a screw. Fig. 103. When using the cabinet clamp, the screw is turned out completely and then the catch or friction end moved in until the clamp is slightly

104. A HAND SCREW CAN BE USED FOR MANY DIFFERENT PURPOSES because it has wooden jaws. Wood can be clamped without danger of injury to its surface. These hand screws are available with jaws ranging from 6 to 20 inches in length.

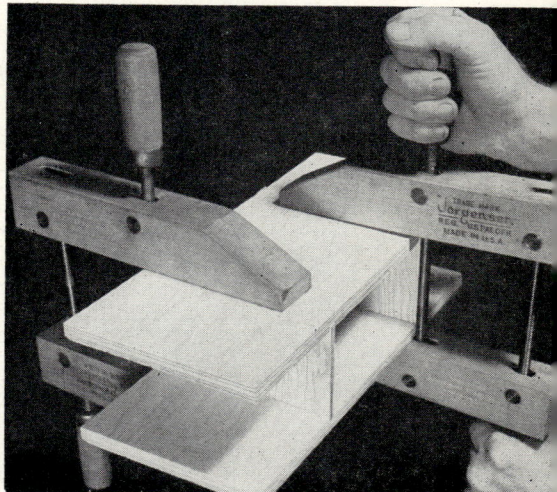

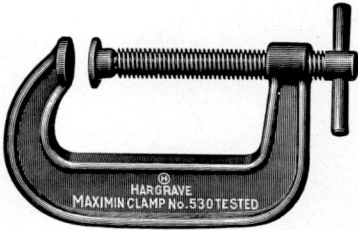

**105. A C OR CARRIAGE CLAMP is for** clamping irregular or odd-shaped pieces and for many special jobs in the woodshop.

**106. SPEED BAR CLAMPS SUCH AS THIS ONE** are easily adjustable. This makes gluing a great deal easier.

wider than the total width of the stock to be clamped. In using cabinet clamps on finished stock, protect the surface of the wood by placing small pieces of scrap stock between the clamp jaws and the wood.

2. Hand screws. Fig. 104. These are wooden parallel clamps with jaws that range in length from about 6 to 20 inches and open to distances of from 4 to 20 inches. When using hand screws, the center screw is grasped in the left hand and the outside screw in the right hand. The clamp can then be opened and closed by twisting the handles in opposite directions. The hand

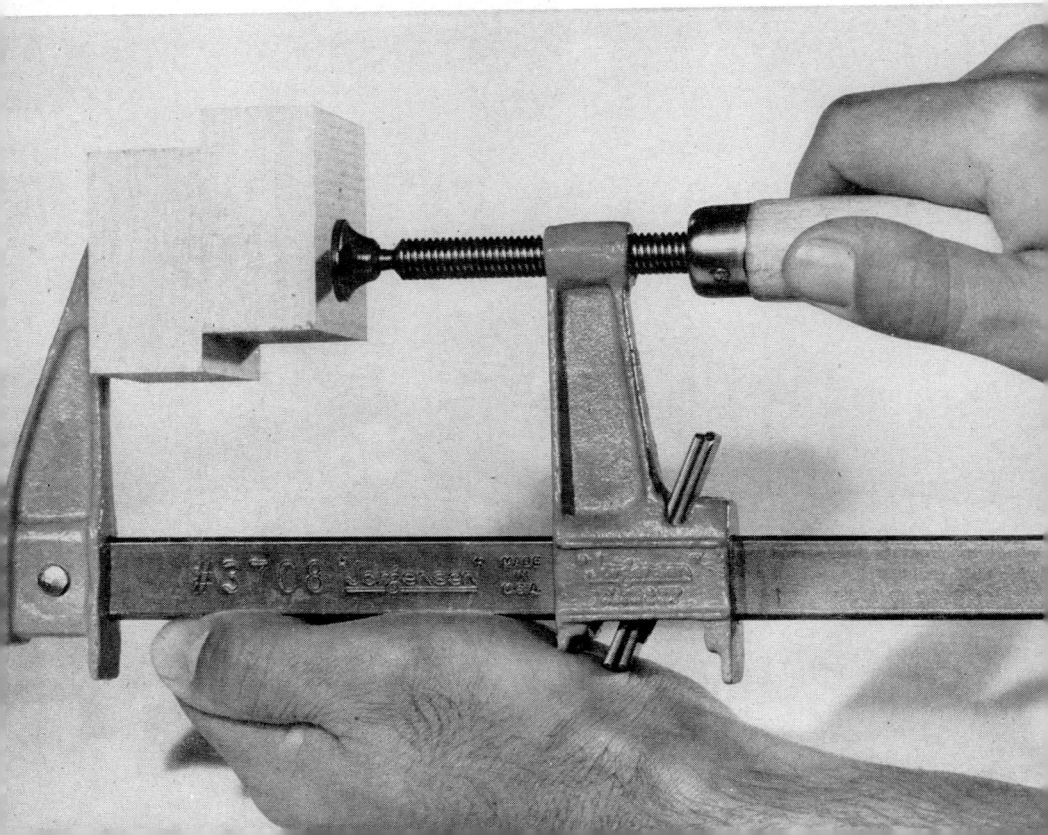

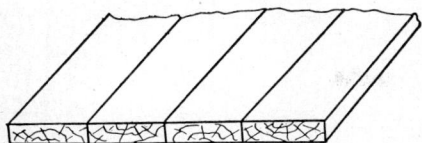

107. THE PROPER METHOD OF ARRANGING STOCK that is to be glued together. Note that the annular rings on the ends are faced in opposite directions on every other board. This is done so that, if there is any warping, the boards counteract each other.

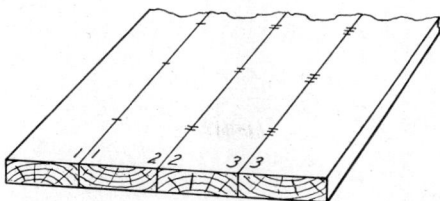

108. MARK ADJOINING BOARDS WITH MATCHING NUMBERS or lines so that it will be easy to assemble them correctly when you are ready for gluing.

screw is for gluing stock face to face or for clamping together any work that is within the range of the clamp jaws.

3. The C clamp is available in many sizes. It is used in assembling and clamping parts. Fig. 105.

4. Speed (instant-acting) clamps are very convenient because they can be instantly adjusted for quick assembly. Fig. 106.

## Making and gluing up an edge joint

1. Select and cut the stock. Select the rough stock that will form the larger surfaces. If it is wider than 8 to 10 inches, it is usually ripped into narrower strips so that the total surface will not warp so much when the pieces are glued together. After the pieces have been cut, try to arrange them in their correct order, taking into consideration the following:

a. Make sure that the grain of all pieces runs in the same direction, so that, after you have glued up the pieces, it will not be difficult to plane.

b. Arrange every other piece with the annular rings on the end, faced in opposite directions. Fig. 107. This will help to prevent the surface from warping unduly.

c. Try to match the pieces to form the most interesting grain arrangement.

When these have been done, mark the end of each matching joint with corresponding numbers in a place where the marks can be easily seen. Fig. 108.

2. First planing. Plane one surface of each piece to take out any wind or warpage. This will also help to determine the direction in which the grain runs. If you have any pieces running in opposite directions, reverse them and re-mark the ends. It will not be necessary to plane this surface accurately now because the assembled stock will have to be planed again.

3. Plane both edges until they are square with the face surface. In

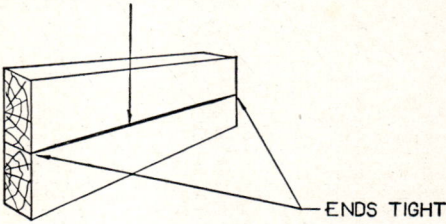

LIGHT JUST VISIBLE

ENDS TIGHT

**109. SPRING JOINT CONSTRUCTION.** Note that the ends are tight and that there is just a small amount of light showing through the center.

**110. CHECKING A SPRING JOINT CONSTRUCTION.** The boards are held together, and then you can sight along them at eye level to see if just a little light comes through at the center.

**111. HOLDING A STRAIGHTEDGE AGAINST THE FACE SURFACES** of the stock to see if these surfaces are straight and do not bow.

planing an edge, the center should be slightly lower than the ends. When the two matching edges are planed, clamp one piece in a vise and set the other piece over it edge to edge. Then observe if a little light is coming through the crack toward the center of the joint and make sure that the ends are tight. Fig. 109. This is called the spring joint construction. Fig. 110. If this is not done, the ends will tend to separate after the pieces have been glued together. As additional checks, hold a straightedge against the face surfaces of all the pieces to make sure that these surfaces do not bow. Fig. 111. Also, tap the top piece with your finger to see that it does not rock. Finally, slide the top piece along the bottom one to see if it tends to have a suction action. Continue to plane one surface and the two edges of each piece and match each of the joints.

## Adding dowels or splines

When joints with additional strength are desired, dowels or splines can be added to each joint. The section on making a dowel joint gives detailed instructions for making an edge dowel joint. To make a spline joint (Fig. 112), cut a groove on the circular saw that is about one third as wide and deep as the thickness of the stock. Then cut and fit splines into these grooves. Allow a small clearance at the bottom of each spline for glue.

## Making a trial assembly of the stock

After all joints have been constructed, place the pieces in position

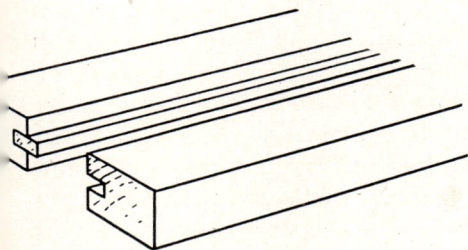

112. AN ENLARGED VIEW OF A SPLINE-JOINT CONSTRUCTION. This type strengthens the two adjoining pieces.

113. A JIG TO HOLD THE BAR CLAMPS. With a jig of this sort, the clamps will be held in correct position, making it a simple job to apply glue to the edges and to place the stock in between the clamps.

again on the top of a bench. If the pieces are extremely long, place them over two sawhorses. If they are placed on top of a bench, use a jig (Fig. 113) to hold the bar clamps. Select three or more cabinet or bar clamps, depending on the length of the stock. There should be a clamp for about every 15 inches of stock. Carefully set all cabinet clamps to the proper openings, so they will be ready to clamp the stock as soon as the edges are glued.

## Gluing up the stock

Hold the two matching edges together so they are flush, and apply the glue with a brush or stick. Make sure that the edges are completely covered but do not apply too much glue, as this will squeeze out of the joint when it is put together, giving you extra trouble in removing it later. Fig. 114.

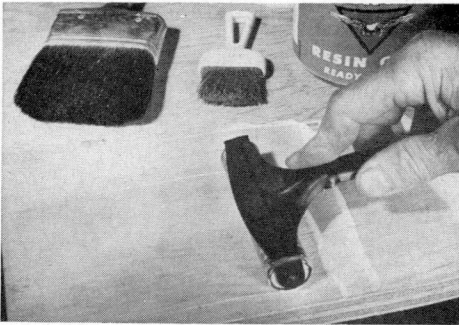

A

B

114. A. Spreading cold liquid glue with a roller after applying it with a brush. B. Applying hot glue with a brush.

When all edges have been glued, rapidly lay the pieces on the lower clamps till all are in place. If possible, rub the two pieces together to work the glue into the pores. Use a rubber mallet to tap the ends or the face surfaces to align them properly. Tighten the outside clamps lightly; then place another clamp upside down on the stock at the

mid-point and clamp this lightly. Check all the joints to make sure that the face surfaces are flush and that the ends align. Use a mallet to strike the pieces to bring them in place. Then turn up each clamp until it applies firm pressure. Don't attempt to squeeze the wood too tightly. If the joint is not constructed properly it will never draw into place. Place a wood cleat above and below the surface at either end and clamp these in place with hand screws or clamps. Fig. 115. A piece of paper under the cleats will prevent them from sticking. This will tend to keep the surface true and free from warpage. Before the glue begins to harden, wipe off the excess from the outside of the joint.

## Making and gluing up stock face to face

Select and cut out several pieces of stock that will make up the correct size when glued together. Arrange the pieces with the annular rings alternating in direction. Also make sure that the grain of the pieces runs in the same direction. Mark the ends so that you will know how the pieces should be arranged for gluing. Plane the face surface of the two outside pieces true and smooth. If more than two pieces are glued together, the center pieces must be planed to thickness. Select several hand screws or C clamps and open them slightly wider than the stock to be clamped. Apply glue evenly to the proper surfaces

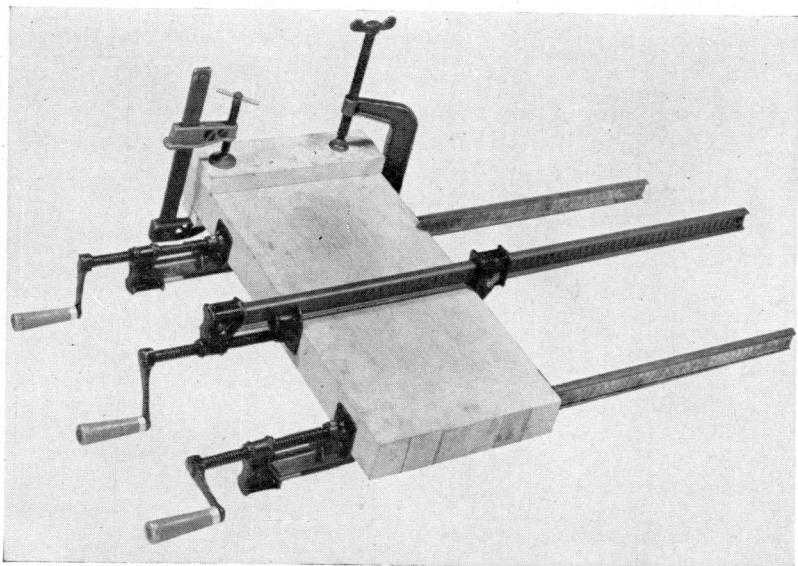

**115.** STOCK GLUED UP AND BAR CLAMPS HOLDING THE STOCK TO-
GETHER. Note the cleat that has been fastened to one end of the stock.

**116.** GLUING STOCK FACE TO FACE. Several different types of clamps hold the
two pieces of stock together. Cleats are fastened underneath the clamps to protect the
surface of the wood.

of the pieces and then clamp them together as shown in Fig. 116. When you tighten the hand screw, you

must take care that the jaws are parallel, to assure even distribution of pressure.

## Can You Answer These Questions on Gluing Up Stock to Form Larger Surfaces?

1. Name five kinds of glue and tell of what they are made.
2. Which glues are waterproof?
3. Which is best for a small repair job?
4. Tell what cabinet or bar clamps are needed for and how they are used.
5. Of what material are the clamps of hand screws made?
6. For what special kinds of gluing jobs can C clamps be helpful?
7. To glue up a large board, wider stock is ripped into narrow strips. Explain the reason for this and how it is done.
8. What three things must you con-

sider when gluing up stock?
9. Describe a spring joint.
10. To make this type of joint, what checks should be made?
11. A trial assembly is always made before gluing. What is accomplished by it?
12. About how much glue should be applied to the edges?
13. With what kind of mallet should wood surfaces be pounded?
14. How can you keep the surface true and free from warpage?
15. Why must the jaws of hand screws be parallel?

### SQUARING UP STOCK

It is usually necessary to plane several or all of the surfaces of the pieces for your project. In some cases, you will be planing only the edges of the stock and sawing the ends. In other cases, such as in making a cutout design, you may plane the face surface, one edge, and the other surface. In many instances in which parts are to be assembled, you will be planing the stock to thickness and width and perhaps finishing the ends by sawing with the backsaw and then sanding.

There are many times, however, when you will need to plane all six surfaces of the board. This is called squaring up the stock. If you apply

the instructions given in the last six units, you should be able to do a good job. It should be remembered, though, that this job is very difficult when done with a hand plane and you should not attempt to plane any more surfaces than are necessary to do the job properly. If machine tools are available, a planer and jointer can be used, following the same procedure as with a hand plane. There are several methods for squaring up stock.

### Method A.

1. Plane the face surface or side (working face).
2. Plane the working edge.
3. Plane the stock to width (second edge).

COMPLETING THE SQUARING OPERATIONS

4. Plane the stock to thickness (second surface or side).

5. Plane one end (working end).

6. Cut stock to length.

7. Plane other end (second end).

## Method B.

1. Plane the face surface (working surface).

2. Plane the working edge.

3. Plane one end square with the face surface and joint edge.

4. Plane stock to width.

5. Plane stock to thickness.

6. Cut off stock to length.

7. Plane other end.

## Method C. (Recommended)

1. Plane the face surface.

2. Plane the working edge.

3. Plane one end square with the face surface and joint edge.

4. Cut off stock to length.

5. Plane other end.

6. Plane stock to width.

7. Plane stock to thickness.

## Can You Answer These Questions on Squaring Up Stock?

1. Must all six surfaces of the board be planed?

2. Name the machine tools that are use-ful in squaring up stock.

3. There are three methods of squaring up stock. Describe them.

# Section IV

## Making Pieces of Curved or Irregular Designs

---

The fourth 3 steps in hand woodworking—what you must know and be able to do.

15. How to transfer curves and irregular lines: using dividers, drawing circles, working with some geometric patterns like the octagon and hexagon, and drawing an ellipse.

16. Cutting many and varied curved patterns with the coping saw

and the compass saw, and the proper way to cut with these saws.

17. Forming and trimming these various shapes to make them smooth and ready for assembly, using the spokeshave, drawknife, homemade scraper, and file or rasp.

---

YOU WOULD find woodwork rather dull if everything were made in flat, straight planes. Curves, geometric designs, and shapes in the form of animals and other representations of Nature are added to lend beauty to your projects and interest to the building of them. Then, too, there are many things which depend for their very usefulness on a curved or molded shape, such as archery bows, canoe paddles, or boat hulls.

In this section, you will begin to work with saws and other cutting tools especially suited to the development of irregular, molded, curved, and formed designs.

The new ideas and skills which you will study and learn in order to create some of these projects and designs are listed in the "box" above. Further woodworking steps are on pp. 12, 37, 53, 97, 111, 119, 148, 174, and 187.

### LAYING OUT AND TRANSFERRING CURVES AND DESIGNS

Many projects contain pieces with irregular designs or geometric shapes that must be transferred to the wood from a drawing before further work can be done. If it is a geometric design, the layout can usually be made directly on the wood. However, if it is an irregular

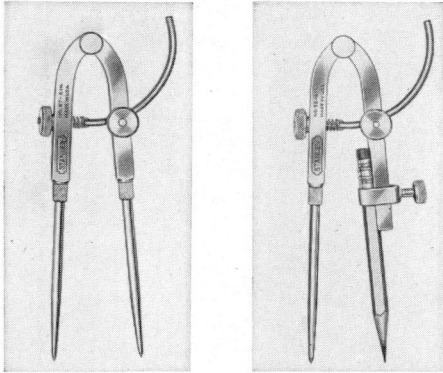

117. Two tools for drawing circles and arcs: A. Dividers. B. Pencil compass.

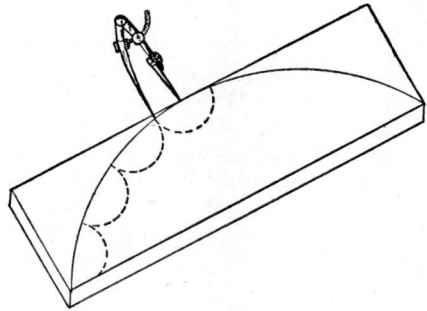

118. USING A DIVIDERS.

design, it is first necessary to draw a full-size pattern on paper and then to transfer it to the wood.

## Dividers

A dividers or an ordinary pencil compass is used for laying out small circles. Fig. 117. The dividers is more accurate and has other uses in layout work, such as dividing space equally, transferring measurements, and scribing arcs. Fig. 118. To set the dividers, place one leg over the inch mark on the rule and then open the other leg to a distance desired. Lock the thumbscrew. On some dividers, there is an additional spring nut that is used to make fine corrections in setting.

## Drawing circles

Set the dividers to equal half the diameter of the circle. Place one leg over the center of the circle, tip the dividers at a slight angle, and,

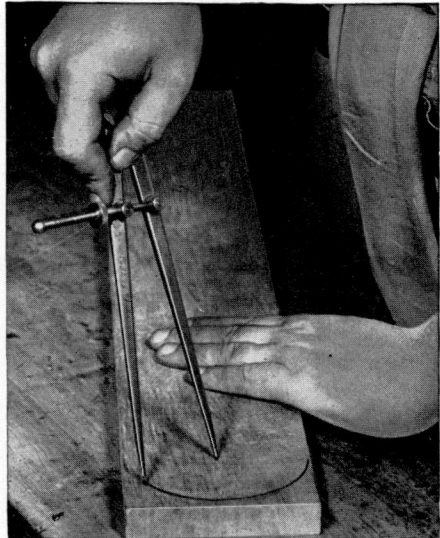

119. LAYING OUT A CIRCLE WITH A DIVIDERS. The dividers is tipped slightly as it is swung around.

working from left to right, scribe the circle. Fig. 119. When drawing circles on finished wood, place an eraser from the end of a pencil over the point of the dividers leg which is to act as the center.

120. TRAMMEL POINTS ARE USED WHEN LAYING OUT LARGE CIRCLES. These points fit on a long, thin board or piece of metal and can be adjusted to any length.

121. LOCATING THE CENTER FOR LAYING OUT A ROUNDED CORNER.

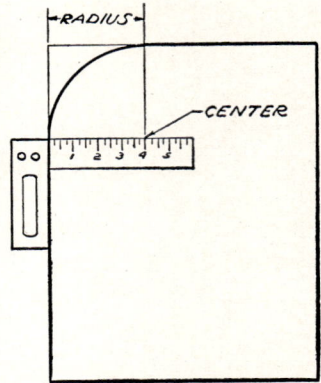

To lay out larger circles, use a set of trammel points (Fig. 120) or tie a piece of string to a pencil and use this as a compass.

## Laying out a rounded corner

The corners on many projects are rounded for appearance and utility. To lay out these corners, first determine the radius of the arc from the drawing. Then mark this distance from the corner on the adjacent side and end. Fig. 121. Then, with a try square held against edge and end, draw two lines that intersect, to indicate the center of the arc. Set the dividers to the proper radius and draw the arc.

## Laying out an octagon

An octagon has eight equal sides and all angles are equal. Determine the distance across the octagon from one side to the other and lay out a square of this size. Next, set a dividers or compass to equal half the diagonal length across the square. Set the point of the

compass at each corner of the square and strike an arc from one side of the square to the other. Do this from each of the four corners. Join the points where the arcs intersect the sides of the square. Fig. 122.

## Laying out a hexagon

A hexagon has six equal sides and all angles are equal. Determine the length of one side. Set a compass or dividers to equal this measurement and draw a circle with this

122. LAYOUT OF AN OCTAGON.

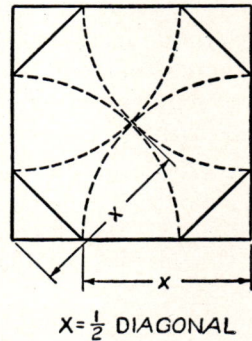

X = ½ DIAGONAL

radius. Begin at any point on the circle and without changing the setting draw a series of arcs, moving the point to the place where the preceding arc has intersected the circle. Fig. 123. The last arc should intersect the circle at the first point made by the compass. Join these points with a straightedge.

## Drawing an ellipse

An ellipse is a regular curve that has two different diameters. Lay out the two diameters at right angles to each other—namely, AB and CD as shown in Fig. 124a. Set a dividers equal to half the longest diameter. Place the point of the dividers on point D and strike an arc to intersect the longest diameter at points X and Y. Fig. 124b. Place a thumbtack at these two points and another at one end of the longest diameter. Tie a string around the two outside thumbtacks. Remove the outside thumbtack and place a pencil inside the string. Fig. 124c. Hold the pen-

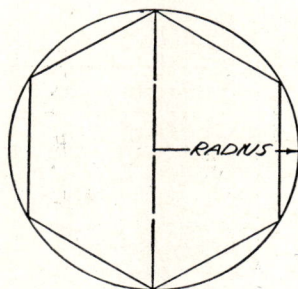

123. LAYOUT OF A HEXAGON.

cil at right angles to the paper and carefully draw the ellipse.

## Enlarging irregular designs

Frequently a project that is found in a book or magazine will not be drawn to full size. If the project contains irregular parts, it will be necessary to make an enlarged drawing to use as a pattern in making the layout on the wood. You can do this in the following manner:

1. Determine how much the original drawing is reduced from full size. Usually drawings in books or

124. HOW TO MAKE AN ELLIPSE. A. Laying out the two diameters at right angles to each other. B. Striking an arc to intersect two points X and Y on the long diameter. C. Drawing the ellipse. Note that the outside thumbtack has been removed and a pencil put in its place. Be sure that the pencil is held at right angles with the work in forming the ellipse.

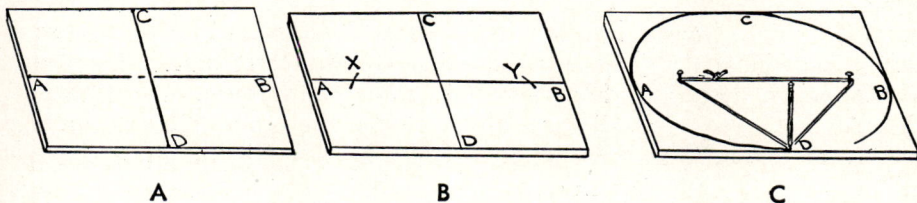

A     B     C

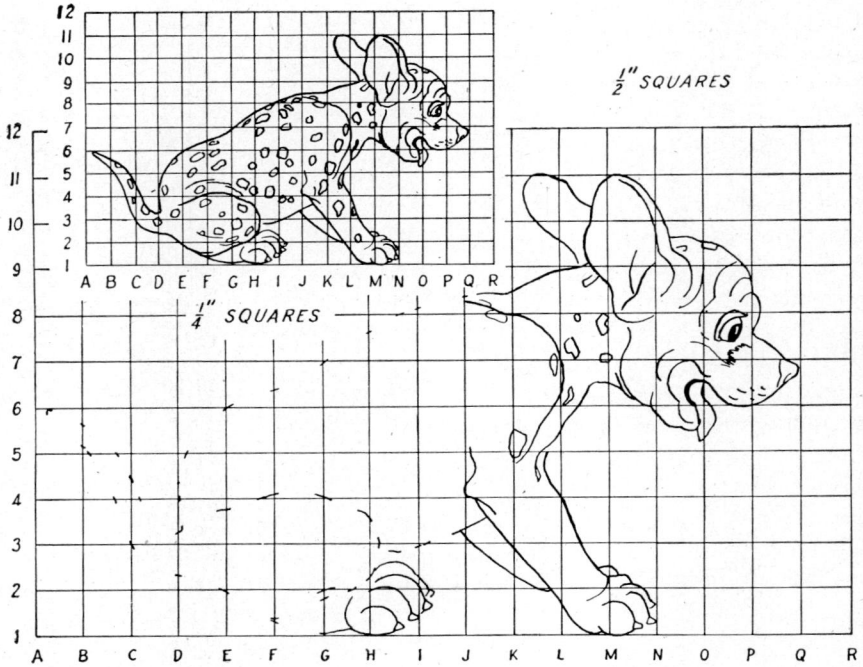

**125. ENLARGING AN IRREGULAR DESIGN.** The crosshatch paper is numbered the same, both in the original and the enlargement. This helps to locate the points needed to make the enlargement.

magazines will be one half or one fourth of full size. If the original drawing is not already on squared paper, lay out squares over the print representing the amount of reduction. *For example, if the pattern is ¼ of full size, draw ¼" squares.*

2. On a large piece of wrapping paper, carefully lay out 1" squares. From the lower lefthand corner of both the original drawing and the layout paper, letter all horizontal lines A, B, C, etc., and all vertical lines 1, 2, 3, etc. Using these letters and numbers, locate a position on the original drawing and then trans-

fer it to the full-size pattern. Fig. 125. Continue to locate and transfer positions until enough points are marked for the full-size pattern.

3. With these points located, sketch the full-size pattern. Use a ruler to connect points that represent straight lines. On curved sections, a piece of wire solder can be bent to serve as a templet, or pattern gauge, in drawing these lines. Now examine your design. A little change here and there may smooth out the curve and give it the attractive appearance you desire.

4. If the piece is symmetrical,

you need to lay out only half the design, then fold the sheet of paper down the center and cut out the full pattern.

5. Place this paper pattern on your pieces of stock and trace around it. You may need a little transparent adhesive or masking tape to hold it in place. Care is essential at this point.

6. If you are making a large number of parts of the same design, make a templet of thin wood or sheet metal from the paper design

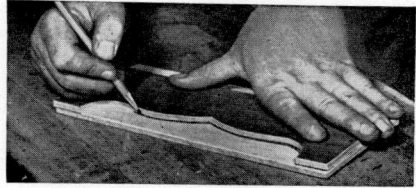

126. USING A TEMPLET TO MAKE A LAYOUT. When several pieces of the same design are to be cut, it is much simpler to use a templet of thin wood or metal.

and use this templet to make the lay-out. Fig. 126.

## Can You Answer These Questions on Laying Out and Transferring Curves and Designs?

1. Name three uses for a dividers.
2. How should a dividers be set to measurement?
3. What precautions should be taken when drawing a circle on a finished piece.
4. What are trammel points?
5. Why is it customary to round the corners of projects?
6. How many sides has an octagon? A hexagon?

7. How is an octagon drawn?
8. Define an ellipse. Describe the method of drawing one.
9. When is it necessary to enlarge an irregular design?
10. Why are most of the designs in books drawn on squared paper?
11. Is it always necessary to lay out the whole design. Why?
12. Describe a templet and how used.

### CUTTING OUT CURVES

Many projects contain curves or irregular shapes that must be cut to form the design. To saw curves, the saw must have a thin blade. The two most commonly used are the coping and compass saws. This work can also be done on the jig or band saw. (See Machine Woodworking.)

### The coping saw

The coping saw has a handle

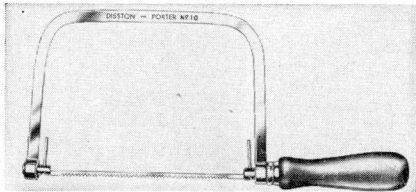

127. A COPING SAW. This type is tightened by screwing up the handle. The blade can also be adjusted to any angle to the frame.

and a U-shaped frame into which a removable blade is fastened. The more inexpensive type has a wire frame in which the blade is held

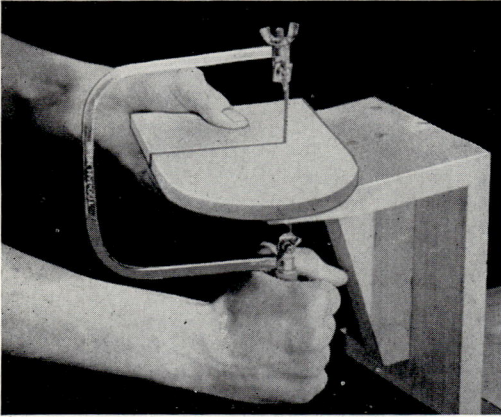

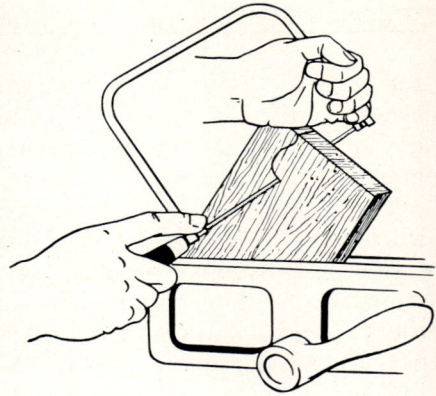

128. CUTTING WORK WITH THE STOCK HELD OVER A SAW BRACKET. When doing this type of sawing, the blade is put in the frame with the teeth pointing toward the handle. This method is especially satisfactory for cutting intricate designs. COURTESY THE JAM HANDY ORGANIZATION.

129. CUTTING WITH A COPING SAW WITH THE WORK HELD IN A VISE. In this type of work, the saw can be held in both hands, thus giving it more support for cutting heavier stock.

taut by the spring of the frame itself. The type shown in Fig. 127 is more practical for general woodworking because the blade is tightened by a screw in the handle. It has the added advantage of permitting the blade to be turned at any angle to the frame. Coping-saw blades have ripsaw-like teeth and are made with several different numbers of points to the inch. For most work, a blade with sixteen points or fifteen teeth to the inch is good.

1. Cutting with the work supported on a saw bracket. Mount the blade in the frame with the teeth pointing toward the handle. If the opening to be cut is internal, drill a small hole in the waste material just large enough for the blade to pass through. Slip the blade through the hole and fasten it into the frame. Hold the work to the bracket with your left hand. Fig. 128. Grasp the handle of the coping saw in your right hand and move the saw up and down. The cutting action takes place on the downward stroke, with the pressure released as the saw is pushed upward. The saw must be worked freely and therefore very little pressure should be exerted. Hold the work firmly. As the cutting takes place, it is better to move the work, keeping the saw blade inside the V cut of the bracket. If it is hard to cut the material, apply a little soap or wax to the blade. Keep the blade moving at a steady pace of about twenty to thirty strokes per minute. At sharp corners, turn the handle slowly in the direction of the line and keep moving the saw up and down without applying any pres-

sure to the blade. Begin cutting again as the blade is turned. Twisting or bending the blade at the corners will usually break it.

2. Cutting with the work held in a vise. Insert the blade in the frame with the teeth pointing away from the handle. Lock the work in the vise with the place to be cut near the top of the vise jaws. Begin the cutting in the waste stock and keep your strokes uniform as you bring the blade to the cutting line. Make sure that the saw kerf is in the waste stock and that the blade is held perpendicular to the work at all times. While the cutting is being done, the saw can be supported with both hands as shown in Fig. 129; or, if the stock is very light, you may support the work itself with your left hand to prevent vibrating.

## The compass saw

The compass saw looks like any other handsaw except that it is much smaller and has a thin, tapered blade. Usually a compass saw has several different-sized blades that fit into the same handle. Fig. 130. The narrow point at the end of the saw makes it possible to start

131A. USING A COMPASS SAW FOR INTERNAL CUTTING. A hole is drilled in the stock to permit the saw blade to enter.

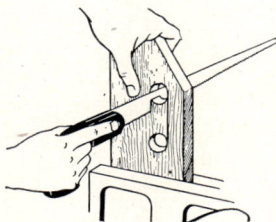

131B. CUTTING AN INSIDE OPENING in which two bored holes are part of the pattern.

132. USING A COMPASS SAW TO CUT A CURVED SURFACE. The handle can be twisted slightly to follow the layout line.

130. COMPASS SAW. This one has several interchangeable blades for different types of jobs.

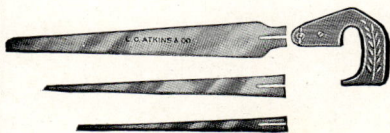

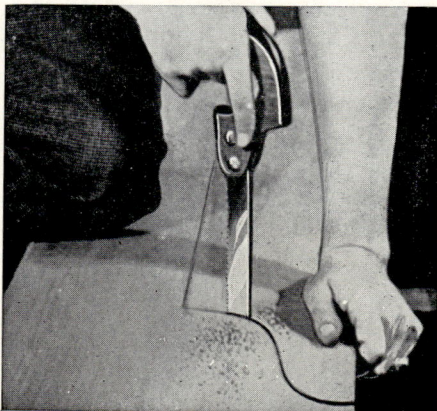

the tool in a small opening and to cut small curves and circles. The saw is made in lengths of from 10 to 18 inches with eight points to the inch. An average size compass saw is 10 to 14 inches long.

A keyhole saw is very similar to the compass saw, except that it is even smaller and is named for its most common use.

*Cutting with the compass saw.* Drill a hole in the waste stock large enough for the saw point to enter. Insert the point of the saw in the first hole and take several short, quick strokes to force more of the blade to pass through the stock. Fig. 131. Cut a curve by twisting the handle of the saw a little to follow the pattern. Fig. 132.

## Can You Answer These Questions on Cutting Out Curves?

1. What machine tools will cut curves in wood? What hand tools?

2. Blades of a coping saw resemble what type of handsaw?

3. When work is cut on a saw bracket, should the teeth be pointed toward or away from the handle?

4. How can the saw be prevented from sticking?

5. About how many strokes per minute should be taken with the coping saw?

6. What are the most common causes of saw blade breakage?

7. Exactly where should the saw kerf be in regard to the layout line?

8. Describe a compass saw. Its use?

### FORMING AND SMOOTHING CURVES

After the curve has been cut, the edge is rough and requires the removal of some excess stock to smooth the edge and to bring it down to the finished line. Also, it is sometimes necessary to form or mold a curved surface. These can be done either with some kind of cutting tool such as a spokeshave or drawknife or with a scraping tool such as a file or rasp. A homemade scraper made from an old hack-saw blade is also a good tool for forming and smoothing curves.

### The spokeshave

A spokeshave consists of a frame with two handles which hold a small cutting blade. It is used to plane convex and concave edges. The depth of cut can be regulated with one or two small thumbscrews. The spokeshave was originally used for shaping the spokes of wheels but since has come to be a common tool for finishing the edges of curves and molding irregular shapes. Fig. 133.

133. A SPOKESHAVE IS USED TO CUT CONCAVE AND CONVEX EDGES and for molding and forming work. This type has two knurled nuts on the top for adjusting the depth of the cutter. The cutter is held in place with a cap, which is fastened by a thumbscrew.

134. HOLDING A SPOKESHAVE WHEN DRAWING IT TOWARD YOU. The blade should be set just deep enough to form a thin shaving. If set too deep, the tool will chatter.

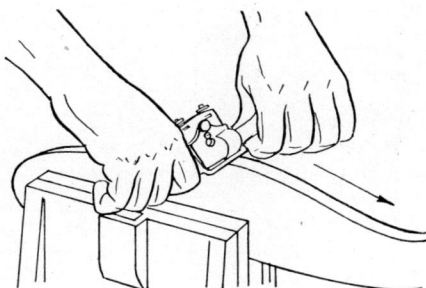

135. HOLDING A SPOKESHAVE WHEN PUSHING IT AWAY FROM YOU. Even pressure can be applied to do the cutting.

136. A DRAWKNIFE IS ESPECIALLY USEFUL in removing large amounts of stock rapidly.

## Cutting with a spokeshave

Place the piece in the vise with the edge to be smoothed near the surface of the vise. Grasp the tool with both hands. Fig. 134. In cutting, you can either draw the spokeshave toward you or, if more convenient, put your thumbs behind the frame and push it as you would a small plane. Fig. 135. Place the cutting edge on the wood and apply even pressure. Work *with* the grain of the wood. Your experience in using a plane will tell you if the proper chip is being formed. If the blade is set too deep, the tool will chatter.

When concave curves are being planed, the cutting is done from the top of the curve downward. Remember, use the spokeshave as you would a small plane.

## The drawknife

The drawknife is a U-shaped tool with a blade 8 or 10 inches long with a handle at either end. Fig. 136. This tool is very effective for removing large amounts of stock rapidly and for doing molding work

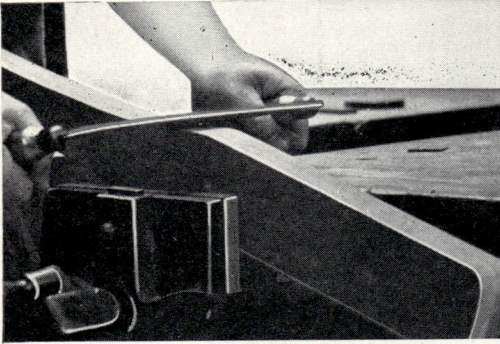

**137. CUTTING WITH A DRAW-KNIFE.** Tip the blade at a slight angle to the work to permit it to enter the stock properly. Be careful not to cut too deeply into the stock.

**139. USING A HOMEMADE SCRAPER TO FORM STOCK.** Note that the blade is held at an angle to the work and is bent slightly. This is really the best tool to use for shaping an archery bow.

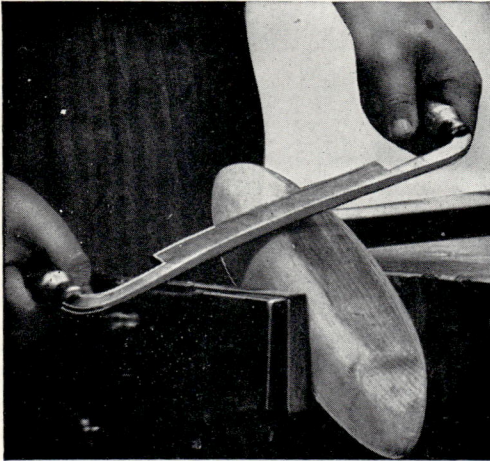

**138. USING A DRAWKNIFE** to shape the hull of a model boat.

such as shaping a canoe paddle or building a model boat, airplane, or other cylindrical model. Be especially careful in using this tool, as the long, exposed blade can be dangerous.

## Cutting with the drawknife

Clamp the work in the vise in such a way that the cutting will take place *with* the grain of the wood. Grasp the tool in both hands, holding the blade firmly against the wood with the bevel side down. Fig. 137. Turn the blade at a slight angle to the work and carefully draw it into the wood until a thin chip forms; then draw the knife steadily toward you. Fig. 138. Do not try to take too deep a cut at one time, as this will split the wood.

## Homemade scraper

For forming and molding curves which you might do to make an archery bow, the best tool is a scraper that can be made by grinding the teeth off an old hack-saw blade. If possible, secure a larger half-hard blade, the kind used in automatic hack saws. Grind off the teeth and cover the ends of the blade by wrapping them with friction tape, to protect your hands.

## Using a homemade scraper

Fasten the stock in the vise so that the piece to be molded extends away from the vise jaw. Grasp the scraper in both hands and hold the blade against the wood at a slight angle, with enough pressure to bend the blade slightly. Now begin to draw the blade toward you. Fig. 139. Continue to draw the blade toward you in long, sweeping strokes to form the stock to the desired shape.

a file, except that the face is cut with individually shaped teeth. Fig. 141. The rasp removes large amounts of stock quickly and leaves a rough surface, while the file produces a smoother finish. Always put a handle on the rasp and file when using them because the tang can injure your hand severely.

## Smoothing with a file or rasp

Clamp the work in the vise securely. Hold the handle in your right hand and the end of the tool

140. A CABINET FILE. Be sure that a handle is attached when you use it for smoothing operations.

141. A RASP. NOTICE THE INDIVIDUALLY SHAPED TEETH. This tool is used for removing larger amounts of stock, but it leaves quite a rough surface.

## The file or rasp

A file or rasp is a scraping tool and should be used only as a last resort. Too often the inexperienced woodworker prefers to use one of these tools when a cutting tool will do a much better job. There are so many kinds of files and so many shapes and sizes that it would be impractical to describe even a few of them here. The two files used most often, however, are a 10- to 12-inch half-round cabinet file or a 10- to 12-inch rattail file. Fig. 140. A rasp is very similar in appearance to

142. USING A FILE TO DRESS AN INTERNAL CURVE. Make sure that you hold the file flat against the stock and that you do not rock it.

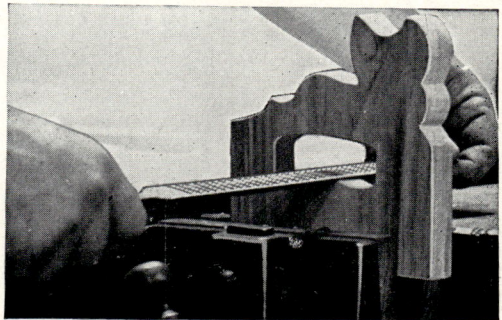

A

B

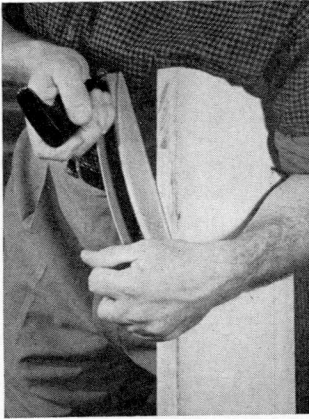

143. A. A FILE TYPE OF SURFORM TOOL. B. Using a plane type of surform tool.

in your left. Apply pressure on the forward stroke, making a slight shearing cut across the edge of the work. Fig. 142. Release the pressure on the return stroke. When you are using a half-round or rattail file for finishing a convex curve,

twist the tool slowly as the forward stroke is made. Don't rock a file or rasp as this will round off the edge of the work. These tools should be cleaned often with a file card.

## The Surform Tool

This is a forming tool that has a hardened and tempered tool-steel cutting blade. Fig. 143A. The blade has 45-degree cutting edges with many small openings that make it easy to cut wood, plastics, or soft metals. The teeth never become clogged. The replaceable blade fits into either a file or plane type holder. This tool is used like a rasp. To obtain best results, apply light, even pressure against the material. Fig. 143B. This produces a smooth, flat surface. It is a good repair tool to smooth an edge or an end that is chipped or splintered. It is also good for shaping gun stocks, canoe paddles, wooden tool handles, and other odd-shaped projects.

## Can You Answer These Questions on Forming and Smoothing Curves?

1. In what ways is a spokeshave like a plane?

2. Where did the spokeshave get its name?

3. Can a spokeshave be both drawn and pushed?

4. To what job is the drawknife best suited?

5. To make the cut, how should the drawknife be held against the wood?

6. Describe how you would make a homemade scraper.

7. What is the main use for a scraper?

8. How is a file different from a rasp?

9. Does a good woodworker use a file or rasp very often?

10. List the safety practices that should be observed when using a file or rasp.

11. Describe the way in which a file or rasp is handled; the surform tool.

# Section V

# Decorating, Shaping, and Bending Woods

The fifth 3 steps in hand woodworking—what you must know and be able to do.

18. Chamfer, bevel, or taper cutting: how it is done, what these are used for, and how they are different from other procedures.

19. Chiseling and gouging operations: kinds of chisels and gouges,

chiseling with the grain, across grain, vertically and horizontally, and many other uses; how to use a gouge.

20. Wood bending; equipment needed and how to heat and bend the wood over forms.

WHEN YOU are making many kinds of articles, you will need to use a number of sharp-edged tools to cut or form the wood either in straight lines or curved designs. This cutting can be done with plane, chisel, or gouge to decorate the pieces, to fit them, and to shape them. Watch particularly the descriptions of the chisel and gouge, since these tools will be used over and over in woodworking.

In some cases the desired shape is more easily attained by bending than by cutting. For example, you might make a boat model by cutting, shaping, and forming it from a single piece of stock, but, when you build the boat to full size, you will probably use bent wood.

Not all of the operations in this section will be done on a single project but eventually you will need all of them. See "box" above. Further steps in woodworking are on pp. 12, 37, 53, 84, 111, 119, 148, 174, and 187.

144. THE CHAMFER IS A DECORATION ON THE EDGE OF STOCK; the bevel is for construction purposes and the taper gives lightness and grace to furniture legs.

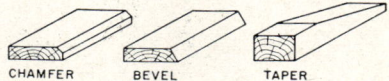

CHAMFER     BEVEL     TAPER

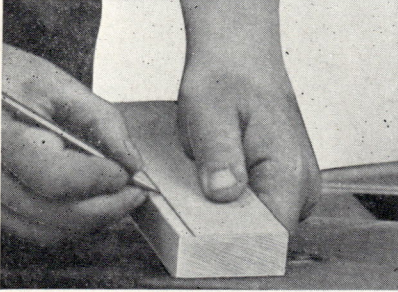

145. MARKING A CHAMFER by using a pencil guided with your fingers held against the edge of the stock.

146. PLANING A CHAMFER WITH THE WOOD HELD IN A HAND SCREW. By this means, you can cut the chamfer with the plane held in a level position.

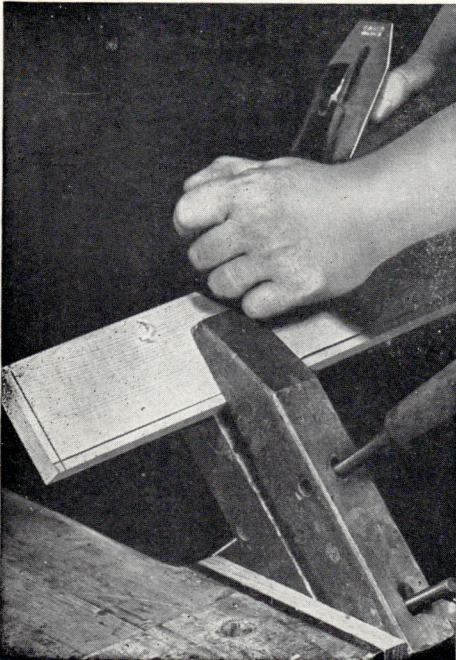

## MAKING A CHAMFER, BEVEL, OR TAPER

Three types of angular cuts that are made much in the same way but used for different purposes are the chamfer, the bevel, and the taper. Fig. 144.

The chamfer is an angular cut across the corner, primarily used as a decoration added to an edge or end. The bevel is an angle cut completely across the edge or end of a piece. This is done when making any project in which one piece is set at an angle to another, such as the troughs of a bookcase. A taper is cut on legs of tables and stools to give them an appearance of light weight and grace. On some projects the taper is on all four sides, but, on many modern pieces, only the two inside surfaces are tapered. (See Fig. 432.)

### Making a through chamfer

1. Determine the amount of chamfer from the drawing. If this is not given, it is a usual practice to cut a chamfer about $\frac{3}{16}$ inch on stock that is 1 inch thick. There are two methods that can be followed for marking the chamfer. One is to hold a pencil between the fingers as a gauge and run it along the face surface and the edge or end as shown in Fig. 145. Another way is to insert a pencil point in a regular marking gauge and then use the marking gauge to lay out the line. Do not, however, use a regular marking

gauge, which would leave a rough edge on the chamfer.

2. Lock the stock in a vise. In some cases it may be easier to clamp the stock first in a hand screw as shown in Fig. 146, and then to lock the hand screw in the vise. This has the advantage of permitting you to hold the plane level as the cutting is done.

3. Plane the corner of the stock with the grain along the total length. Remove the stock evenly so that the chamfer will come down to the marked line on both sides at the same time. Use the fingers of your left hand to guide the plane and to aid in holding it at the proper angle. In taking the last cut, form a chip that is the full width of the chamfer across the total length of the stock.

When cutting a chamfer on end grain, hold the plane at an angle to the surface being cut and take a shearing cut across the edge. Fig. 147. If this is not done, there is danger of splitting out the chamfer on the edge. To check the chamfer, set a sliding T bevel at an angle of 45 degrees and hold it against the chamfer edge.

## Making a stop chamfer

To make a stop chamfer (Fig. 148), it is necessary to cut it with a chisel or drawknife. However, if it is a long stop chamfer, the ends can be formed with a chisel or drawknife and the center section planed with a block plane.

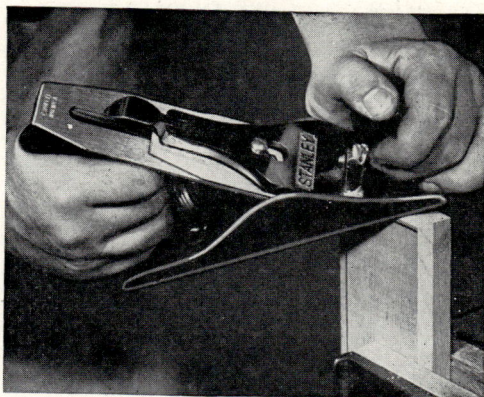

147. **CUTTING A CHAMFER ON END GRAIN.** A shearing cut is being taken to prevent the edge of the stock from splitting out.

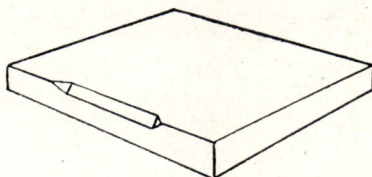

148. **A STOP CHAMFER.** This requires the use of a chisel to form the ends. If it is a long stop chamfer, the center section can be planed.

## Planing a bevel

Determine the angle at which the bevel is to be cut and set a sliding T bevel to this angle with a protractor. Hold the sliding T bevel against the face surface and mark the angle of the bevel on both ends of the stock. Fig. 149. Begin to

149. USING A SLIDING T BEVEL to lay out a bevel on one edge of a piece of stock. As the planing approaches the finished line, the sliding T bevel can be used in the same manner as a try square to check the bevel along the edge.

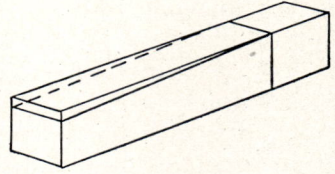

150. LAYING OUT A TAPER. When the taper is to be cut on two adjoining sides, one side should be laid out and cut before the second layout is made.

## Cutting a taper

Square up the legs on which the taper is to be cut. Lay the four legs side by side and mark the position at which the taper is to start. Then square a line around all four sides of each leg. Next determine the amount of stock to be removed at the foot of the taper. Set a marking gauge to this amount and mark a line across the lower end of the leg on the two opposite sides, if all four sides are to be tapered, or on one side, if only two sides are to be tapered. Draw a line along each side to indicate where the taper is to be cut. Fig. 150.

Cut the taper with a handsaw or, if one is available, a band or circular saw. Plane the tapered surface smooth and true. After the one or two sides have been finished, cut the other one or two the same.

plane the bevel as you would plane an edge, except that you must tip the plane at about the angle at which the bevel is to be cut. Check this angle frequently with a sliding T bevel. Continue to plane the edge until the bevel is formed.

### Can You Answer These Questions on Making a Chamfer, Bevel, or Taper?

1. In what way is a chamfer different from a bevel?

2. Would you lay out a chamfer with a regular marking gauge? Discuss two

methods of laying out an ordinary chamfer.

3. How can you hold the plane level and still cut a chamfer?

4. What precautions must be taken in cutting a chamfer on end grain?

5. Describe a stop chamfer.

6. Why is a sliding T bevel necessary when making a bevel?

## SHAPING STOCK WITH A CHISEL OR GOUGE

There are many jobs in which you will need to cut down to a line or to form irregular shapes that cannot be done with a saw or plane. This can be done with either a chisel or gouge. You will find many uses for a set of good chisels.

### Chisels and gouges

The chisels you buy can be either of two types, the socket or firmer chisel and the tang chisel. Fig. 151a and b. The socket chisel is used most commonly, as it will withstand pounding better than the tang type.

Chisels are either standard lengths or shorter lengths. The latter are called butt chisels. Fig. 152. You will need a set of at least six chisels with blades from ¼ inch in width, increasing at ⅛ inch intervals up to 1 inch in width.

Gouges are used in a similar way, except that the blade is curved and may be sharpened either with the bevel on the inside or outside. Fig. 153. They vary in size from ¼ inch to 2 inches.

To cut with a chisel or gouge, it is often necessary to pound the

151. TYPES OF CHISEL HANDLES AND CONNECTIONS. A. Socket-type chisel is made in such a way that the handle fits into a socket of the blade itself. B. Tang-type chisel has the tang of the chisel itself running into the handle.

152. A BUTT TYPE CHISEL that is used by cabinetmakers and other skilled woodworkers for very fine work.

153. THIS IS A GOUGE WITH A BEVEL ON THE OUTSIDE. Gouges can also be purchased with an inside bevel.

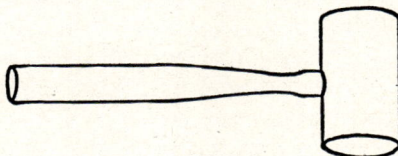

154. A MALLET TO USE FOR POUNDING A CHISEL or gouge should have a wood, rawhide, or hard rubber head.

tool with a mallet that has a head made of wood, hard rubber, or rawhide. Fig. 154.

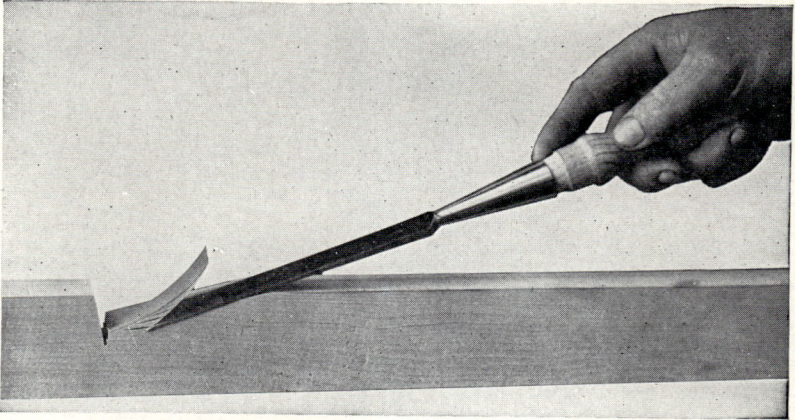

**155.** NOTE THE CUTTING ACTION OF THE CHISEL. You should always cut with the grain, never against.

## Cutting horizontally with the grain

Lock the work in a vise in the proper position for working with the grain of the wood. Fig. 155. Never attempt to cut against the grain, as the wood will split out.

For rough cutting, hold the chisel with the bevel side against the stock. Grasp the chisel handle in your right hand and the blade in your left. Fig. 156. Use your right hand to apply pressure to the tool and your left hand to guide the cutting action.

The cutting action may be taken in two ways. The blade may be forced into the stock parallel to the wood or a shearing cut made with the blade moving from right to left as it cuts. You will find that the straight cutting will require that more pressure be applied to the tool

and that it is more convenient to hold the tool in your left hand and pound with a mallet held in your right hand. When making light, paring cuts with the chisel, turn the tool around with the flat surface next to the wood and take a light, shearing cut. Hold the blade between your thumb and forefinger to guide it in taking these cuts.

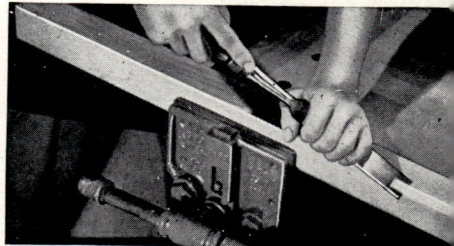

**156.** HOLDING A CHISEL FOR DOING HEAVY HORIZONTAL CUTTING with the grain. The blade of the chisel is held firmly in the left hand. COURTESY THE JAM HANDY ORGANIZATION.

**157. ROUGHING OUT A CUT ACROSS GRAIN.** The chisel is held with the bevel side down and a mallet is used for driving. This illustrates the cutting of a lap joint.

**159. MAKING LIGHT PARING CUTS ACROSS GRAIN.** The blade of the chisel is held between the thumb and forefinger for accurate control. The chisel is held with the flat side down.

**158. THE PROPER METHOD OF CUTTING A LAP JOINT** from both sides, leaving the center high and then trimming the center down.

## Horizontal cutting across the grain

Lock the work in a vise or clamp it to the top of the bench. Rough cutting can be done with the bevel downward or by paring with the flat side down. In cutting across the grain to make a rabbet, dado, or lap joint, work from one side to about halfway across the stock. Fig. 157. Never go completely across the stock, as this will chip out the opposite side. Work from both sides to the finished line, leaving the center higher. Fig. 158. Then with light, paring cuts bring the center down to the proper depth. Fig. 159. To clean out the corners, hold the chisel in one hand with the flat side toward the shoulder and draw it across as you would a knife. Fig. 160.

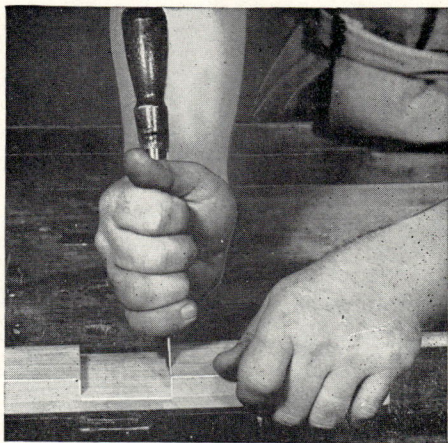

**160. CLEANING OUT THE CORNERS OF THE LAP JOINT** by drawing the chisel across with the flat side held against the shoulder of the joint.

## Cutting convex curves horizontally

Remember when you lock the work in the vise that you will be cutting with the grain. Begin by taking straight cuts that tend to follow the curve. Fig. 161. Remove

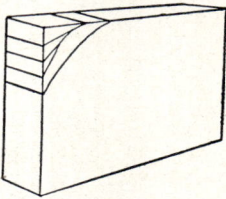

**161. CUTTING A CONVEX CURVE.**
Note that several straight cuts have been taken to form the curve to the approximate arc.

most of the excess stock with these straight cuts until the curve is almost formed. Then hold the chisel with the flat side down and carefully cut the curve by applying forward pressure and raising the handle to follow the arc. Fig. 162.

**162. FINISHING A CONVEX CURVE.**
Forward pressure is applied and the handle is raised gradually to follow the proper curvature. COURTESY THE JAM HANDY ORGANIZATION.

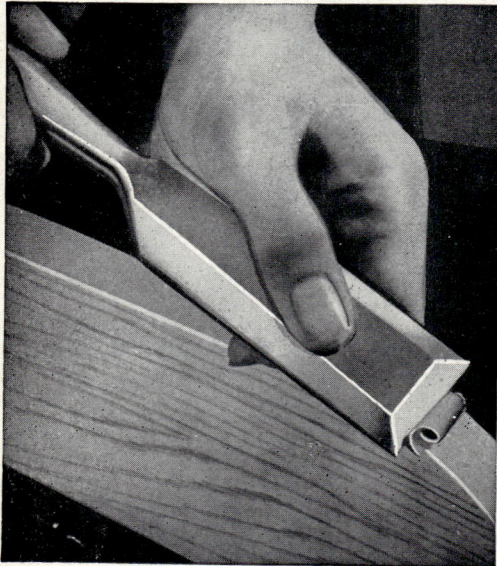

## Cutting vertically across the grain

Hold the stock over a bench hook or clamp it over a scrap piece of wood. Never do vertical chiseling directly on the top of a bench, as this would mar it.

Hold the chisel in a vertical position with the handle gripped in your

**163. CUTTING END GRAIN VERTICALLY.** Note that the stock is held over a bench hook and pressure applied to the handle at the same time that it is rotated slightly to obtain a shearing cut.

right hand and the blade guided between your thumb and forefinger. Take a shearing cut, working from right to left, to remove the stock. On wide stock, you can regulate the depth of the cut by holding the flat side of the chisel against the surface that has been previously cut.

## Cutting end grain vertically

Lay the work flat over a bench hook or piece of scrap stock and clamp it firmly in place. Begin at one corner of the stock to make the cut by tipping the handle to one side, rotating it to get a shearing cut. Fig. 163. Always start from the corner and work toward the center. Working in the opposite way would tend to split out the end grain.

## Cutting concave surfaces vertically

Lock the work in the vise with the concave surface to be removed just above the end of the vise. Take straight cuts until as much of the waste stock as possible is removed, working as always from the edge toward the end to avoid splitting out the stock. To form the concave curve, hold the chisel with the bevel side toward the stock. Apply forward pressure, at the same time moving the handle in an arc. Fig. 164.

## Cutting with a gouge

Gouges are used in the same general manner as chisels. Outside bevel

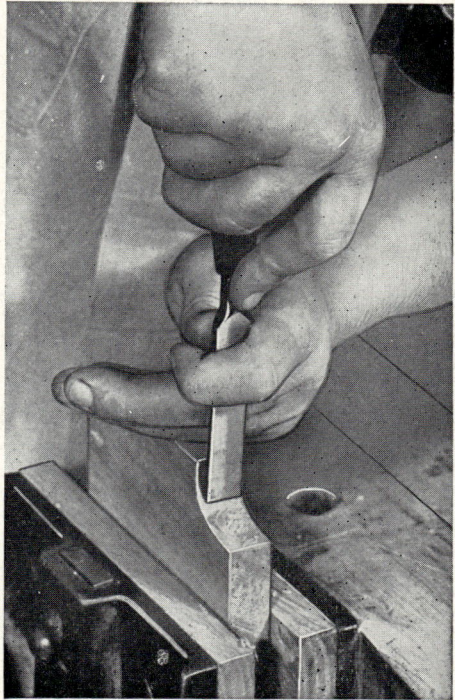

164. CUTTING A CONCAVE CURVE. The chisel is held with the bevel side down and the cut is being taken from the edge to the end grain, so that the cut is made with the grain of the wood.

gouges are manipulated in the same way that a chisel with the bevel side down is, while an inside bevel gouge is handled like a chisel with the bevel turned up.

To do heavy gouging with an outside bevel gouge, hold the handle in your right hand and the blade in your left hand. Fig. 165. Push the gouge forward and rock it from

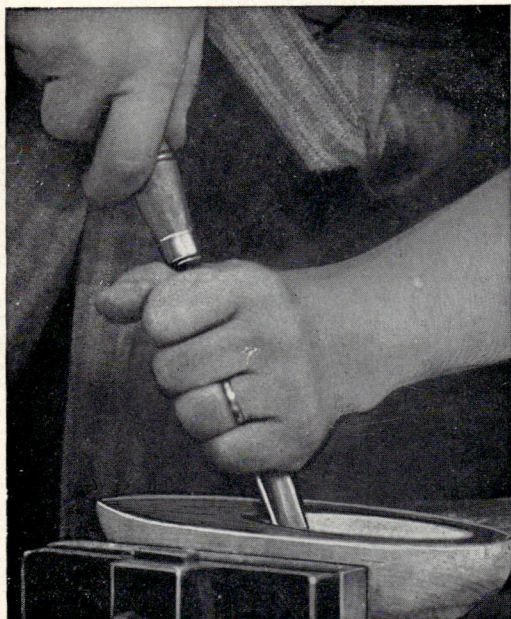

165. DOING HEAVY GOUGING to shape out the inside of a model-boat hull. The left hand holds the blade firmly, while the right hand applies pressure.

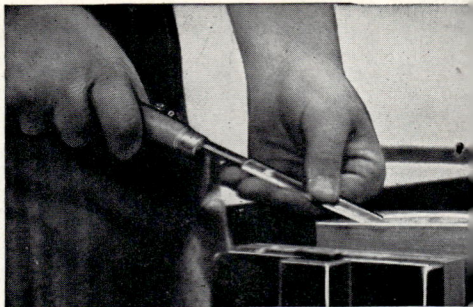

166. DOING LIGHT GOUGING with the gouge held between thumb and other fingers for accurate, light work.

side to side slightly to get a shearing cut. If extremely heavy work is being done, the gouge can be held in the left hand and a mallet used to apply force to the tool. If a large surface is to be gouged out, it is better to work across the grain, since the gouge is less likely to dig in than when cutting in the direction of the grain.

To do light gouging, hold the blade in your left hand as shown in Fig. 166, and take a thin, long shaving by forcing the tool into the wood lightly and then pushing on the handle to finish it.

Gouging is done to form recesses, to do veining and decorating work on the surface of wood, to shape such articles as boat hulls, wooden bowls, and shallow trays, and to imitate the appearance of age as on the treasure chest.

## Can You Answer These Questions on Shaping Stock With a Chisel or Gouge?

1. Name the two types of chisels. What is a butt chisel?

2. How are gouges sharpened?

3. Do you cut with or against the grain of the wood?

4. How should a chisel be held for making heavy cuts?

5. What are the two ways to do the cutting?

6. When making light, paring cuts, how should the blade be held?

7. Give the procedure for cutting a rabbet, dado, or lap joint.

8. How can the corners be chiseled out?

9. In cutting convex curves, why are straight cuts made first?

10. Should vertical chiseling be done directly on the top of a bench?

11. What kind of chisel action is best for cutting end grain vertically?

12. Can a concave surface be cut with a chisel?

NOSE CAP

0-24 16

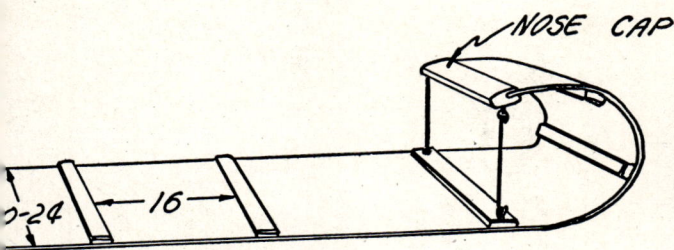

167. THE TOBOGGAN AND WATER SKIS are two of the many pieces of sports equipment that require bending. The length can be varied to suit your own needs.

13. How does a gouge differ from a chisel?

14. What kind of gouge is best for heavy gouge work?

15. To remove a great deal of stock, is it better to work with or across the grain?

16. What is the purpose of gouging?

## BENDING WOOD

To make sports equipment such as toboggans, skis, surfboards and other things in which the wood is formed, the stock must be bent. Fig. 167. Sometimes stock is bent to form a part of furniture that must be curved, such as the front of a drawer. There are many types of wood for building these projects, but ash, hickory, birch, and oak are the most successful.

## Equipment

The best method of bending wood is to soften it by steaming it or boiling it in hot water. A necessary piece of equipment is a heating tube which is closed on the lower end and has a cover for the upper end. Fig. 168. You will note that the lower end of this tube is placed directly above a gas flame. Water is poured into this tube and the end closed. The heat then turns the water hot enough to soften the wood through the addition of moisture and heat, as explained later, on page 108.

Another piece needed is the form over which the wood is to be bent. A form with the specifications shown in Fig. 169A can be used for forming the staves for a toboggan. Another form (Fig.

168. DRAWING OF A TYPE OF HEATING TUBE you will need for bending wood. The tube is fastened to the wall at a slight angle and a burner is placed under the lower end.

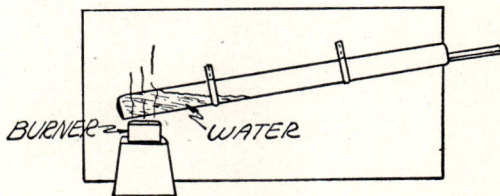

BURNER      WATER

A

I" SQUARES              $\frac{3}{4}$ x I x 2I$\frac{1}{2}$        $\frac{3}{4}$ x I0 x 28

$\llcorner\frac{3}{4}$ x I$\frac{1}{2}$ x 20, 2" APART ALONG CURVE

28

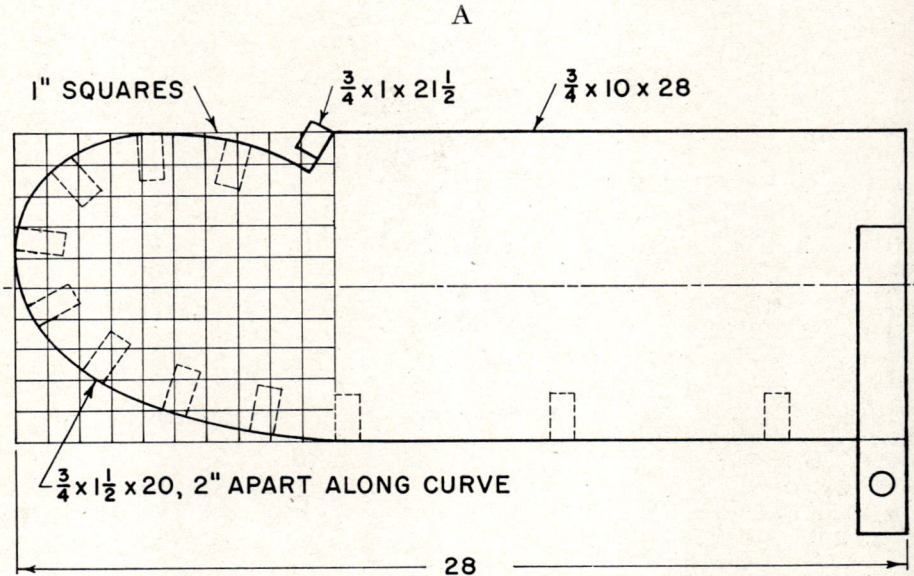

169A. A FORM SIMILAR TO THIS ONE is required to shape the front of the toboggan staves or slats.

169B) will be found satisfactory for bending the tips of water skis.

## Heating the wood

Fill the heating tube about half full of water. Light the gas flame and close the end of the tube with a tight cover. To prevent the cover from blowing off, there should be a tiny hole in it. At the same time, prepare the staves. These should be cut to the thickness and width desired and the edges chamfered or rounded off with a $\frac{1}{8}$-inch radius. When the water in the tube is boiling, insert the wood pieces in the tube. Make sure that you do not put in too many at one time, as the water should completely surround each one. Leave the wood in the tube about two to three hours.

Prepare the bending equipment while the wood is being heated. You should have available the form over which you are to bend these pieces, several C clamps, and parallel hand screws. Also cut a piece of thin sheet metal the same width as the staves and the length of the bend.

## Bending the wood

When the pieces have been heated, remove them from the tube and insert the heated end under the

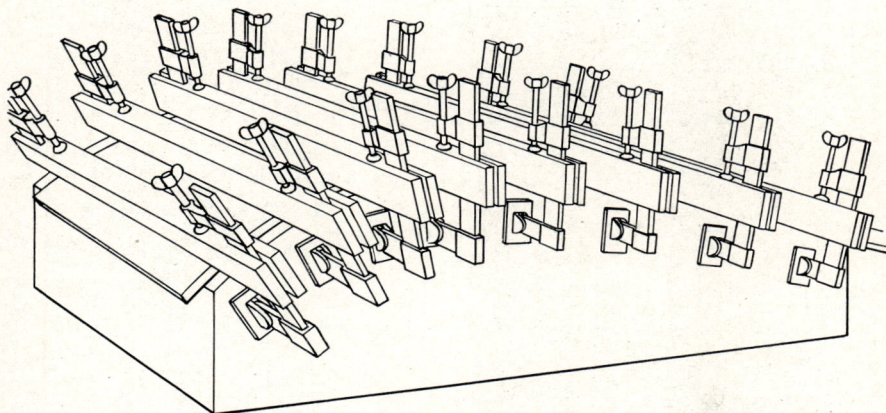

B

169B. A FORM SIMILAR TO THIS IS NEEDED to bend the tips of water skis. Each clamp must be tightened a little at a time.

170. CLAMPING A STAVE OR SLAT TO THE FORM with C clamps. A piece of sheet metal is placed directly over the wood to protect it.

171. CUT SEVERAL SAW KERFS FROM THE END OF THE STOCK as you would do in resawing lumber. This will make the tips of the skis easier to bend.

protecting bar at the top of the form. Insert the thin sheet metal directly under it. Then begin to draw the stave around the form. Work slowly and clamp the staves at each cross support with a C clamp.

Do not try to pull the stave

around the form too rapidly or the wood may split out. Continue to clamp the stave to the form as shown in Fig. 170. Then allow the piece to dry for at least twenty-four hours before removing from the form. You are now ready to sand, shape, and assemble the pieces.

## Bending without Heat and Moisture

Water skis can be made by bending flat stock to shape without steam. Make the skis of mahogany, spruce or ash. A bending form, shown in Fig. 169B, is needed. Cut the stock to size and square it up. Resaw two or more saw kerfs, staggering the cut 13 to 15 inches in length from one end. Fig. 171. Then cut veneer the thickness of the saw kerf to a shape that is slightly wider than the stock and as long as the saw kerf. Apply waterproof glue to both sides of the veneer and slip it into the kerfs. Clamp the stock in the form and allow to dry for at least 12 hours. Then shape and complete the skis as with pre-bent blanks. See Project No. 427, Page 282 and 284.

## Can You Answer These Questions on Bending Wood?

1. Toboggans, skis, and surfboards are most commonly made from what kinds of wood?

2. Wood is softened for bending in two ways. What are they and how is this done?

3. List the equipment needed for bending wood.

4. Can wood ever be bent rapidly?

# Section VI

# Cutting Holes

The sixth 2 steps in hand woodworking—what you must know and be able to do.

21. Boring holes with the auger, expansion, and Foerstner bits held in a bit brace, boring holes in both horizontal and vertical positions, through boring to prevent breaking out the opposite side of the hole, and using the depth gauge for regulating the depth of hole.

22. Drilling holes with a drill and small holes with a bit, using a hand drill for both vertical and horizontal drilling, and regulating the depth of the hole with a depth gauge.

Have you ever stopped to think why most holes are round? In woodworking, it's because it is easier to make cutting tools that will cut a round hole, although later you will find that it is possible to drill a square hole with a mortising attachment on the drill press. Another reason is that the whole process of assembly is based on the use of circular objects such as nails, screws, and dowels.

Holes are cut in wood by boring or drilling. It is called *boring* if the hole is ¼ inch or larger in diameter and cut with some kind of bit, and *drilling* when it is a small hole cut with a drill. You will find many different types of bits and drills, and each is a very fine cutting tool that must be handled with care.

Since there is usually no more than one set of bits or drills in the woodshop, you should be especially careful not to break one.

The tools and methods involved are listed in the "box" above. Further steps are on pp. 12, 37, 53, 84, 97, 119, 148, 174, and 187.

## BORING HOLES

The construction of many projects requires boring holes— to cut out a design, to make a mortise-and-tenon joint, to fit dowel rods, and other boring operations.

A

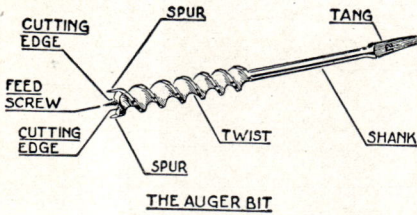

CUTTING EDGE  SPUR  TANG

FEED SCREW

CUTTING EDGE  TWIST  SHANK

SPUR

THE AUGER BIT

B

**172. KINDS OF AUGER BITS. A.** A single twist auger bit with solid center. A good set of these bits is absolutely essential in woodworking. B. An auger bit showing the parts. C. Dowel auger bit.

C

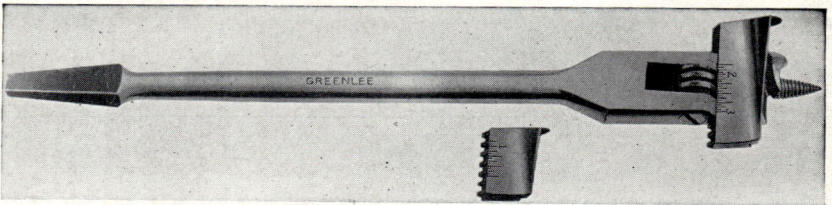

**173. AN EXPANSION BIT.** There are two cutters, a smaller one for holes of 1 inch to 2 inches in diameter and a larger one for holes 2 inches and above in diameter.

**174. USING AN EXPANSION BIT.** Care must be taken, as the bit begins to go through the opposite side, to prevent it from splitting out. It is a good idea to cut a little over halfway through, reverse the stock, and cut through the other side.

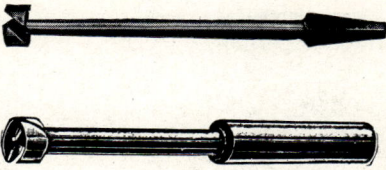

175. A FOERSTNER BIT IS USED to enlarge existing holes or to cut a hole part way through thin stock. Both the machine and hand types are shown.

## Bits

For holes from ¼ to 1¼ inch in size, an auger bit is used. Fig. 172a, b and c. The size of the auger bit is stamped on the shank, always in a single number such as 4, 5, or 6, etc., indicating that it will bore a hole ⁴⁄₁₆, ⁵⁄₁₆, ⁶⁄₁₆, etc., inch in diameter. For holes larger than 1 inch, use an expansion bit. Fig. 173. This tool can be adjusted with different cutters for a diameter of from 1 to 3 inches. Fig. 174. When you want to bore a hole part way into a thin board or when you want to enlarge an existing hole, a Foerstner bit will be found useful. Fig. 175.

## Installing a bit in a brace

The auger bit is held in a bit brace. Fig. 176. To install the bit, grasp the shell of the chuck in your left hand and turn the handle to the left until the jaw is open slightly larger than the shank of the bit. Then insert the bit and turn the handle to the right to fasten the auger bit in the brace. Most bit braces are made with a ratchet attachment which makes it possible

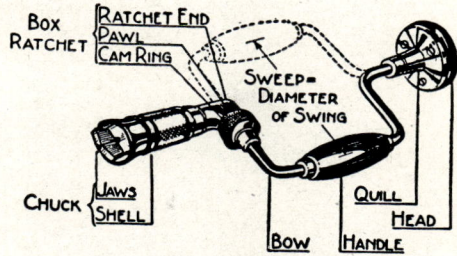

176. THE BIT BRACE IS FOR HOLDING AUGER BITS, Foerstner bits, and other tools with rectangular-shaped shanks. Most bits have a ratchet arrangement, making it possible to bore in corners and otherwise inaccessible places.

to do drilling in corners or other places where it is impossible to make a complete revolution with the handle.

## Boring holes in a horizontal position

If it is convenient, place the stock in a vise on which the boring will take place so that the brace can be held in a horizontal position. Be sure that the center of the hole is properly located and is punched with a scratch awl to aid in starting the point correctly. Fig. 177. Hold the head of the brace with your left hand cupped around it and with your body against the head for added pressure. Turn the handle with your right hand to start the point. Fig. 178. Be especially careful in starting to keep the auger bit square to the work. It is easy to sight from the top to see if it is

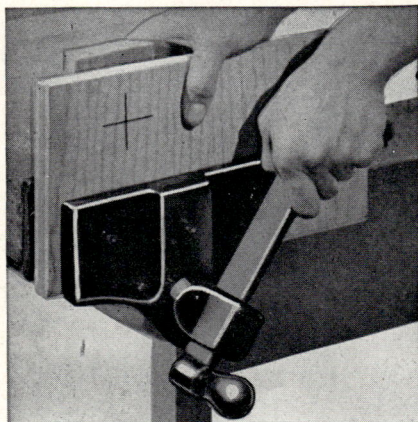

**179. USING A GUIDE FASTENED TO THE STOCK TO BE BORED.** This helps the operator to guide the auger bit and to keep it square with the surface of the work.

**177. THE PROPER LAYOUT FOR A HOLE TO BE BORED.** The center has been accurately located. On thin stock, a piece of scrap wood should be fastened to the back to support the wood while boring, as shown. COURTESY THE JAM HANDY ORGANIZATION.

be done by attaching a jig to the board. Fig. 179.

Do not apply too much pressure to the brace, as the very construction of the auger bit will tend to feed the bit into the wood. Continue to bore the hole until the point of the bit just protrudes through the opposite side. Then reverse the wood to complete the hole. If this is not done, the hole will split out on the opposite side as the auger bit comes through. Fig. 180. You can, however, put a piece of scrap

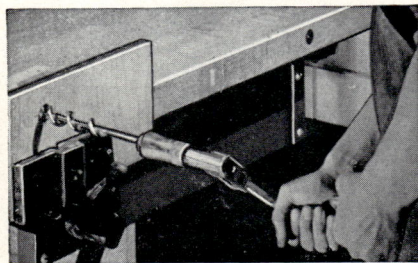

**178. BORING WITH A BIT AND BRACE.** Make sure that the auger bit is held at right angles to the stock. COURTESY THE JAM HANDY ORGANIZATION.

**180. THE CORRECT METHOD OF BORING WITH AN AUGER BIT.** The auger bit should go through the stock until the point appears on the other side and then the piece reversed and the boring completed from the opposite side. This is to keep the hole from splitting out.

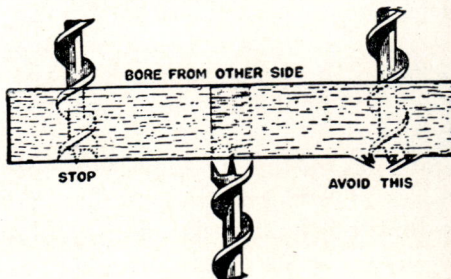

square to right and to left but, if there is another person present, have him sight to make sure that it is square up and down. This can also

**181. BORING HOLES WITH THE BIT AND BRACE** held in a vertical position. The hand is cupped around the head of the brace. Sometimes the chin is rested on the hand to steady the tool. Most boring in the shop will be done in the vertical position.

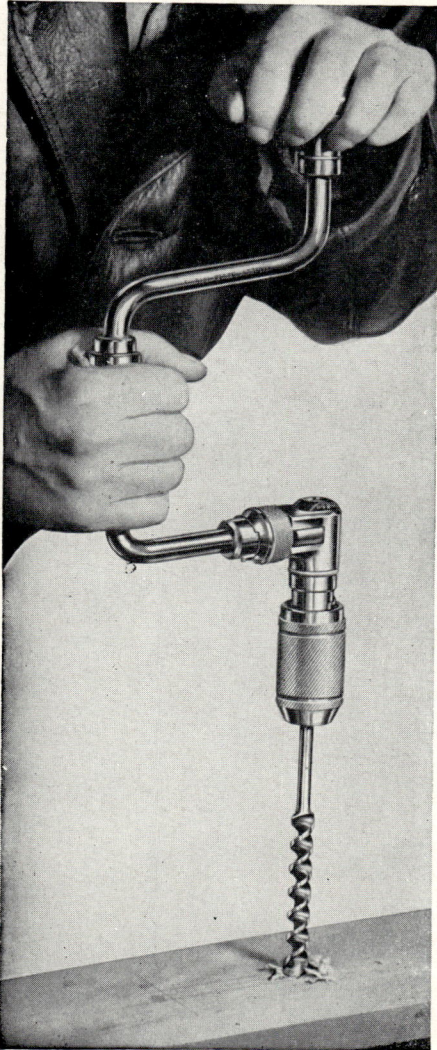

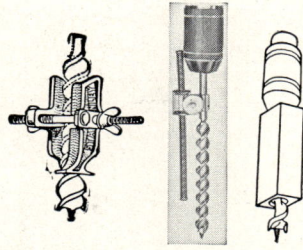

**182. DEPTH OR BIT GAUGES.** These commercial gauges can be fastened to the bit to control the depth of the hole.

**183. A DEPTH GAUGE** can be made from a piece of stock through which a hole has been bored, exposing the bit to the desired length.

wood back of the piece you are boring to make it possible to go completely through from one side without the danger of splitting out the wood.

## Boring holes in a vertical position

Frequently it will be necessary or more convenient to bore holes with the auger bit held in a vertical position. Lay out and locate the positions of the holes as before. Put your left hand over the head of the brace and use your right hand to turn the handle. Fig. 181. Sometimes you will find it natural to rest your chin on the handle to steady it. To make sure that you are boring square with the surface, you can test by sighting along the board or by using a try square.

Very often you will need to bore only part way through the

stock, as in removing stock for making a mortise-and-tenon joint. In this case, you will use a depth gauge. You can use either a commercial one that can be clamped on the auger bit to the proper depth (Fig. 182), or you can bore through a piece of wood or dowel rod, exposing the auger bit to the depth desired. Fig. 183.

## Can You Answer These Questions on Boring Holes?

1. What is an auger bit?
2. How is the size marked on the auger bit?
3. What is an expansion bit and how is it used?
4. The Foerstner bit has what primary use?
5. Name the parts of a brace.
6. Why do some braces have a ratchet attachment?
7. To bore holes in a vertical position, how can the tool be kept square with the work?
8. Should you bore the hole completely through the stock from one side? Explain.
9. Describe how the brace should be held when boring in a vertical position.
10. Describe a depth gauge and tell how it is used.
11. How is a depth gauge made?

## DRILLING HOLES

Small holes must be drilled to assemble projects with nails and screws, for starting an inside cut and for many other purposes. Holes ¼ inch or less in diameter are drilled.

### Drills and Drilling Devices

A small set of twist drills ranging in size from $\frac{1}{16}$ inch to $\frac{1}{2}$ inch in intervals of $\frac{1}{64}$ inch are used for drilling both metal and wood. Fig. 184. If the drills are used only for wood, they can be made of carbon steel and the point ground at an angle of 80 degrees. An *automatic drill* with drill points is handy to have when many small holes must be drilled. The drill points are numbered from one to eight. Number 1 is $\frac{1}{16}$ inch, 2 is $\frac{5}{64}$ inch, 3 is $\frac{3}{32}$ inch, 4 is $\frac{7}{64}$ inch, 5 is $\frac{1}{8}$ inch, 6 is $\frac{9}{64}$

A

B

184. KINDS OF DRILLS: A. The straight-shank twist drill can be used for drilling both wood and metal. B. The bit-stock drill can be used in a brace.

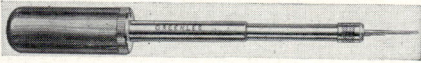

185. THE AUTOMATIC DRILL IS VERY EFFICIENT for drilling many small holes such as in boat construction.

has three jaws in the chuck for holding round shanks. Fig. 186. A *breast drill* is very similar but larger.

## Using a Hand Drill

Select the correct size twist drill.

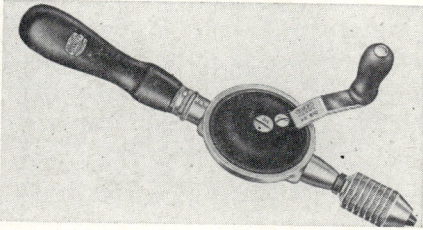

A

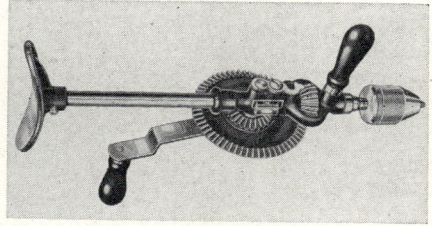

B

186. A. HAND DRILL. B. Breast drill.

inch, 7 is $5/32$ inch, and 8 is $11/64$ inch. To use this tool, insert the drill in the chuck. Tighten the chuck. Place the drill point where the hole is needed. Then simply push down a few times, allowing the handle to spring back after each stroke. This will give you a good clean hole. Fig. 185.

The *hand drill* is used to hold the twist drill for drilling holes. It

Hold the shell of the chuck in your left hand. Pull the crank backward until the jaws are open slightly wider than the shank. Then place the shank in the chuck and tighten the chuck by pushing the crank forward. Make sure the drill is in the chuck straight. Locate the position of the hole and mark it with a scratch-all. Hold the handle in your left hand and turn the crank with

187. VERTICAL DRILLING WITH A HAND DRILL. The handle is grasped in one hand and the crank turned with the other. Be sure to hold the drill square with the work.

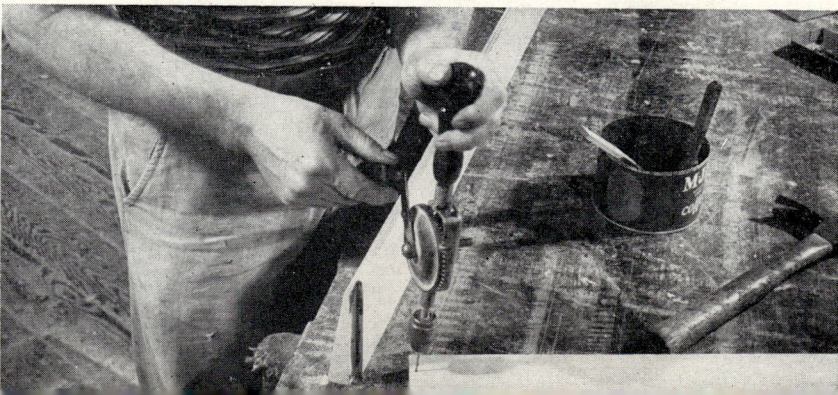

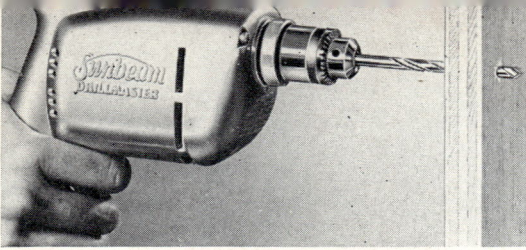

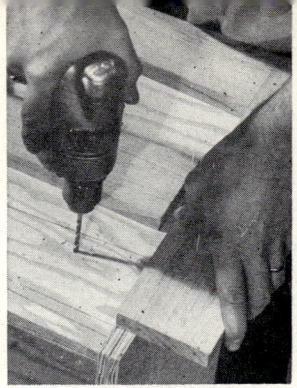

188. A. AN ELECTRIC HAND DRILL.
B. Using an electric hand drill for drilling screw holes.

your right hand. Make sure the drill is square with the work. Fig. 187. Never bend the hand drill to one side or the other. Small drills would break. Continue to turn the handle until the holes are drilled.

## Using the Electric Hand Drill

The electric hand drill is an excellent all-around tool for drilling and boring holes. Drill size is indicated by the size of the chuck. The most common sizes are $\frac{1}{4}$, $\frac{3}{8}$, and $\frac{1}{2}$ inch. Fig. 188A. The horsepower rating is also important.

Light-duty, $\frac{1}{4}$-inch electric drills may develop as little as $\frac{1}{8}$ horsepower. A good $\frac{1}{2}$-inch electric drill should develop at least $\frac{2}{3}$ horsepower.

Use the chuck wrench to open the jaws until the twist drill will slip in. Then tighten the drill firmly. Always remove the chuck wrench.

Never use an auger bit with a screw point and a square shank as a power bit. There are several types of power wood bits. Fig. 189. These are ideal to use with the electric hand drill for boring larger holes.

## Can You Answer These Questions on Drilling Holes?

1. Name the kind of cutting tool used for drilling holes in wood.
2. Describe a hand drill.
3. How can a twist drill be faster than a hand drill?
4. How is the hand drill held for doing horizontal drilling?
5. How is the size of an electric hand drill indicated?
6. What kind of bit should be used for boring larger holes?

189. A SPEED OR MACHINE BIT that can be used in a portable electric drill or a drill press.

A

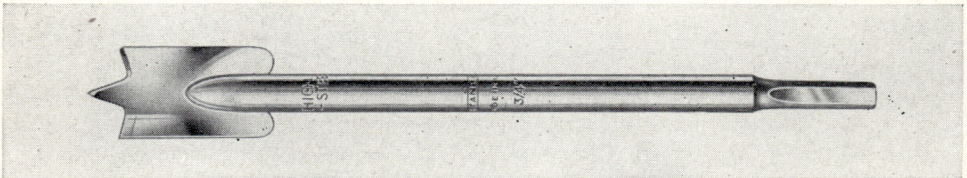

B

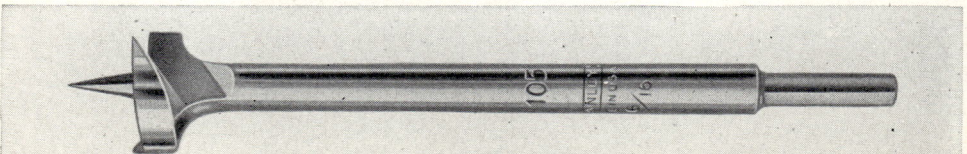

# Section VII

## Making Joints

The seventh 8 steps in hand woodworking—what you must know and be able to do.

23. The dowel joint and its variations, such as the edge dowel joint, corner dowel joint, and leg and rail dowel joints: what they are and how to make them, including layout, cut, fit, assembly, and fastening.

24. The rabbet joint and the steps in making this joint, including its assembly.

25. Constructing and assembling the dado joint and its variations, such as the rabbet and dado joint and blind dado joint.

26. Kinds of lap joints. Laying out, cutting, and assembling a cross-lap joint and what it is used for.

27. Using a miter box, either commercial or homemade, for cutting a miter joint, assembling the miter joint, and applications of this joint.

28. Kinds of mortise-and-tenon joints. Layout, construction, and assembly of the mortise and the tenon.

29. How to make a table or desk which has fitted drawers which make necessary special work in fastening down the table or desk top, building the drawers and their guides, and fitting the drawers in place.

30. The paneled door or frame: its parts and how to build and fit it.

WOULD IT surprise you to know that there are over a hundred different types of woodworking joints? Of course, there are many that are similar, but each is used to join two pieces of wood together in a special way. All joints in woodworking are made first by making a layout, then by cutting, fitting, and assembling. To do these things well, you must have learned to use all of the common hand tools. Of course, you will not use more than one or two kinds of joints on any one project, but these ought to be chosen wisely, for each has a particular purpose.

When you begin to make larger articles, such has desks and tables, you will have added problems of joinery in making drawers and doors. See "box" above. Further

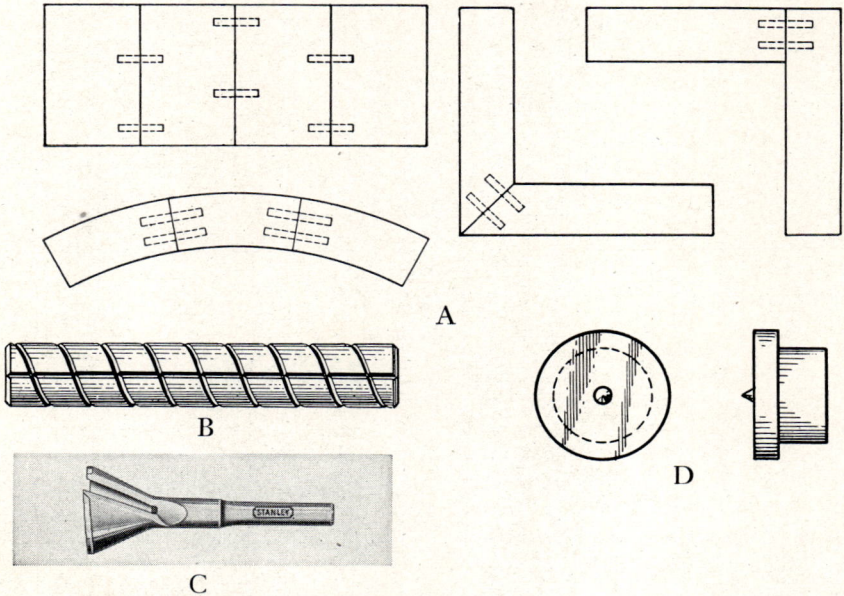

190. A. DOWEL JOINTS ARE SIMPLE TO CONSTRUCT. B. Dowel pins usually
have a spiral groove which helps the glue to flow. C. Dowel sharpener. D. Dowel
centers are useful in locating adjoining holes. The locations for the dowels are
marked on the first piece and drilled. Then the dowel centers are put in place. When
the two pieces are held together the dowel centers show the hole locations on the
second piece.

woodworking steps are on pp. 12, 37, 53, 84, 97, 111, 148, 174, 187.

## MAKING A DOWEL JOINT

A dowel joint on a leg and rail is sometimes used as a substitute for a mortise-and-tenon joint. Dowels are also used to strengthen an edge, butt, or miter joint. Fig. 190.

## Dowel Tools and Materials

*Dowel rod* is usually made of birch in diameters from ⅛ to 1 inch in 3-foot lengths. Small *dowel pins* are made with a spiral groove and pointed ends. A *dowel sharpener* points the ends of the dowels. *Dowel centers* are small metal pins used for spotting the location of holes on two parts of a joint.

## Making an edge dowel joint

To make this joint, clamp the two pieces to be joined with the edges flush and with the face surfaces out. With a try square mark across the edge of both pieces at the several points at which the dowels are to be located. Next set a marking gauge to half the thickness of

191. MARKING THE POSITION FOR
AN EDGE DOWEL JOINT. The
pieces are placed in a vise with the
face surfaces outward. Then a marking gauge is set to half the thickness of
the stock and the center location is
marked. The location for the three
dowels has already been marked with
a try square and pencil.

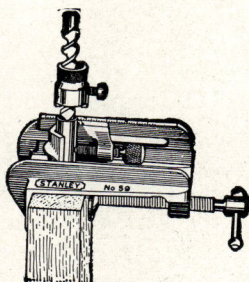

192. A DOWELING JIG. This device can
be automatically set to drill holes in
the center of a piece of stock.

the stock and mark the center location of the dowel joints. Fig. 191.
Make sure that you mark these
from the face side.

Select the size dowel you plan
to use and the depth to which the
dowel is to be inserted. The diameter of the dowel should never be
more than half the thickness of the
stock being used. Usually the dowel
should be no longer than 3 inches,
and therefore the holes will be
drilled about $1\frac{5}{8}$-inch deep, providing about $\frac{1}{8}$-inch clearance at
the bottom on each side.

After the points have been located, make a small indentation with

a scratch awl. Select an auger bit the
same size as the dowel rod. Carefully bore the hole to the proper
depth, making sure that you are
working square with the edge of
the stock. Use a depth gauge as a
guide. A doweling jig should be
used, if one is available. Fig. 192.
With it you will always be able to
bore the holes square and in the
proper location. Fig. 193.

After the holes are bored, cut
off the dowel and cut a slight bevel
at either end to make the dowel
pieces slip into the holes easily.
When gluing, dip the dowels about
halfway in glue and drive them into
the holes on one edge. Then coat
the other half and other edges and
assemble. Fig. 194.

## Making a dowel joint on a frame

One way to strengthen a butt
joint on a simple frame is to install
two or more dowels at each corner.
Do this in the following manner:

1. Square up pieces of stock
that are to go into the frame and

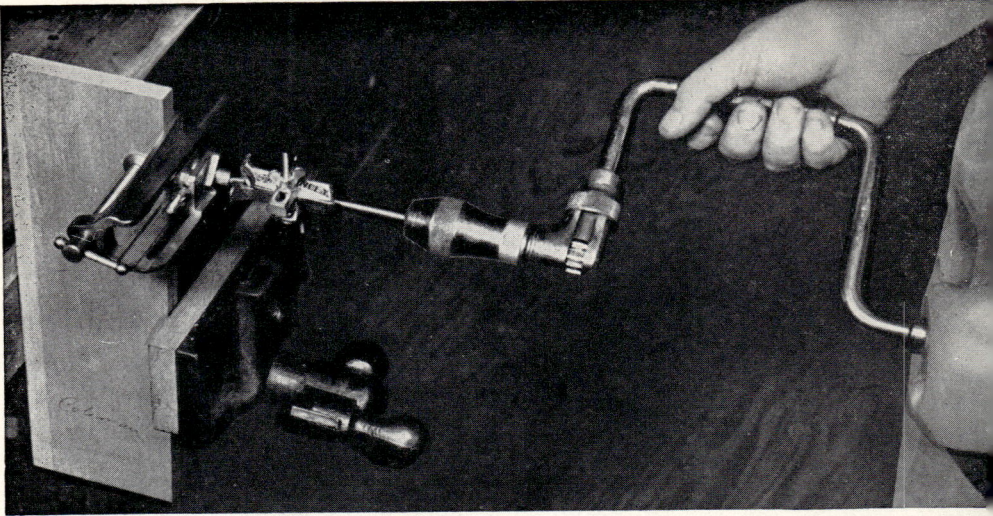

**193. USING A DOWELING JIG.** The jig has been clamped to the stock and the proper size guide fastened in it. An auger bit of the correct size is being used and a depth gauge is attached to control the depth of the hole.

**194. GLUING AN EDGE DOWEL JOINT.** This illustrates the proper method of performing this operation. The dowels have already been dipped in the glue and driven halfway in one edge. Cold casein glue is being applied to the two edges and to the other half of the dowels.

**195. LAYING OUT THE POSITION FOR BORING A DOWEL JOINT IN A FRAME.** Here the butting edge and end are held in a vise, while a try square is being used to lay out the position of the two dowels.

carefully saw and sand the ends.

2. Lay out the frame and mark the corners with corresponding numbers.

3. In a vise, place the two pieces that are to form one of the corners with the butting end and the butting edge protruding, and with the face surfaces of the two pieces out and the end and edge flush.

4. Hold a try square against one of the face surfaces and mark lines across to indicate the location of the dowel rods. Fig. 195.

5. Set a marking gauge to half the thickness of the stock, hold it against the surface of each piece, and mark the exact location. Mark these points with a scratch awl and bore the holes as described above.

## Making a dowel joint on a leg and rail

Frequently a dowel joint is made on a leg and rail as a substitute for a mortise-and-tenon joint because it is more easily and quickly made.

Square up the leg and rail as for any joint, making sure that the end of the rail is square. Next clamp the leg and rail in a vise with the butting end and the butting edge protruding and the face surface of each turned out. Hold a try square against the face surface of the rail and mark the location of the dowels on the end of the rail and the edge of the leg. Next set a marking gauge to half the thickness of the rail and, from the face surface of the rail, mark the crossline that will indicate the location of the dowel joints. Then determine how far you want the rail to set back from the face surface of the leg. Add this amount to the setting you already have on the marking gauge. From the face surface of the leg, mark the crossline that will indicate the exact location of the dowel. Bore the holes, cut the dowels, glue, and assemble as previously described in this section on joints.

## Can You Answer These Questions on Making a Dowel Joint?

1. From what kinds of wood is dowel rod usually made?

2. Dowel joints are sometimes used as a substitute for another kind of joint. What is this joint and why is the dowel joint substituted?

3. Why are dowels used in making an edge joint?

4. State the rule for choosing the correct dowel diameter.

5. Should there be clearance at the bottom of a dowel hole? Why?

6. What is a doweling jig? Explain how it is used.

7. List the steps in making a dowel joint on a frame.

8. Why is it necessary to lay out a dowel joint very accurately?

9. What would happen if the dowel holes of two joint pieces were not aligned perfectly?

10. How do you think a dowel joint on a leg or rail will compare with a mortise-and-tenon joint?

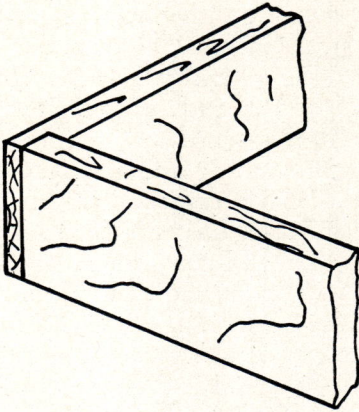

196. A RABBET JOINT is a simple type of joint construction that is found on much of the modern furniture.

## MAKING A RABBET JOINT

One of the simplest joints to make is the rabbet joint. Fig. 196. In making this joint, a recess is cut across the grain at the end of one piece into which the end of the second piece fits. Fig. 197. It is made with the end grain concealed from the front. This type of joint is commonly found in drawer construction, boxes, cabinet frames, and in much of the modern furniture, since it provides great simplicity in both construction and appearance. Fig. 198.

## Laying out a rabbet joint

Make sure that the end on which the joint is to be made has been squared properly. Place the board into which the rabbet is to be cut on the bench with the face surface down. Hold the other piece

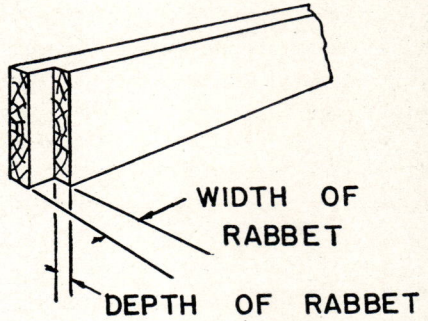

WIDTH OF RABBET

DEPTH OF RABBET

197. A RABBET.

directly over the first, with the face surface of the second piece flush with the end grain of the first. Fig. 199. This is called superimposing. You will frequently use this method

198. THE BOTTOM OF THIS TABLE is attached with a rabbet joint.

**199. SUPERIMPOSING ONE PIECE OVER ANOTHER** to lay out the width of the rabbet. The surface of one piece is held flush with the end of the stock and a pencil used to mark off the width of the rabbet.

**200. MAKING THE SHOULDER CUT ON A RABBET JOINT.** Note that a piece of scrap stock is clamped over the layout line with hand screws; then the backsaw is held against the edge of the scrap stock. This prevents the saw from jumping out of the kerf and damaging the wood.

in laying out many of the different kinds of joints.

With a sharp pencil or knife, mark the width of rabbet to be cut. Then remove the second piece and, with a try square held on the joint edge, square the line across the surface of the first piece. Then mark a line down each edge. From the face surface, mark the depth of the rabbet on the sides and end with a marking gauge. This type of joint is usually cut half to two thirds the thickness of the stock.

## Cutting the rabbet

In cutting the rabbet joint, the piece should be held firmly against a bench hook or, for a beginner, it is better to clamp the stock directly to the bench top. Using a backsaw to make the cut, make sure that the saw kerf is in the waste stock or inside the layout line. It is wise for a beginner to take a piece of scrap stock that has a true surface and edge and clamp this directly

over the layout line. Then the backsaw can be held against this edge to make the saw cut. Fig. 200. Cut the joint to the proper depth as indicated by the layout line.

**201. AFTER THE RABBET HAS BEEN CUT**, it should be trimmed with the chisel. The blade of the chisel is being held between thumb and forefinger **to trim out the excess stock.**

202. NAILING A RABBET JOINT. It is being nailed so that the front has no visible joint. It is a good idea to drive in the nails at a slight angle so they will have more holding power, since they are being fastened in end grain.

To remove the excess stock from the joint, you can either saw out the remaining stock or pare it out with a chisel. If you decide to saw out the rabbet joint, lock the stock in a vise with the joint exposed. With a backsaw, carefully saw out the excess stock.

If you use a chisel, leave the stock clamped to the top of the bench and pare out the excess stock as you have learned from the unit on cutting with a chisel. Regardless of which method you follow, you will need to use the chisel for trimming the joint and making it fit properly. Fig. 201.

It is a good idea to mark this joint on both edges with corresponding numbers, so that, if there are several to be made, they may be easily identified when the project is ready for assembly.

## Assembling the joint

This type of joint will usually be assembled with glue or with both glue and nails or screws. If the joint is nailed, drive the nails in at a slight angle to enable them to fasten the joint more tightly. Fig. 202. Screws should be long and thin, as they will have to go into end grain.

## Can You Answer These Questions on Making a Rabbet Joint?

1. What is a rabbet?
2. How is the rabbet used?
3. Explain superimposing.
4. What tools should be used to mark a rabbet?
5. What kind of saw should be selected for cutting a rabbet?

6. When can a chisel be chosen for making a rabbet joint?
7. How can the pieces of several different rabbet joints be kept in order?
8. If you decide to assemble a rabbet joint with nails, how would you proceed to insert them?

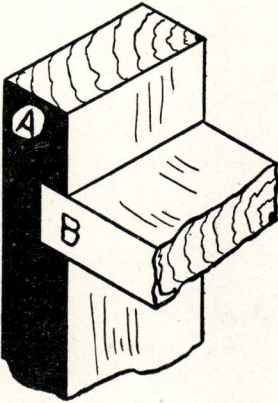

**204. MAKING THE LAYOUT FOR THE DADO JOINT.** One line is laid out on the surface and then, by superimposing, the width of the dado is marked. Then lines are drawn across the surface and down the edge of the stock as shown.

**203. A DADO JOINT IS COMMONLY USED** whenever the crosspiece must support considerable weight, such as in shelves and steps of ladders.

## MAKING A DADO JOINT

A dado is a groove cut across the grain of wood. Fig. 203. This type of joint is commonly found in bookracks, drawers, cabinet shelves, and such things as ladders and steps.

### Laying out a dado joint

From the end of the board measure in the correct distance to one side of the dado. Then square off a line across the surface of the piece at this point. Superimpose the other piece with one arris directly over this line and, with a sharp knife or pencil, mark the correct width of the dado.

Remove the second piece and square off a line across the surface to indicate the proper width. Continue both lines down both edges. Fig. 204. Then, with a marking gauge, lay out the correct depth of the dado joint.

### Cutting the dado

Use a backsaw and, following the directions for cutting out a rabbet joint, cut the dado to the proper depth at both layout lines. Make sure that the saw kerfs are in the

**205. MAKE SURE THAT THE SAW KERFS** in the dado joint are inside the waste stock.

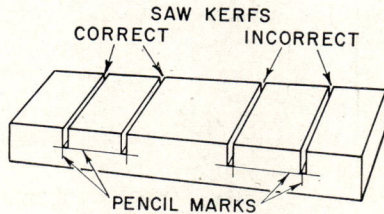

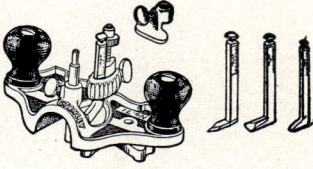

206. A ROUTER PLANE is equipped with blades of different widths and is used for surfacing the bottom of grooves and other depressions.

With a depth gauge (Fig. 208) check the dado to make sure that it is the same depth throughout. Check the dado joint by inserting the piece into the joint. Fig. 209.

You may find it necessary to trim the joint to make it a little wider, or it may be easier to plane the side of the second piece slightly

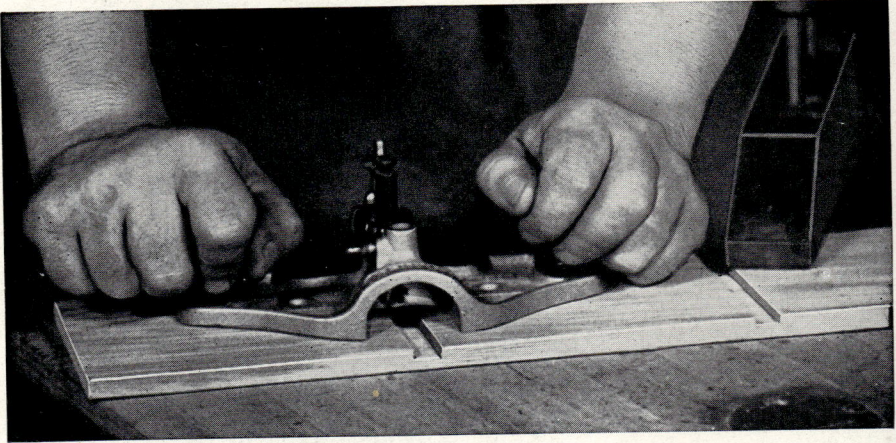

207. USING A ROUTER PLANE to trim out the bottom of a dado joint. A cutter that is the same width or slightly narrower than the width of the dado should be selected. The thumb screw is adjusted to the proper depth, and the cut is taken by holding the router plane firmly on the surface of the work and applying pressure with both hands. Do not attempt to cut to the total depth with one setting.

waste stock and not outside the layout line. Fig. 205.

With a chisel, cut and trim the dado to the proper depth. If one is available, a router plane may be used to trim out the waste stock. Figs. 206 and 207.

If the dado is a particularly wide one, you may need to make several saw cuts to depth so that the waste stock can be easily trimmed out.

to make it fit into the joint.

## Assembling the joint

The dado joint is usually assembled either with glue or with glue and nails or screws, in the same manner as a rabbet joint.

## Making a rabbet-and-dado joint

A rabbet-and-dado joint (Fig. 210) is frequently used when add-

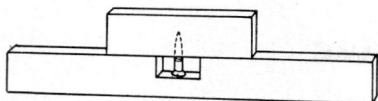

208. THE DEPTH OF A DADO JOINT can be checked with a simple, home-made depth gauge, as shown here. A flathead screw is driven into a piece of scrap stock until the head extends from the stock an amount equal to the depth of the dado. This gauge can also be used to check the dado.

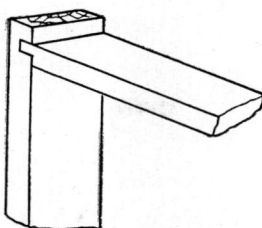

210. HERE IS A RABBET-AND-DADO JOINT which gives added strength and rigidity. It is therefore in common use for the corners of drawers.

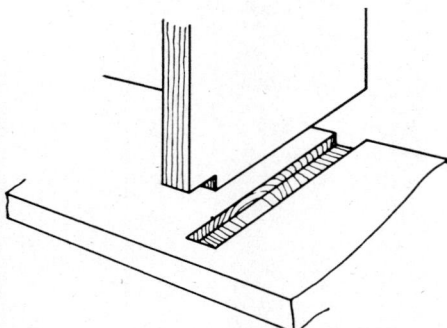

209. CHECKING A DADO JOINT. The second piece is inserted in the dado to check it. If it is necessary to fit the joint, it is simpler to remove a little stock from the second piece rather than to cut the dado wider.

tional strength and rigidity are needed as in cases involving drawer construction.

211. A BLIND DADO JOINT has the same advantage of strength of construction as the dado joint but does not have the disadvantage of showing the joint. It is built into bookcases, especially, and other projects of this type, on which a neat appearance on the front of the shelves is desirable.

The joint consists of a rabbet, the tongue of which is fitted into a dado. To make this kind of joint, lay out and cut the rabbet first. Then lay out the position of the dado joint and, by superimposing the tongue of the rabbet, mark the width of the dado. Make the dado as previously described and fit the tongue of the rabbet into it.

## Making a blind dado joint

A blind dado joint is one in which the dado is cut only part way across the board. Fig. 211. The piece that fits into the dado is notched so that the joint appears invisible when viewed from in front.

Lay out the width of the dado as described previously. Mark the depth of the dado on the back edge only. Also lay out the length of the dado from the back edge to within ½ to ¾ inch of the front edge. The dado can be cut by boring a series of holes in the waste stock and then trimming out with a chisel.

## Can You Answer These Questions on Making a Dado Joint?

1. What is a dado?
2. Point out the difference between a dado and a rabbet.
3. When cutting a dado, where should the saw kerf be formed?
4. Explain a router plane. What is it used for?
5. How could you make a depth gauge to check a dado?
6. In fitting a dado joint, is it better to plane the side of the second piece or to cut a wider dado?
7. What advantage does a rabbet-and-dado joint have? Where is it frequently found?
8. Sketch a blind dado joint.
9. Why would a blind dado joint be found in more expensive furniture?

HALF LAP    EDGE CROSS LAP

END LAP    MIDDLE LAP

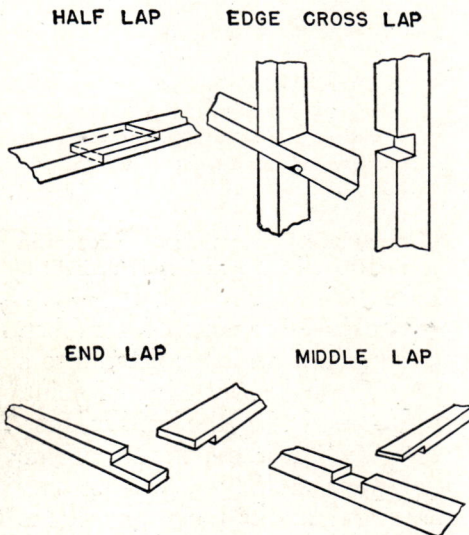

**212. HERE ARE SEVERAL TYPES OF LAP JOINTS** that are varied in their usefulness.

## MAKING A LAP JOINT

There are many different types of lap joints. Fig. 212. The end lap is found in screen doors, chair seats, or any type of corner construction in which the surfaces of the two pieces, when assembled, must be flush. The middle lap is also found in screen-door construction, in making cabinets, and in framing a house. The cross lap is widely used in furniture building whenever two pieces must cross and still be flush on the surface. An example is the ring game. Fig. 403. The cross lap is by far the most common and therefore will be emphasized. Should you need to make any of the other types, follow the same general directions. observe the way each is made, and you will have **no** difficulty.

## Laying out the cross-lap joint

The cross-lap joint is usually made in the exact center of the two pieces that cross at a 90-degree angle. The two pieces must be exactly the same thickness and width. Lay the two pieces on the bench side by side, with the face surface of one, piece A, and the opposite surface of the other, piece B, upward. Divide the length of each into two equal parts and lay out a center line across the two pieces. Measure the width of the stock being used and divide this measurement in half. Lay out a line this distance on either side of this center line. Fig. 213.

Now check this measurement by superimposing piece B over piece A at right angles and in the position that the joint will be when assembled. Fig. 214. The layout line should be just barely visible beyond the edge of each piece.

Now continue the lines that indicate the width of the joint down the edge of each piece. Next, set a marking gauge to half the thickness of the stock and from the face surface of each piece mark along the edge on each side to indicate the depth of the joint. If you make this measurement from the face surface, the two pieces will be flush when the joint is made because you will be cutting the joint from the

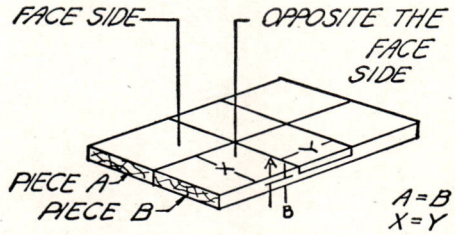

213. THE CORRECT LAYOUT FOR A LAP JOINT. Both pieces should be marked at the same time.

face surface of one piece and **the** opposite surface of the other **piece.**

## Cutting the lap joint

Hold the piece in a bench hook or clamp it to the top of the bench and cut with a backsaw to the depth of the joint just inside each of the

214. CHECKING A LAP JOINT. The layout has been made and the lap joint is being checked. A try square keeps the pieces at right angles. The lines on the lower piece, which indicate the width of the lap joint, should be just visible.

FACE SIDE

PIECE B

FACE SIDE

PIECE A

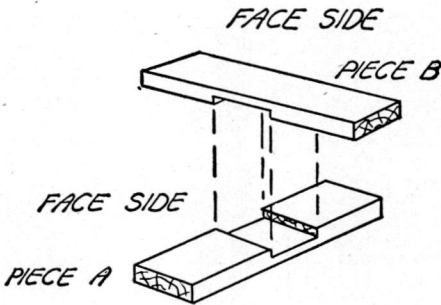

**215. FITTING A LAP JOINT.** The lap joints should fit in such a way that they will go together with a moderate amount of pressure. It is simpler to trim off a little from the edges of the stock than it would be to make the joint wider.

**216. A LAP JOINT ASSEMBLED WITH SCREWS** provides very neat construction when done from the underside.

layout lines, as you did to make a dado joint. If the joint is wide, it is wise to make several cuts in the waste stock. This will help remove the waste and will also serve as a guide when you chisel out the waste stock.

Next, use a chisel to remove the waste stock. Work from both sides of each piece, tapering up toward the center. If you try to chisel out across the stock from only one side, you may chip out the opposite side.

After you have brought the joint down to the layout line on

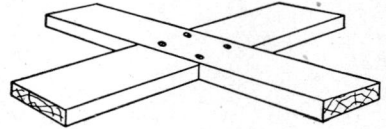

either edge, continue to pare the high point in the center of the joint. (See the unit on shaping stock with a chisel.)

Complete this on both pieces; then try to fit them together. Fig. 215. The pieces should fit snugly but should not be so loose that they will fall apart or so tight that they must be forced together. If the two pieces will not slip together, it is better to plane a little from the edge of one piece rather than to try to trim the shoulder.

## Assembling the joint

When assembled, the surfaces of both pieces should fit flush with one another. In assembling this joint, both glue and nails or screws are used. If the nails or screws are installed from the underside, they will not be visible and the joint will be very neat. Fig. 216.

## Can You Answer These Questions on Making a Lap Joint?

1. Name several lap joints. What are the common uses of each?
2. Which type of lap joint is most common?
3. At what angle do the pieces of a lap joint usually cross?
4. How can you make sure that the two

pieces will be flush when the joint is assembled?
5. To what other joint is cutting a lap joint similar?
6. At what point in the fitting can you say that the two pieces fit together properly?

7. If nails or screws are selected for fastening the joint, how would they be inserted?

## MAKING A MITER JOINT

A miter joint is made when it is undesirable to have the end grain showing on the finished project. Fig. 217. It is not a very strong joint and therefore is used primarily to make picture frames, casings, and decorative edges for furniture such as the hot-dish holder in Fig. 391.

### Miter boxes

The metal miter box and saw consist of a metal box in which a saw can be adjusted to any angle from 30 to 90 degrees. Fig. 218. If one is not available, it is relatively simple to make one of your own. This can be done by fastening two pieces of stock to a base and then, with a sliding T bevel, laying a 45-

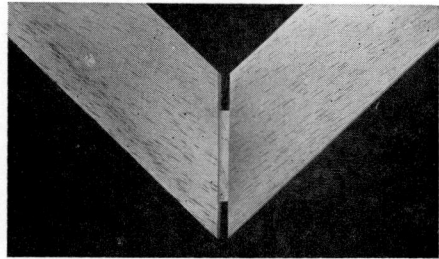

217. THE MITER JOINT IS USED FOR FRAMES, modern furniture and in other places where end grain should not show. The corner can be strengthened by adding a dowel or spline.

degree angle in both directions. Usually this and a 90-degree angle cut are all that is ever needed. Fig. 219. Since cutting a picture frame or similar device is the most common use for the miter joint, this procedure will be described.

### Cutting a picture frame

If a metal miter box is available,

218. A METAL MITER BOX. This box consists of a frame and a saw. The saw can be adjusted at various angles.

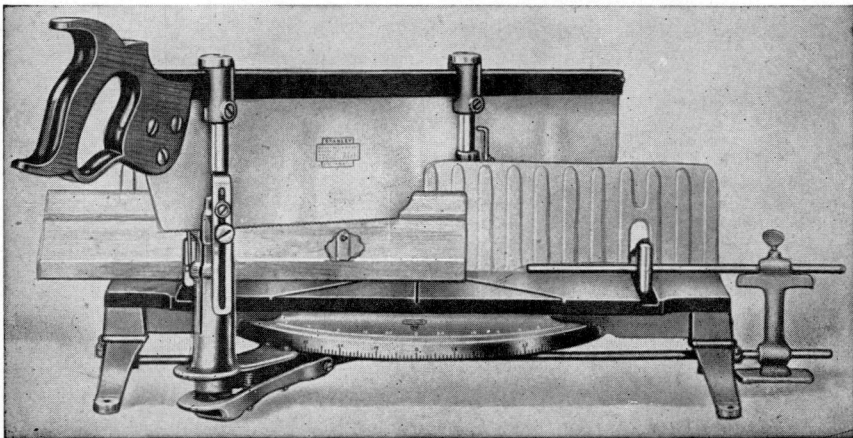

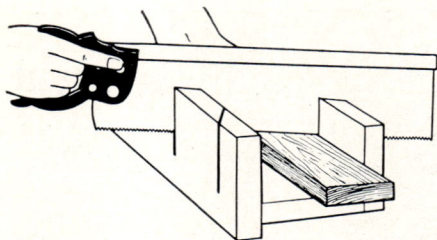

219. CUTTING A MITER JOINT with a homemade miter box and back saw. When cutting, be certain that the line to be cut is directly under the saw teeth. Hold the work tightly against the back of the box; start the cut with a careful back stroke.

220. USING A MITER BOX. Make sure that the stock is held firmly against the back of the box so that it does not slip when the saw kerf is started.

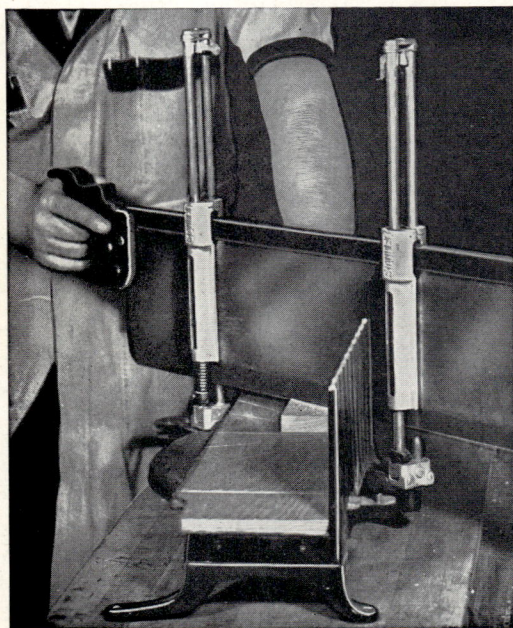

swing the saw to the left and set it at 45 degrees; or, if a wood box is used, use the cut that is to the left as you face it. Place the edge of the frame in the box with the rabbet edge down and toward you. Hold the stock firmly with the thumb of your left hand against the side of the box. Fig. 220. Then carefully bring the miter saw (or backsaw or fine crosscut saw, if the box is homemade) down on the stock and cut the angle. Be especially careful not to let the stock slip when starting the cut, or you may ruin the surface of the frame.

Next, determine the length of the glass or the picture. Add to this length twice the width of the frame, measured from the rabbet edge to the outside edge. Lay out this measurement along the outside edge of the stock. Fig. 221. Then swing the

221. LAYING OUT THE PROPER MEASUREMENT for cutting miter joints on a picture frame. The length as marked on the outside of the frame is equal to the length of the glass plus twice the width of the stock measured from the rabbet to the outside edge.

LENGTH OF GLASS OR PICTURE

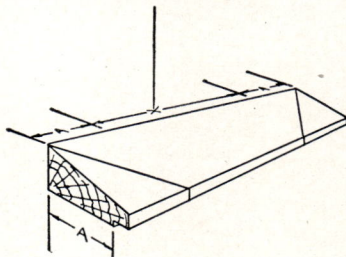

222. NAILING A MITER JOINT. One piece is locked in a vise and the second piece held over it, with the corner extending slightly.

223. A. THIS MITER-AND-CORNER CLAMP holds the corners together as they are glued or fastened. B. A four-corner miter-frame clamp.

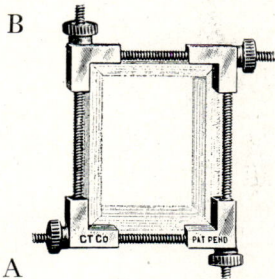

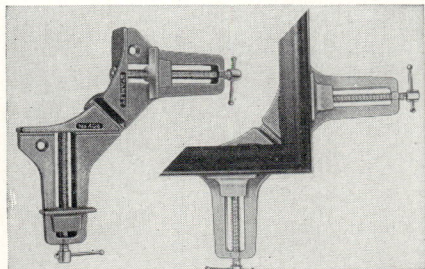

224. ANOTHER METHOD OF GLUING UP A MITER JOINT. In this simple example, an engineering principle nevertheless is involved. Pressure must be so exerted as to drive the joint together. The clamps can be readily adjusted for the purpose.

225. TRIMMING THE SPLINE OFF A MITER JOINT. This spline strengthens the joint.

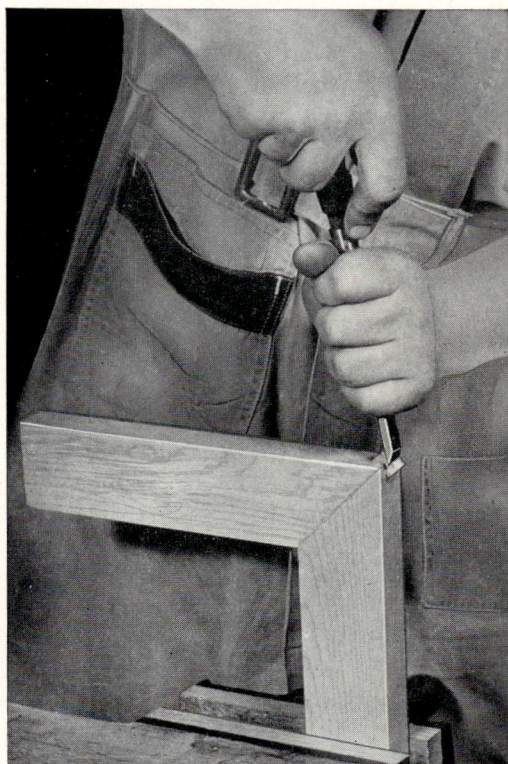

miter-box saw to the right and set it at 45 degrees. Hold the stock again firmly with your right hand and cut the stock to length, using your left hand to operate the saw. If you find this awkward to do, clamp the stock to the box with a hand screw and then operate the saw with your right hand. Repeat the same procedure for the second side and a similar procedure for making the ends.

## Assembling the miter joint

The miter joint is usually assembled by gluing and nailing. Sometimes dowels are added to strengthen the joint. To nail a miter joint, drive

the nail part way into one piece. Lock the other piece in a vise in a vertical position. Hold the first piece over the vertical piece with its corner extending somewhat outside the edge of the vertical piece. Fig. 222. As you nail the corners together, the top piece will tend to slip down until it fits squarely. If you are using glue only, you can use a little jig like the one in Fig. 223 or 224 to hold the corners while the glue dries. If only glue is used in assembling the frame, it is sometimes desirable to strengthen the corners by inserting a spline across each corner. Fig. 225.

## Can You Answer These Questions on Making a Miter Joint?

1. What is the advantage of a miter joint? Disadvantage?
2. Name the common uses.
3. Describe a miter box.
4. Could you construct a miter box?
5. At what angle is a miter joint made?
6. What kind of saw is best for cutting

a miter joint?
7. Are there any precautions that should be observed in starting a miter cut?
8. In what two ways can a miter joint be strengthened?
9. What implements would you choose for holding a miter joint after it is glued?

## MAKING A MORTISE-AND-TENON JOINT

The mortise-and-tenon joint is found in better furniture construction. You may have an opportunity to make it, especially if you are constructing a table, bench, or stool. There are many kinds of mortise-and-tenon joints, a few of which are shown in Fig. 226, but by far the most common is the blind mortise-and-tenon joint. As you will

see, this is a rectangular projection on the end of a rail that fits into a rectangular hole in a second piece, usually a leg. Making a mortise-and-tenon joint by hand requires considerable skill and should not be attempted if another type of joint will fit the needs of the project just as satisfactorily. Before beginning, note the names and measurements indicated in Fig. 227, because these will be referred to constantly.

IND MORTISE & TENON

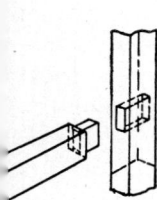

OPEN MORTISE & TENON

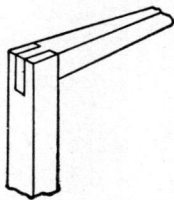

RU MORTISE & TENON

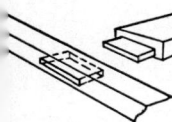

STUB MORTISE & TENON

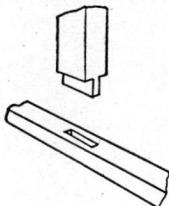

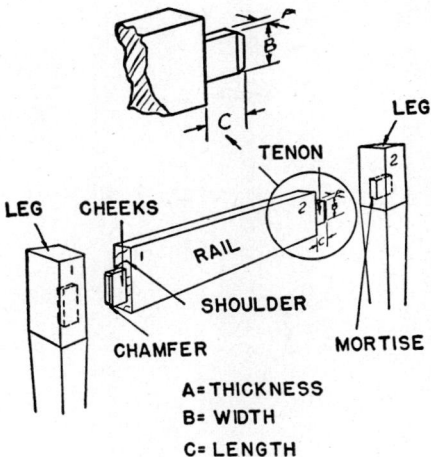

**226. TYPES OF MORTISE-AND-TENON JOINTS.** The use of each particular kind will depend upon the construction of the project.

LEG

TENON

LEG     CHEEKS

RAIL

SHOULDER

CHAMFER                    MORTISE

A = THICKNESS
B = WIDTH
C = LENGTH

**227. STUDY THE PARTS OF THE MORTISE-AND-TENON JOINT,** as these will be referred to in its layout and construction.

## Making the preliminary layout

In most cases, it will be necessary to make several mortise-and-tenon joints in the construction of a single project. For example, in making a simple table consisting of four rails and legs, eight mortise-and-tenon joints are needed. Before laying out the joints, hold the several pieces to be assembled in approximately the position they will be when the project is finished. With the face surface of the rails and the face surface and joint edge of the legs outward, begin at one corner to mark No. 1 on the leg and No. 1 on the adjoining rail, No. 2 on the next, etc., until you have marked with matching numbers the pieces that make up each mortise-and-tenon joint. In this way, you will be sure that the pieces will fit together in the proper order when you are ready to assemble them.

## Laying out the tenons

The size of the mortise-and-tenon joint is usually indicated on the drawing and, if so, these measurements should be followed carefully. However, if they are not specified, the tenon is made half the thickness of the total thickness of the piece and about ½ to ¾ inch

WIDTH OF TENON

THICKNESS OF TENON

FACE SIDE

LENGTH OF TENON

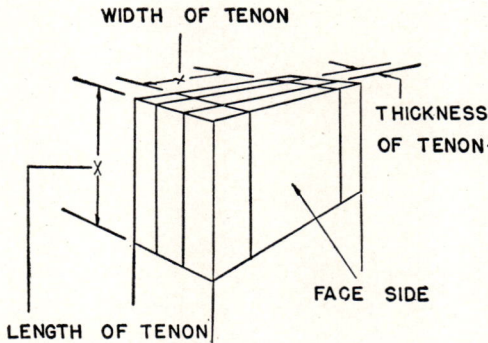

**228. PROPER LAYOUT FOR A TENON.** These lines should be accurately made, so that the tenon will be the correct size and shape.

A= DISTANCE FROM EDGE OF LEG TO FACE SIDE OF RAIL
B= THICKNESS OF RAIL
C= THICKNESS OF TENON

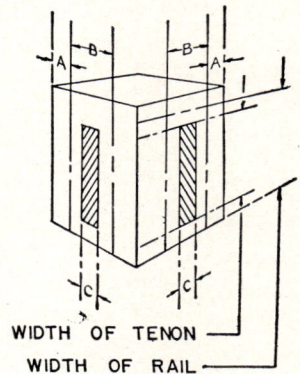

WIDTH OF TENON
WIDTH OF RAIL

**229. THE PROPER LAYOUT OF THE MORTISE.** Only the part indicated by the cross hatch is absolutely essential to the layout.

narrower than the total width of the piece.

From the ends, mark out the length of the tenon and square a line completely around the end of each piece. Do this on all pieces and then check to see that all of the rails are of identical length from shoulder to shoulder. Next, set the marking gauge to half the thickness of the stock to be removed and, working from the face side, mark a line across the end and down either edge.

Next, add to this measurement the thickness of the tenon and check the gauge. Again mark a line across the end and down the sides. Subtract the width of the tenon from the total width of the stock, divide this amount in half, and set this measurement on a marking gauge.

From the joint edge of the rail, mark a line across the end and down the side. Next, add to this measurement the width of the tenon and set the gauge again. Repeat the mark across the end and down the side.

Now you have all of the necessary measurements on the tenon. Fig. 228. If several tenons are to be marked, make sure that you do them simultaneously to avoid error.

## Laying out a mortise

Use a pencil point on your marking gauge to make all lines simultaneously on all four legs. From the top end of each leg, lay out two lines on the inside surfaces (those opposite the face side and joint edge) that indicate the total width of the rail.

Next, lay out two more lines on these surfaces to indicate the width of the tenon. Determine how far back the rail is to set from the outside edge of the leg. Add to this measurement the thickness of the stock removed from one side of the tenon. Set the marking gauge to this measurement and, holding the marking gauge against the face side and joint edge, mark a line between the lines that indicate the width of the tenon. Add to this measurement an amount equal to the thickness of the tenon and mark another line to complete the outline, which will be exactly the same as the thickness and width of the tenon. Fig. 229. If an auger bit is to be used to remove the waste stock from the mortise, lay out a line down the center of the outline.

## Cutting the tenon

Lock the stock in a vise with the marked tenon exposed. Use a backsaw or fine crosscut saw to make four saw cuts in the waste stock that will shape the thickness and width of the tenon. Fig. 230.

Next, remove the stock from the vise and clamp it on the top of the bench. Make the shoulder cuts to remove the waste stock which forms the thickness and the width of the tenon. *Be especially careful,* as it is essential that these saw marks be accurate for a tight-fitting tenon. The cutting of a tenon can be simplified by using a circular saw. The

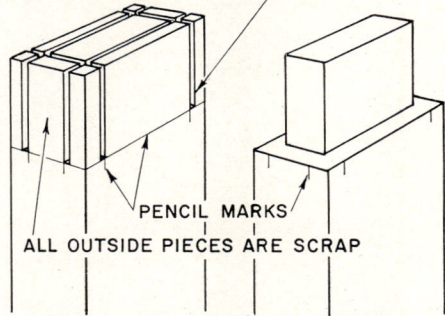

230. CHEEK CUTS COMPLETED. This shows the four cuts that will shape the thickness and width of the tenon. *Make cuts in waste stock.* Fig. 100.

tenon must then be trimmed with a chisel. Fig. 231.

Cut a small chamfer around the end of the tenon to help it slip easily into the mortise opening. This must be very slight.

231. TRIMMING A TENON WITH A CHISEL. After the shoulder cuts are made, the tenon should be trimmed to make it fit accurately into the mortise.

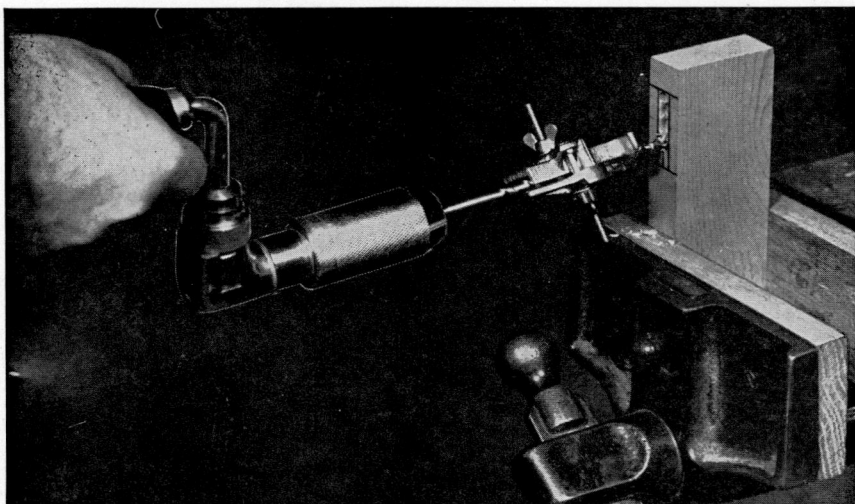

**232. BORING OUT A MORTISE.** Note that a bit has been selected that is the same diameter as the thickness of the tenon or the width of the mortise. A depth gauge controls the amount of stock removed.

## Cutting the mortise

The most common way to remove most of the stock from the mortise opening is with an auger bit and brace. Select an auger bit that is the same diameter or slightly smaller than the width of the opening. Then bore a series of holes to remove most of the stock from the mortise opening. Fig. 232. Use a depth gauge that is set to make the holes slightly deeper than the length of the tenon.

Next, use a chisel to pare out the sides and ends of the opening to the layout line. Fig. 233. To finish the ends, use a narrow chisel. Some woodworkers prefer to use a chisel to remove all of the stock. If so, it is necessary to use a mortise chisel, which is a heavy, thick chisel that can stand quite a bit of pounding. The width of the chisel should be exactly the width of the opening. Begin to cut at the center of the mortise, holding the chisel in a vertical position with the bevel side toward the end of the mortise. Cut out a V-shaped notch to the depth required and then continue to remove the stock by driving the chisel down with a mallet and then drawing down on the handle to remove the chips. Fig. 234. Stop when you are within about ⅛ inch of the end of the opening. Turn the chisel around with the flat side toward the end of the mortise and cut out the remainder of the stock. Fig. 235.

**233. TRIMMING OUT A MORTISE WITH A CHISEL.** After the holes are drilled, it is necessary to trim out the sides and end of the mortise. To do this, hold the chisel with the flat side against the side of the mortise and take a shearing cut. It will be necessary to use a narrow chisel to trim out the ends.

## Assembling the mortise and tenon

After the mortise-and-tenon joint has been cut, it will be necessary to do some fitting before the tenon will fit into the mortise properly. Use a chisel to pare off stock from the thickness and width of the tenon until you can force the tenon into the mortise with a moderate amount of pressure. Make sure that the shoulder of the tenon fits squarely against the face of the mortise.

For permanency, this type of construction is usually glued.

Gluing is treated extensively in a discussion of the subject elsewhere in the book.

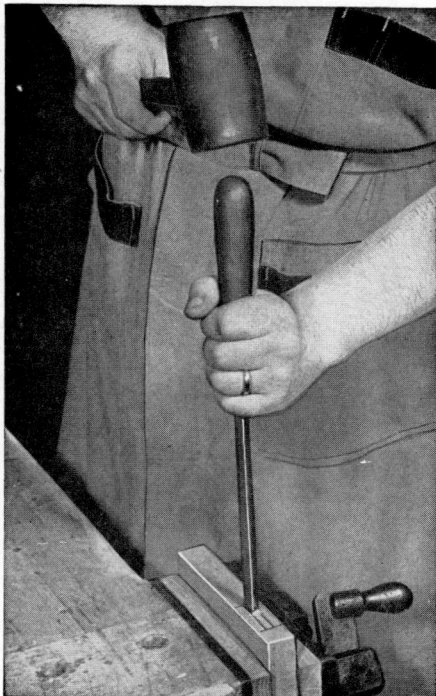

**234. CUTTING A MORTISE WITH A MORTISING CHISEL.** This is a heavy chisel that will take considerable pounding. The chisel selected must be the same width as the mortise.

**235. PROPER METHOD OF CUTTING A MORTISE** with a mortising chisel. The center cuts are taken with the chisel held with the bevel toward the outside, other cuts with the bevel turned in.

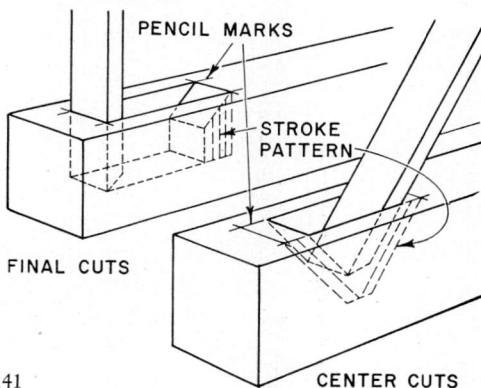

PENCIL MARKS

STROKE PATTERN

FINAL CUTS

CENTER CUTS

## Can You Answer These Questions on Making a Mortise-and-Tenon Joint?

1. Is a mortise-and-tenon joint found on better-quality furniture? Why?

2. Which part is the mortise? The tenon?

3. Make a sketch showing the cheek. The shoulder.

4. Name several types of mortise-and-tenon joints.

5. How many mortise-and-tenon joints could be found on a simple table?

6. What is the rule for the thickness of the tenon? What should the length of the tenon be?

7. Tell how to lay out a tenon.

8. Could a marking gauge be used to lay out a mortise? Explain.

9. How do the width of the mortise and the thickness of the tenon compare?

10. Should the shoulder cuts be made first? Why?

11. Which of the two methods of cutting a mortise is the most common? What are these two methods?

12. How are mortise-and-tenon joints usually fastened for permanency?

## BUILDING TABLES AND DESKS WITH DRAWERS

In building a table or desk, there are several steps added to those already covered in this book.

### Strengthening Corners

Most tables, chairs, and simple desks are made with four legs joined by rails. The rail and leg are fastened together with dowel construction or a mortise-and-tenon joint. To add strength to the adjoining parts, a *corner block* is cut and fastened in each corner. Fig. 236. The block helps to hold the table square and gives added support at its weakest point.

### Fastening Table Tops

Fig. 237 shows three of the common ways of attaching a table top to the rails.

### Drawer Construction

In installing a drawer in a table,

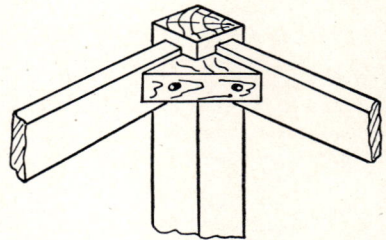

236. A CORNER BLOCK USED TO STRENGTHEN CORNERS of a table.

there are three steps: cutting the rail to receive the drawer, making a drawer guide and making the drawer. In desk-and-chest construction only the last two steps must be done.

1. Cutting the rail. To cut the rail to receive the drawer, first determine the exact size of the drawer. Then cut an opening that is $\frac{1}{16}$ inch wider and $\frac{1}{8}$ inch longer than the drawer front.

2. Making the drawer.

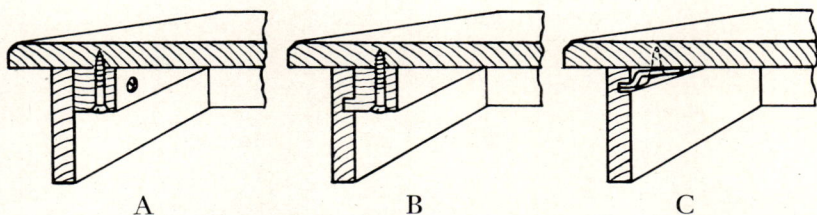

**237. SEVERAL WAYS OF ATTACHING A TABLE TOP TO THE RAILS:** A. Square cleat. B. Square cleat with rabbet and groove. C. Metal table-top fastener.

a.  The drawer may be made to fit flush with the opening, or it may be a lip drawer (fit over the frame). To make a lip drawer, a $\frac{3}{8}$-inch rabbet is cut around the inside edge of the drawer front. Then the drawer will fit over the frame.

b.  The front is usually made of $\frac{3}{4}$-inch material. The grain and color should match the material used in the project. The sides and back are made of $\frac{1}{2}$-inch material such as pine, birch, or maple. The bottom is usually made of $\frac{1}{4}$-inch fir plywood or hardboard. Fig. 239A.

c.  A common way of joining the front to the sides is with a rabbet joint. The rabbet is cut to a width of two thirds the thickness of the drawer front and to a depth slightly more than the thickness of the sides. This will allow some clearance for the drawer. Other kinds of drawer joints can also be used.

d.  The back is joined to the sides with a butt or dado joint. The back should be cut so that the drawer is slightly narrower at the back than at the front.

e.  Cut a $\frac{1}{4}$-inch by $\frac{1}{4}$-inch groove about $\frac{1}{2}$ inch above the bottom on the inside front and sides. Sometimes a groove is also cut across the back.

f.  Cut the drawer bottom slightly smaller (about $\frac{1}{16}$ inch) than the width between the grooves. This will allow for shrinkage and swelling.

g.  Assemble the drawer. Glue and nail the sides to the front. Never use glue in the grooves for the bottom. Slip the bottom in place and then glue or nail the sides to the back.

3.  Making drawer guides. The three most common drawer guides are the slide-block guide and runner (simple drawer guide), the center guide, and the side guide. Drawer guides support the drawer and keep it from slipping from one side to the other.

a.  To make a slide-block guide and runner for a table drawer, cut a rabbet in a piece of wood. This piece will fit between the rails at the lower corner of the drawer.

b.  Fig. 240A shows a side

DRILL AND COUNTERSINK
ON THE INSIDE

GLUE AND NAIL

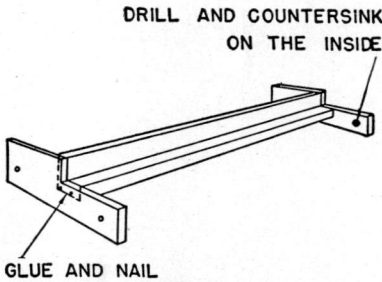

**238. A SIMPLE DRAWER GUIDE.** This type can be easily made, will work well when fitting a drawer between rails.

guide with a groove in the side of the drawer and with the runner attached to the project itself. Another method is to attach a runner to the side of the drawer and then cut a groove in either side of the project.

The bottom can be made to serve as a runner. Fig. 240B.

c. The center guide is made by attaching a runner to the project. Then two extra pieces are attached to the bottom of the drawer to act as the guide, or a groove is cut in an extra piece that is fastened to the bottom as a guide.

For heavy drawers such as those for letter files, special ball-bearing guides should be fastened to either side of the drawer. If it sticks, rub a little paraffin at the tight points. In best quality furniture, the dovetail joint is used to fasten the sides to the front and a rabbet-and-dado joint joins the back and sides. When there are several drawers, a dust panel is usually placed between drawers.

**239. A. SIMPLE WAYS OF FASTENING THE SIDES** to the front and the sides to the back in drawer construction. B. Parts of a drawer.

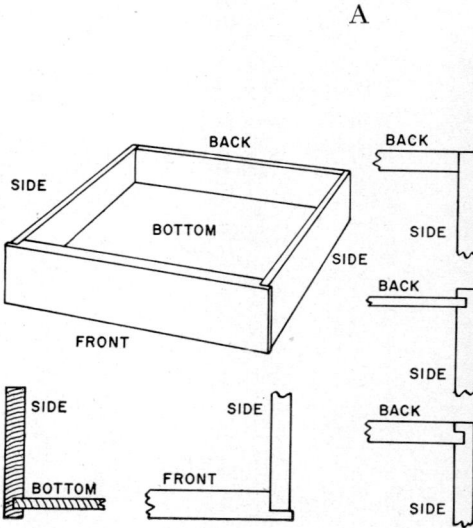

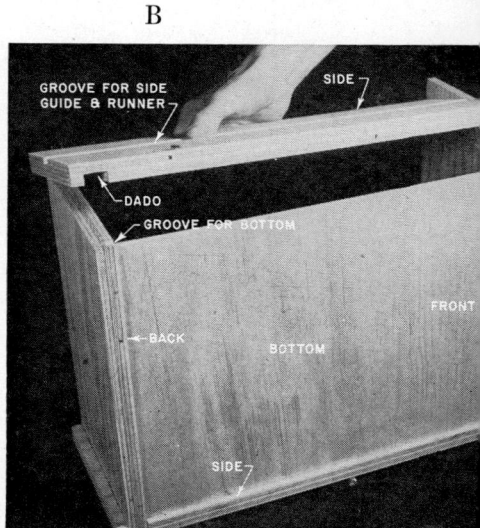

A

B

SIDE · BACK · BOTTOM · FRONT · SIDE · BOTTOM · FRONT · BACK · SIDE · BACK · SIDE · BACK · SIDE

GROOVE FOR SIDE GUIDE & RUNNER · SIDE · DADO · GROOVE FOR BOTTOM · BACK · FRONT · BOTTOM · SIDE

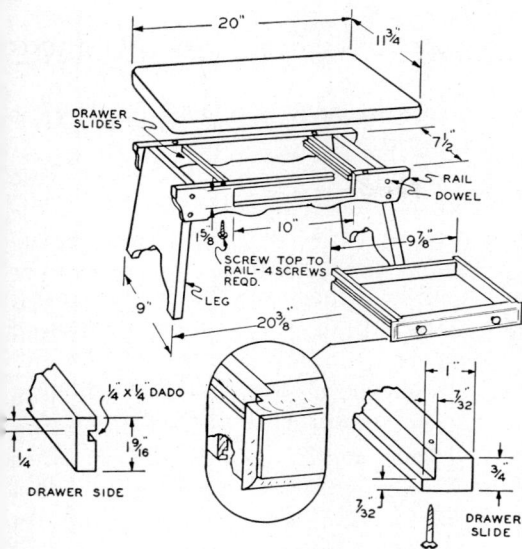

240A. A SIDE GUIDE AND RUNNER
used in a drawer fitted between rails.

240B. THE BOTTOM OF THIS drawer
serves as the runner that fits into the
dado cut in the side of the chest.

## Can You Answer These Questions on Building Tables and Desks With Drawers?

1. How can the corners of a table be strengthened?

2. What are three ways of fastening a table top to the base?

3. Describe a drawer guide. What purpose does it have?

4. Relate the three steps in installing a drawer in a table.

5. What is the best type of drawer guide?

6. How can a simple drawer guide be constructed?

7. What things should you think about when choosing the wood for the front of the drawer?

8. What joints are found in a drawer?

9. Explain why the sides of the drawer are not parallel.

## MAKING AND FITTING A PANELED DOOR OR FRAME

Panel construction is found in such things as chests, desks, and other pieces of cabinet furniture. Fig. 241. It consists of a frame into which is fitted a piece or panel of plywood. It has the advantage of less warpage over solid construction, since only the frame can change in size, while the panel inside is free to expand or con-

tract. The construction is the same whether the panels are made for parts of furniture or for doors.

### Parts of a door

The upright parts of a door are called stiles and the cross parts are called rails. Fig. 242. Door construction is similar to the other panel construction in which the frame fits together with a haunched mortise-and-tenon joint. Window construc-

145

though it can be done with a hand combination plane.

The mortise should be far enough away from the ends of the stiles to prevent it from breaking out under pressure. The mortise should be made the same width as the width of the groove, and the length should be about two thirds the width of the rail. The tenon should be cut as thick as the width of the groove. The length of the tenon should equal the depth of the mortise plus the depth of the groove.

Cut the notch out of the tenon so that the long part of the tenon will fit into the mortise opening and the short part will fit into the groove of the stile. Fig. 243. Sometimes in making a panel frame, no mortise is cut and only a stub tenon is made that fits into the groove in the stiles.

Fit the panel temporarily into the frame to check it. Take the

241. HERE IS ILLUSTRATED PANEL CONSTRUCTION IN A COFFEE TABLE. The outside top panels are fitted with leather inserts. The center panel is fitted with a piece of glass.

tion is very similar, except that the open mortise-and-tenon joint is used.

## Making a paneled door

Lay out and cut the stock for the frames, allowing extra length to provide for making a haunched mortise-and-tenon joint. Square up the stock. Select the panel to be used to fill the frame. Check this thickness and then cut a groove along the joint edges of each piece into which the panel will fit. This groove should be as deep as it is wide. The simplest method of cutting it is to use the circular saw, al-

242. THE PARTS OF A DOOR. Here is another example of panel construction.

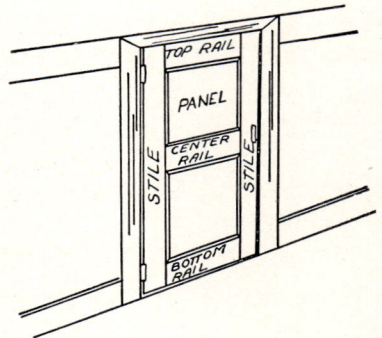

frame apart and cover the edge of
the panel with soap or wax to keep
any glue from getting into the
groove or edge of the panel. Apply
glue and clamp the frame together.

## Fitting a panel door

Check the opening into which
the door is to be fitted. Plane the
edge of the stile that is to fit against
the frame to which the hinges will
be fastened. After the edge has
been planed true, hold the door
against the opening as close as possible to get a rough check on how
well it fits. Also make sure that
each stile will be about the same
width when the door is fitted. Use
a framing square and check the
frame. If it is square, then square
off a line on the upper rail. Cut
and plane this end square with the
edge that has been fitted. It is a
good idea, however, to check and
plane until the door fits properly,
since frequently the frame will be
a little "out of square." Measure
the height of the opening, and lay
out and cut the bottom rail. If the
frame is square, plane this end
square with the first edge. Measure the width of the opening at the

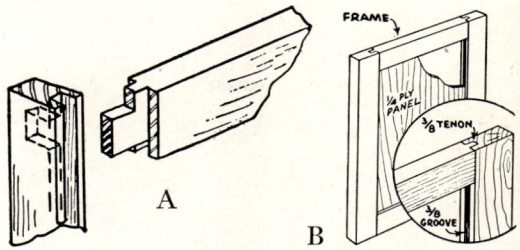

243. A. THE HAUNCHED MORTISE-
AND-TENON JOINT. This is a
common type of joint construction
for making a panel. B. A frame for a
panel can be made with a stub tenon
that fits into a groove.

top and at the bottom. Sometimes
the frame opening will not be exactly parallel from top to bottom.
Lay out these measurements on the
top and bottom rail and join these
lines with a straightedge along the
stile. Cut and plane the edge until
the door fits properly. The door
must not fit too snug since, after
the hinges are installed, it must have
some "play" to swing open. This
edge should be planed at a slight
bevel toward the back of the door.
This gives the stile proper clearance when the door is opened and
closed.

## Can You Answer These Questions on Making and Fitting a Paneled Door or Frame?

1. Why are doors and frames made of
panel construction?

2. Make a sketch of a door naming its
parts.

3. What kind of joint is found most
frequently in panel construction?

4. Should the panel be glued to the
frame? Explain your answer.

5. List all of the steps in fitting a door
in an opening.

# Section VIII

## Assembling

THE BEST part of woodworking comes when you begin to assemble your project. However, you must not hurry this work because you can easily ruin an article if you put it together poorly. Even before you begin to plan for assembly, be sure that each part of the project is scraped and sanded.

There are three common methods of permanently fastening pieces together; namely, with nails, screws, and glue. You will probably have a chance to use all three devices.

The assembled project is not ready for finishing until you have gone over the entire surface carefully to remove all glue, to fill in dents, and to scrape and resand the surface. Also, the hardware should be fitted and then removed. See "box" above. Further steps in woodworking are on pp. 12, 37, 53, 84, 97, 111, 119, 174, and 187.

## ASSEMBLING STOCK WITH NAILS

The simplest and easiest way to join two pieces of wood is with nails. You have undoubtedly had some nailing experience; yet, while it appears rather simple, considerable skill is required to do it properly.

### Tools for nailing

The most common tool is the *claw hammer*. Fig. 244. The face of the head, the part at the contact point, should be slightly rounded, as this will permit you to drive the nail flush with the surface of the wood without damaging the wood itself. Be sure the face is free from dirt, glue, etc., to keep it from slipping and marring the surface of the wood or bending a nail.

A *nail set* is a short metal punch with a cup-shaped head, used to drive the head of the nail below the surface of the wood. Fig. 245.

### Kinds of nails

There are so many kinds of nails, brads, and tacks that it would be impossible to list them here. Nails are made of mild steel, copper, brass, and aluminum.

Mild steel nails are sometimes

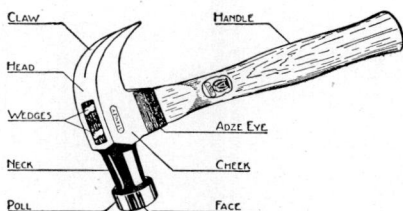

244. CLAW HAMMERS ARE AVAILABLE IN VARIOUS SIZES with heads that weigh from 5 ounces to 20 ounces. You should have several sizes of hammers of good quality. Parts of a claw hammer are shown.

galvanized to protect them from rusting. There are four kinds that you will probably use oftenest: common, box, casing, and finishing. Fig. 246.

The system of marking nails is rather antiquated, that of marking with "penny" or "d." This term stems from one of two sources: either it was considered to be the weight per thousand or the cost per thousand. Regardless of its origin, it is still used.

Nails range in size from 2d, the smallest, to 60d, the largest. Fig. 247. However, you will find that a 2d common nail will have a larger diameter than a 2d finishing nail.

245. THE NAIL SET IS USED TO DRIVE THE HEAD of a nail below the surface of the wood. This hole is then filled with putty or plastic wood before the project is finished.

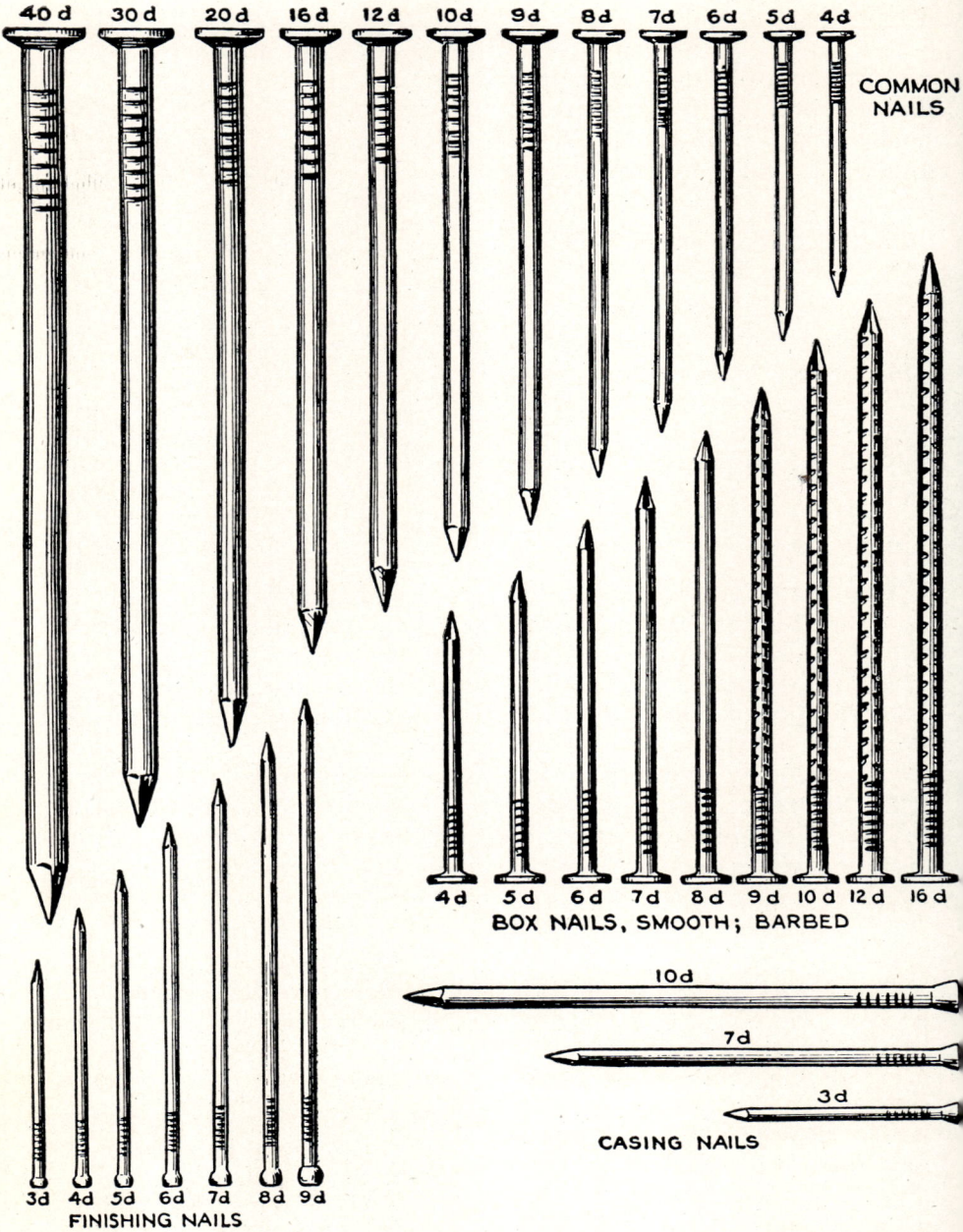

40 d   30 d   20 d   16 d   12 d   10 d   9 d   8 d   7 d   6 d   5 d   4 d

COMMON NAILS

4 d   5 d   6 d   7 d   8 d   9 d   10 d   12 d   16 d
BOX NAILS, SMOOTH; BARBED

10 d

7 d

3 d

CASING NAILS

3d   4d   5d   6d   7d   8d   9d
FINISHING NAILS

246. THE COMMON TYPES OF NAILS that you should be acquainted with.

The larger sizes are called *spikes*. *Box nails* are mostly for construction of packing cases and other somewhat more finished carpentry work. The *casing nail* has a small head but is a rather heavy nail for more finished carpentry or for the assembly of projects on which the heads of the nails are to be recessed. The *finishing nail*, the finest of all nails, is used for all fine cabinet and construction work. *Brads* are similar to finishing nails but are marked a little differently. They are indi-

## NAIL CHART

| Size | Length in Inches | American Steel Wire Gauge Number | | |
|------|------------------|--------|----------------|-----------|
|      |                  | Common | Box and Casing | Finishing |
| 2d | 1 | 15* | 15½ | 16½ |
| 3d | 1¼ | 14 | 14½ | 15½ |
| 4d | 1½ | 12½ | 14 | 15 |
| 5d | 1¾ | 12½ | 14 | 15 |
| 6d | 2 | 11½ | 12½ | 13 |
| 7d | 2¼ | 11½ | 12½ | 13 |
| 8d | 2½ | 10¼ | 11½ | 12½ |
| 9d | 2¾ | 10¼ | 11½ | 12½ |
| 10d | 3 | 9 | 10½ | 11½ |
| 12d | 3¼ | 9 | 10½ | 11½ |
| 16d | 3½ | 8 | 10 | 11 |
| 20d | 4 | 6 | 9 | 10 |
| 30d | 4½ | 5 | 9 | |
| 40d | 5 | 4 | 8 | |

* Note: The decimal equivalent of common gauge numbers is:

| | | | |
|---|---|---|---|
| 15 = .072 | 12 = .106 | 9 = .148 | 6 = .192 |
| 14 = .080 | 11 = .121 | 8 = .162 | 5 = .207 |
| 13 = .092 | 10 = .135 | 7 = .177 | 4 = .225 |

**247. A CHART SHOWING THE COMPARATIVE SIZES OF NAILS.** Note, for example, that a 2d common nail is larger in diameter than a 2d finishing nail.

cated by the length in inches (¼ inch to 3 inches) and a gauge number from 11 to 20. The higher the gauge number, the smaller the diameter. They are sold in pound boxes. *Escutcheon nails* or pins are small brass nails with round heads. They are used to assemble small projects, especially if a decorative head is desirable. They come in lengths from ¼ inch to 1¼ inches

**248. CORRUGATED FASTENERS OR WIGGLE NAILS** are used in place of nails in repair work and in box-and-frame construction.

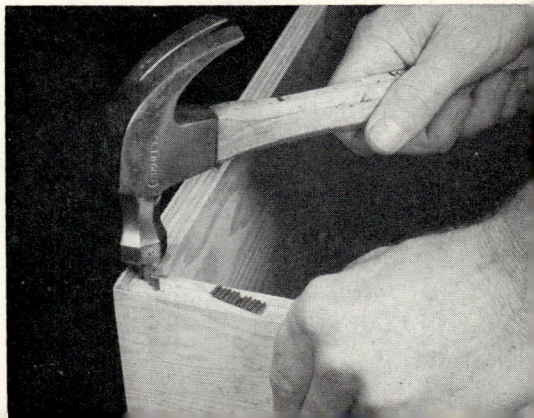

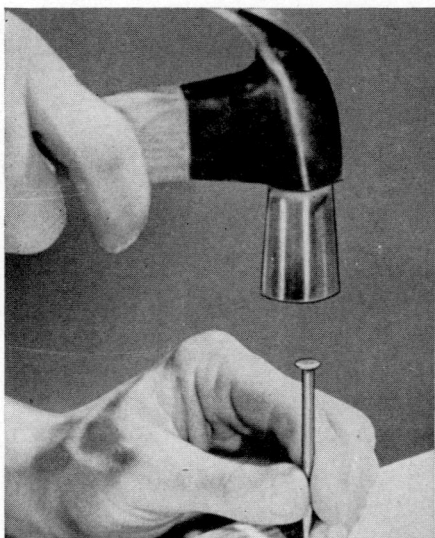

**249. STARTING A NAIL.** The nail is held between the thumb and forefinger and the hammer grasped close to the head when starting the nail. COURTESY THE JAM HANDY ORGANIZATION.

**250. DRIVING A NAIL.** Hold the hammer handle at the end so you can strike the hammer with firm, even blows. A few, well-placed blows are better than many light taps. COURTESY THE JAM HANDY ORGANIZATION.

**251. USING A NAIL SET.** The nail set is held between the thumb and forefinger and guided by the other fingers. It is important to guide the nail set in this way to keep it from slipping off the head of the nail and marring the wood surface.

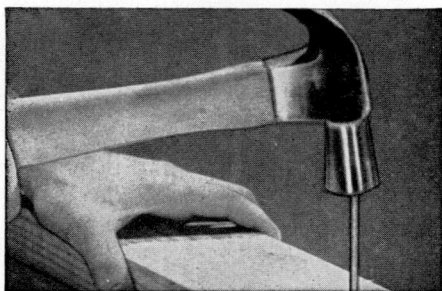

and gauge numbers of 20 to 16. Corrugated fasteners such as shown in Fig. 248 are used for holding joints. They are particularly good for repair work.

## Selecting nails

The first thing to consider is the proper kind and size of nail. You will find from experience that smaller diameters should be used for thinner stock and larger diameters on heavier work. Nails can be driven either straight into the wood or, for a tighter joint, they may be driven at a slight angle. If two pieces are to be nailed together, as the corner of a box, it is well to drive one or two nails through the first piece and then to hold this piece over the other piece to finish driving the nails in place.

## Driving nails

Hold the nail in your left hand between thumb and forefinger close to the point. To start the nail, grasp the hammer near the hammer head. Fig. 249. To hammer, hold the handle near its end and use a wrist movement as well as an elbow and arm movement, depending on the size of the nail being driven. Tap the head of the nail with the hammer to get it started and then remove your fingers from the nail before continuing to strike it with firm blows. Fig. 250.

Watch the head of the nail and not the hammer and try to drive the nail with a few well-placed blows rather than with many quick taps. If a nail begins to bend over, it is better to remove it and start over with a new one.

When nailing any two pieces together, choose the location for the nails wisely and do not put several nails along the same grain as this will split the wood. A neatly arranged series of nails will do a better job of holding than a larger number haphazardly placed.

If you are using casing or finishing nails, do not drive the head completely down to the surface but finish driving it with a nail set. Hold the nail set in your left hand with the middle finger against the surface of the work and the side of

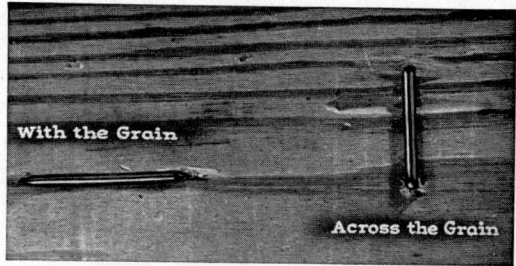

252. CLINCHING A NAIL. It is better practice to clinch a nail with the grain than across it because with the grain the nail will sink in more easily, since it does not have to break the fibers. COURTESY THE JAM HANDY ORGANIZATION.

the nail. Then drive the nail in until it is about $\frac{1}{16}$ inch below the surface. Fig. 251.

If you are nailing hardwood, special steps must be taken. In the piece of wood, drill holes slightly smaller than the diameter of the nail, apply a little wax to the surface of the nail, and drive it in.

Sometimes you will need to use nails that are longer than the total

253. TOENAILING. When it is necessary to nail the end of one piece to the side of another piece, they should be toenailed by driving the nails in at an angle on either side.

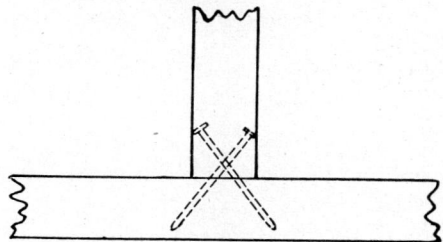

together. In this case, the points of the nails should be driven completely through the pieces and then bent or clinched. Bend the nails over with the grain so they can be flattened easily. Fig. 252.

Sometimes it will be necessary to nail the end of one piece of wood to the side of another as in framing up a house. The nails are then driven into the wood at an angle from both sides. This is called "toe-nailing." Fig. 253.

## Removing nails

Force the claws of the hammer under the head of the nail and pull on the handle. When the nail is drawn part way out slip a piece of scrap wood under the hammer head before continuing to draw out the nail. Fig. 254. It is a good idea to protect the wood as in this photo.

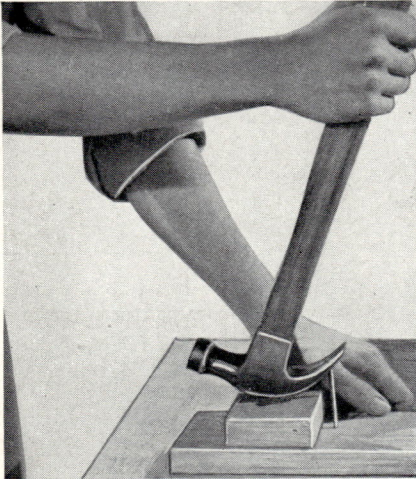

254. REMOVING A NAIL. A piece of scrap wood is placed under the head of the hammer to provide leverage for drawing the nail out. COURTESY THE JAM HANDY ORGANIZATION.

thickness of both pieces being nailed

## Can You Answer These Questions on Assembling Stock With Nails?

1. Name the parts of a claw hammer.
2. Explain how to use a nail set.
3. Can you name and describe the four most common kinds of nails?
4. What does the word "penny" mean?
5. How large is a 7d finishing nail?
6. What are the larger sizes of common nails called?
7. How is a brad different from a finishing nail?
8. Tell how you would start a nail.
9. When you use a hammer, would you watch the head of the hammer or the nail?
10. How are finishing and casing nails set?
11. Hardwood is very difficult to nail. What would you do to overcome the difficulty?
12. Tell how to clinch a nail. Is this done with or across the grain?
13. Explain what toenailing is.
14. When it is necessary to remove a nail, how can you keep from marring the surface of the wood?

## ASSEMBLING WITH SCREWS

Screws take more time to assemble, but they are far superior to nails because they make a stronger bond and because the pieces can easily be taken apart. If screws are

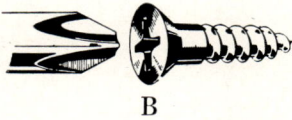

255. A. A SCREW DRIVER SHOULD ALWAYS BE THE CORRECT SIZE. This type is used for screws with slotted heads. B. The recessed, or Phillips head, screw driver.

A

installed correctly, a few will do the work of several nails and hold much better.

## The screw driver

In selecting a screw driver, Fig. 255, it is well to choose as large a one as possible for the work. The size is determined by the length of the blade rather than by the total length. Make sure that the point is

about the same width as the diameter of the head of the screw. If it is wider, it may mar the surface of the wood as it is set in place. Fig. 256.

Notice in Fig. 297A the proper method of grinding a screw driver. This is very important because a screw driver, if ground to a sharp edge, will tend to slip out of the slot and either mar the surface of the wood or injure the head of the screw. The head of a screw that has been set with a poor screw driver usually has a ragged metal edge exposed.

## Screws

There are several things you should know about the size and kind of screw to use. These are: the kind of head, the diameter or gauge size, the length, the kind of metal, and the finish. As you see in Fig. 257, screws are roundhead, flathead, oval head, and drive screw. They

256. SELECTING THE PROPER SIZE OF SCREW DRIVER. Note that in (A) the screw driver is too narrow, with the result that it causes a burr on the head; (B) the screw driver is of the correct width; (C) the screw driver is too wide, with the result that it will mar the surface of the wood. COURTESY THE JAM HANDY ORGANIZATION.

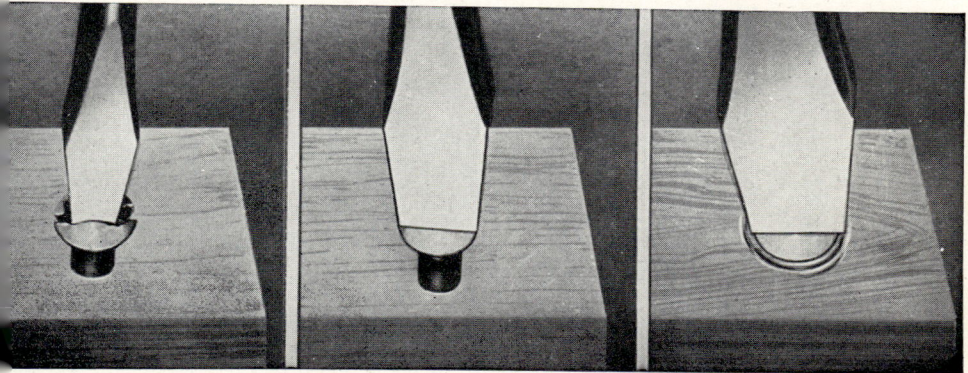

A                              B                              C

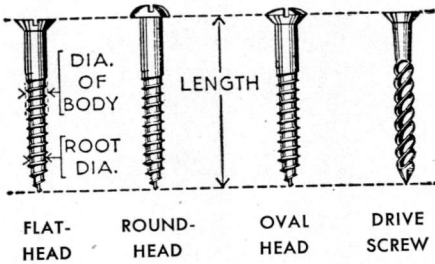

FLAT-   ROUND-   OVAL   DRIVE
HEAD   HEAD   HEAD   SCREW

**257. THE FOUR KINDS OF SCREWS.**
The portion of each style of screw
included in the length measurement is
indicated in the diagram. Learn the
names of the parts and the method of
measuring the lengths.

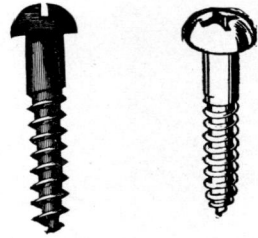

**258. THE DIFFERENCE BETWEEN** the
slotted head and the recessed Phillips head screws.

are available with either a slotted
head or a Phillips head, and are almost any length from ¼ inch to 6
inches. Fig. 258. Most screws are
made of mild steel, although it is
possible to buy them in brass or
aluminum, which are primarily for
boat construction or wherever moisture would rust the other kind.
Most flathead screws have a bright
finish, while roundhead screws are
generally finished in a dull blue.

Wood screw sizes are determined by a special gauge with numbers from 0 to 24. 0 is the smallest
number and has a diameter of .060.
The diameter of each succeeding
number is .013 larger. For example,
a number 5 screw is .125 (.060 +
.013 × 5) or ⅛" in diameter. A
number 11 screw would be .203 or
$^{13}/_{64}$" in diameter. You will notice
that the shank clearance hole is always approximately this diameter.
See Fig. 259B. Two screws can be
the same length but have a different
gauge size (Fig. 259A), which

**259A. THE DIFFERENT GAUGE SIZES OF 1¼-INCH SCREWS.** Wood screws range
in length from ¼ to 6 inches and in gauge sizes from gauge 0 to gauge 24. Of
course, each length is not made in all gauges, as is shown by the 1¼-inch screw.

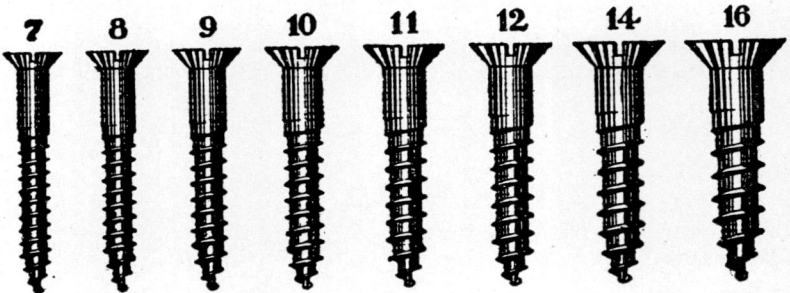

7   8   9   10   11   12   14   16

1¼ INCH

| No. of Screw | For Shank Clearance Holes | For Pilot Holes* | | No. of Auger Bit to counter-bore for sinking head (by 16ths) |
|---|---|---|---|---|
| | | Hardwoods | Softwoods | |
| 0 | 1/16 | 1/32 | 1/64 | |
| 1 | 5/64 | 1/32 | 1/32 | |
| 2 | 3/32 | 3/64 | 1/32 | 3 |
| 3 | 7/64 | 1/16 | 3/64 | 4 |
| 4 | 7/64 | 1/16 | 3/64 | 4 |
| 5 | 1/8 | 5/64 | 1/16 | 4 |
| 6 | 9/64 | 5/64 | 1/16 | 5 |
| 7 | 5/32 | 3/32 | 1/16 | 5 |
| 8 | 11/64 | 3/32 | 5/64 | 6 |
| 9 | 3/16 | 7/64 | 5/64 | 6 |
| 10 | 3/16 | 7/64 | 3/32 | 6 |
| 11 | 13/64 | 1/8 | 3/32 | 7 |
| 12 | 7/32 | 1/8 | 7/64 | 7 |
| 14 | 1/4 | 9/64 | 7/64 | 8 |
| 16 | 17/64 | 5/32 | 9/64 | 9 |
| 18 | 19/64 | 3/16 | 9/64 | 10 |
| 20 | 21/64 | 13/64 | 11/64 | 11 |
| 24 | 3/8 | 7/32 | 3/16 | 12 |

*Sometimes called "anchor holes."

**ACTUAL SHANK SIZES**

#0  #1  #2  #3  #4
#5  #6  #7  #8  #9
#10  #11  #12  #14  #16
#18  #20  #24  #30

To determine Sizes of Screws, lay screws flat within parallel lines shown in border.

259B. TABLE SHOWING THE PROPER SIZE BIT OR DRILL needed for the shank hole and the pilot hole for assembling stock with screws.

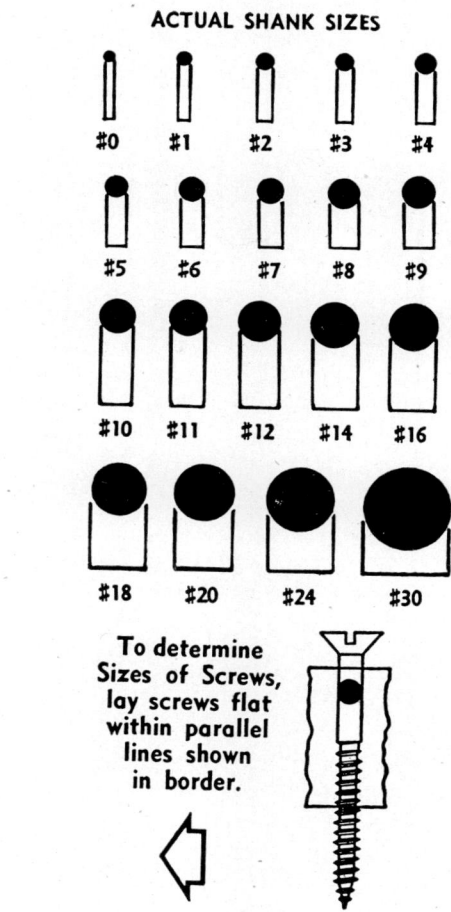

CUP HOOK  SCREW HOOK  "L" SCREW HOOK  SCREW EYE

260. CUP HOOKS (USUALLY OF BRASS) COME IN SIZES FROM ½ TO 1½ INCH. *Screw hooks* are made in lengths from 1¼ to 2½ inches. "L" (square-bent) *screw hooks* come in lengths from 1 inch to 2¼ inches. *Screw eyes* are made with either small or medium eyes in many sizes.

means that they have different diameters. In most cases, the size of the screw is indicated on the drawing; for example, No. 8 R. H. 1½, which means that the screw is No. 8 gauge size, roundhead, and 1½ inches long. If the size isn't indicated, it is well to select a screw that will go at least two-thirds of its length into the second piece. If the second piece is end grain, however, it should be even longer, since end grain does not provide a good holding condition. Other screw devices are shown in Fig. 260.

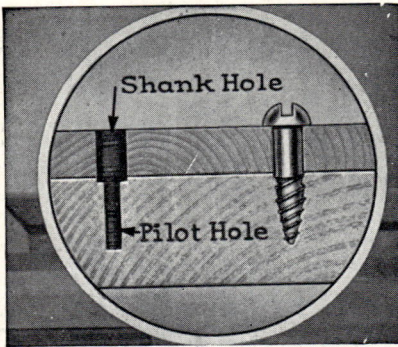

261. HERE IS THE SHANK HOLE AND PILOT HOLE, properly drilled and the screw installed. COURTESY THE JAM HANDY ORGANIZATION.

## Drilling the clearance holes

Select the kind and size of screw needed. Note in Fig. 259B the two sizes of drills you will need. The first one is for the shank clearance hole, drilled in the first piece, and the second one is for the pilot hole, drilled in the second piece. Fig. 261. The shank clearance hole should be the same size or slightly smaller than the shank of the screw so that the screw can be inserted in the first piece without forcing.

Drill the shank clearance hole in the first piece of stock. Then hold this piece over the second and mark the location for the pilot hole with a scratch awl. If you are assembling pieces of softwood, drill the pilot hole only about half the depth to which the screw is to go. If you are drilling hardwood, make sure that it is drilled to the total depth of the screw.

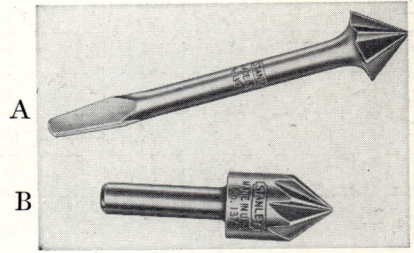

262. TWO TYPES OF 82-DEGREE COUNTERSINKS: A. For use in a brace. B. For use in a drill press.

## Countersinking for flathead screws

If flathead screws are being installed, countersink the upper surface of the first piece to allow the head of the screw to be flush with the surface. Fig. 262. Check the

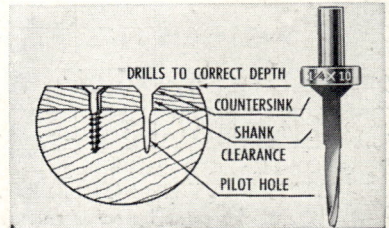

DRILLS TO CORRECT DEPTH

COUNTERSINK

SHANK CLEARANCE

PILOT HOLE

263. THIS TOOL WILL DO FOUR THINGS: (1) drill to the correct depth, (2) do countersinking, (3) make the correct shank clearance, and (4) drill the correct pilot hole.

264. A PLUG CUTTER. Available in different sizes for cutting wooden plugs.

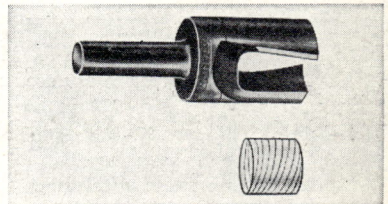

A

**265. USING A PLUG CUTTER. The** plug should be cut from the same kind of wood as is used in the project.

**266. STARTING A SCREW. Hold the** screw between the thumb and forefinger to guide it while starting.

B

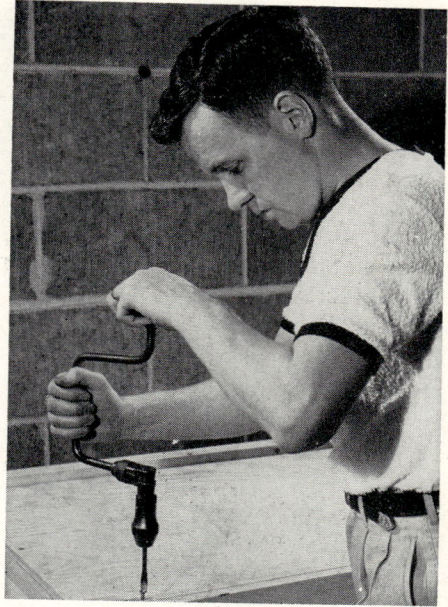

**267. A. A SCREW-DRIVER BIT TO USE IN A BRACE. B.** Installing a wood screw with a bit and brace.

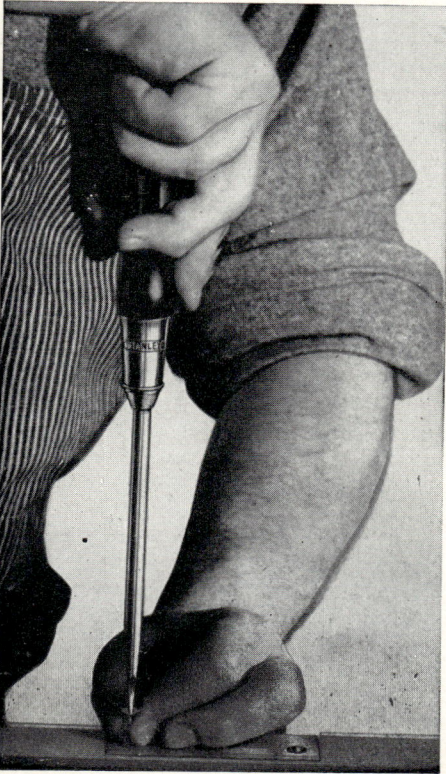

depth of the countersunk hole by turning the screw upside down and fitting it in the hole. A screw-mate drill countersink can be used with flathead screws. Fig. 263.

## Plugging screw holes

In furniture construction, it is frequently desirable to have the screws completely invisible. In this case, you should use a drill or auger bit the same size as the head of the screw to counterbore a hole in the first surface about ⅜ inch deep. The screw will then be below the surface of the wood. After the parts are assembled, this hole can either be filled with plastic wood or you can make a little screw plug with the tool shown in Figs. 264 and 265. Furniture and supply companies can supply fancy, decorated plugs.

## Driving the screw

To install a screw, hold the body of the screw between your thumb and forefinger. Fig. 266. Grasp the handle of the screw driver in the palm of your hand, with the thumb and forefinger extending toward the shank. Start the screw and then move your left hand up just back of the point of the screw driver to guide the tool and to keep it from slipping off the head as the screw is set in place. Continue to turn the screw in until it is firmly set, but do not try to force it, as this may either strip the threads or shear off the screw from the wood. Fig. 267. This is especially true if the screws are small or made of brass.

## Can You Answer These Questions on Assembling Stock With Screws?

1. A screw has several advantages over a nail. Name them.

2. How do you know what size screw driver to choose?

3. Describe the proper way of grinding a screw driver.

4. What information must you have in order to secure the proper kind and size of screw for your work?

5. As the gauge number increases, how is the diameter of the screw affected?

6. What is the general rule for selecting screw lengths?

7. Name two types of screws.

8. What is the shank clearance hole and what purpose does it serve?

9. Why must a pilot hole be drilled?

10. Is the pilot hole drilled in softwood in the same way it is drilled in hardwood?

11. When is it necessary to countersink the hole?

12. How can you check the depth of the countersink hole?

13. What is the purpose of screw plugs?

14. Describe the proper method of holding a screw driver when starting a screw.

15. Why is it important to set the screw with the correct size screw driver?

268. SCRAPING A SURFACE BY HAND. Note that the scraper is held in both hands and tipped at an angle to the surface of the wood.

## SCRAPING A SURFACE

To obtain a really fine surface on open grain wood such as oak, mahogany, and walnut, the wood frequently is scraped after the planing is done. This scraping removes the small irregularities that have been left there by the plane iron. Some woods, such as curly maple and cedar, that cannot be planed successfully, can be scraped to produce a very smooth surface. It is very important to have a sharp hand scraper. It is always necessary to sharpen the scraper before each time it is used and frequently during its use.

## Scraping a surface

Clamp the stock firmly in a vise or on top of the bench. Hold the hand scraper with both hands between the thumbs and forefingers with the cutting edge toward the surface of the wood. Fig. 268. Turn the blade at an angle of about 50 to 60 degrees to the surface of the wood. Apply firm pressure to the scraper blade and push or draw it across the surface. Be careful to keep the cutting edge flat against the wood so that the corners do not dig in or mar the wood. Always scrape *with* the grain of the wood. Sometimes the scraper is turned a little and a shearing cut made across the surface. If you are working on curly maple or other burly type wood, always change the direction of the scraping action to correspond with the direction of the grain.

## Can You Answer These Questions on Scraping a Surface?

1. On what kinds of wood is scraping necessary to produce a smooth surface?
2. At what times should a scraper be sharpened?
3. The scraper is held at what angle to the surface of the wood?
4. How can you prevent the corners of the scraper from marring or digging into the wood?
5. Tell how the scraper should be used on burly woods.

## SANDING A SURFACE

One of the last steps before a project is assembled is sanding. All planing, cutting, and forming should be completed before beginning to use sandpaper. Sanding is done only to finish the surface of wood and not to form or shape it. Too frequently sandpaper is used in place of cutting tools.

## Kinds of sandpaper

There is really no such thing as "sand" paper, though the name is given to two types of abrasives: quartz, more commonly called flint, which has a yellowish cast, and garnet, which is a tawny red. For hand sanding, the flint paper is often used, even though garnet is harder, sharper, and better for most woods, especially harder woods.

Sandpaper is made by applying a coat of animal glue to a tough paper and then coating the surface with the quartz or garnet. Garnet

| | Aluminum Oxide | Flint and Garnet | | Aluminum Oxide | Flint and Garnet |
|---|---|---|---|---|---|
| Very Fine | 240 | 7/0 | | 100 | 2/0 |
| | 220 | 6/0 | Medium | 80 | 0 |
| | | | | 60 | ½ |
| | | | | 50 | 1 |
| Fine | 180 | 5/0 | Coarse | 40 | 1½ |
| | 150 | 4/0 | | 36 | 2 |
| | 120 | 3/0 | | 30 | 2½ |

269A. Table of abrasive numbers.

269B. GRADES AND TYPES OF SANDPAPER. Nine- by 10-inch sheets of flint or 9- by 11-inch sheets of garnet paper are used for hand sanding. For the belt sander, narrow-roll garnet paper or cloth, or prepared belts, can be selected. On disk sanders, wide-roll garnet paper or cloth is needed. For machine sanding, No. 1 garnet with paper or cloth back is used for general sanding. No. 0 garnet paper and No. 3/0 garnet cloth are used for smoothing woods.

paper is sold in 9-inch by 11-inch sheets. The paper ranges from 2½, which is very coarse, to 7/0, which is very fine. You will need about three different coarsenesses of paper for most jobs. Figs. 269A and B.

## Tearing sandpaper

To make the sheet of sandpaper more flexible, draw it over the edge of the bench. A 9″ x 11″ sheet is usually divided into four or six pieces, depending upon the kind of work to be sanded and the size of your sanding block. To tear the sheet, fold it lengthwise with the abrasive surface toward the inside, then hold one half of the sheet over the bench and tear the paper along the folded line. Sometimes you can tear the piece by holding a straight-edge or the cutting edge of a saw over the folded line.

For most sanding, a sandpaper block (Fig. 270) is a good backing. If the sheets are torn into six pieces, a block 1½″ thick, 3″ wide, and 5″ long is convenient.

A piece of foam rubber or felt can be glued to the base to provide a more flexible surface.

## Sanding a flat surface

Fasten the piece between the vise dog and bench stop or hold it firmly against the surface of the bench. If the piece is held in the vise, grip the sanding block as

271. SANDING A SURFACE. The sanding block is held firmly against the surface and is moved back and forth with the grain.

270. TWO KINDS OF SANDING BLOCKS. On the left is a commercial block with a foam-rubber base. The one on the right is homemade, with a piece of leather tacked to it under the sandpaper.

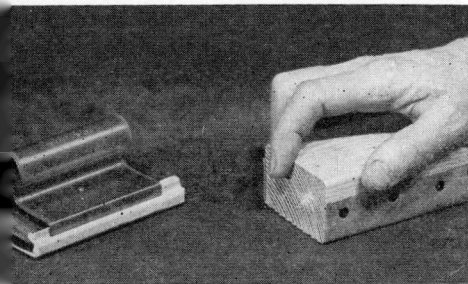

shown in Fig. 271. Apply even pressure to the block and sand the surface *with* the grain of the wood. Move the block back and forth and work slowly from one side to the other to obtain an even surface. Take special care to keep from sanding the edges too much.

After the coarser paper has been used, finer grades are substituted to produce a progressively smoother finish. If the piece is held against the top of the bench, you can operate the block with one hand.

## Sanding an edge

Lock the work in a vise with the edge exposed. Grasp the sanding block in both hands, using the forefinger on either side of the edge to keep it square with the sides. Fig. 272. It is just as important to sand an edge square as it is to plane it square.

After the edge has been sanded,

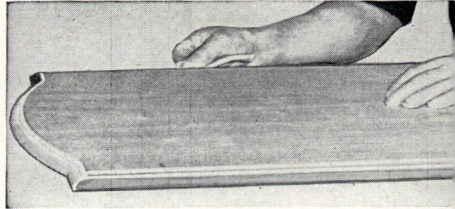

273. SANDING A MOLDING BY HAND. The sandpaper is held in the fingers and guided along the edge.

272. SANDING AN EDGE. The sanding block is grasped in both hands with the thumbs on top and the fingers curled underneath. This will help keep the block square with the surface. If this is not done, there is danger of rounding the edges.

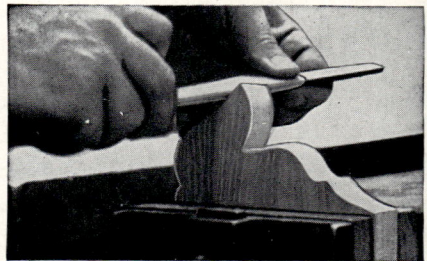

274. SANDING THE CONCAVE SURFACE. Here the sandpaper is wrapped around a half-round file so that it will conform to the general curve of the concave surface.

the arris is rounded slightly by drawing the paper over the edge.

## Sanding an end

To sand an end, the same procedure as for sanding an edge is followed, except that the surface is sanded in only one direction rather than back and forth. This produces a smoother finish.

## Sanding convex surfaces

Convex surfaces can usually be sanded with a block in the same way as an edge is sanded, but convex surfaces such as rounded ends can be done more satisfactorily by holding the paper in the fingers or palm of your hand. Fig. 273.

## Sanding concave or other inside surfaces

These surfaces are most easily finished by wrapping the paper around a stick such as part of a broomstick or the handle of a tool. The half-round surface of a file also makes a suitable backing. Fig. 274.

## Can You Answer These Questions on Sanding a Surface?

1. Is sanding done for the purpose of forming or shaping wood?
2. At what point in building the project should the sanding be done?
3. Is there any sand on sandpaper? What are the two abrasives used in sandpaper?

4. Which sandpaper is best for hard-wood? For softwood?

5. How is sandpaper usually sold?

6. What number would you ask for when buying very coarse sandpaper? Very fine sandpaper?

7. What grades of sandpaper are commonly found in use in school shops?

8. How would you soften a sheet of sandpaper before using it? How would you tear it into smaller pieces?

9. How is a sanding block useful?

10. Is it correct to sand across grain? Why?

11. There is a very common error often made in sanding a flat surface. What is it?

12. How can you keep the edge square when sanding?

13. Describe how you would sand a convex surface.

14. How would you sand a concave surface?

## FITTING, ASSEMBLING, AND GLUING UP THE PARTS

You are now ready to assemble your project. The difficulty of this step is, of course, largely determined by the kind of project and its size. If you have built a simple, three-member project such as a footstool, the problem of assembly is relatively simple. On the other hand, if you have constructed an end table, a bookcase, or a table or desk with drawers, the problem is much more complicated. There are, however, certain things to watch regardless of the size of the project.

## Collecting the parts

Get all the parts together that are to go into the finished project. If you were careful when you made

them, you will have kept identification marks on all pieces so that you will know how each part, joint, and piece fits to the next. This is very important because you will find yourself in a very unhappy position if, when you begin to glue, the joints don't fit or the parts don't match. This can easily happen.

## Checking all the parts to see that they are finished

To be considered finished, the parts should have properly constructed joints and they should be scraped and sanded. If there are duplicate parts, rails or legs, check each one of them to make sure that they are identical in size and shape. If the project has a joint construction, try each of the joints to see whether it fits properly and to check whether it is clearly marked in a place which can be seen after glue is applied and after the joint is assembled. These checks are especially important, since you will usually find that there is some small correction to be made before you can go ahead with the assembling. If the parts have been in storage for some time, the wood may have swelled slightly, and therefore the joints may not fit just right.

Your plan of procedure or the drawing of your job will indicate whether the project is to be assembled with glue, screws, or nails. If screws or nails are used, carefully check to see that you have the correct type and number to complete your job. You should usually figure a couple of extra screws or several more nails than are indicated, as you may spoil a few. If glue is to be used, decide whether it is to be hot animal glue, cold casein or plastic resin glue, or cold liquid fish glue. Be sure that you have a sufficient amount of the glue ready to apply.

## Making protective pieces

Before attempting to clamp the pieces together, cut out of softwood some protective pieces to place between the clamps and the project. These protective pieces are not needed if you use hand screws. It is a good idea to plane the surface of the pieces which are to be placed against the finished project, thus keeping it from being marred. It may be necessary to cut special shapes if the project is of an irregular design—for example, if you are clamping a table that has legs that taper outward, or if you are assembling a stool that has an irregularly shaped design at the point where the clamps are to fasten. Of course, you will know when this is necessary.

## Assembling the project temporarily

Now use cabinet clamps and hand screws temporarily to clamp all parts together. This will give you an idea of how your pieces fit together and will also give you a chance to see if any small correc-tions need to be made. If you are assembling such a thing as a bookcase or hanging wall shelves made with parallel sides and crosspieces with dado or rabbet joints, all you will need are flat pieces of protective scrap stock and cabinet clamps that will fit across the project both on the front and back, and a pair of clamps for each shelf. If you are assembling such projects as end tables, stools, small desks, etc., that have legs and rails, the corners will usually be made with mortise-and-tenon joints or dowel joints. In either case, you will need clamps to go across the ends and cabinet clamps to go across the sides in completing the work.

After the project is assembled with clamps, check with a square to make sure that the project is squared up. Fig. 275. Also use a steel tape or rule to take measurements across and up and down to see that the sides and ends are parallel and that the project is of the same height throughout. Fig. 276. By shifting the clamp or tapping a side or leg with a mallet, you can bring it into place.

This trial assembly will give you a chance to have all clamps adjusted to correct width, and you will be all set to assemble.

## Assembling with nails and screws

Follow the directions given in the unit on assembling stock with nails and screws.

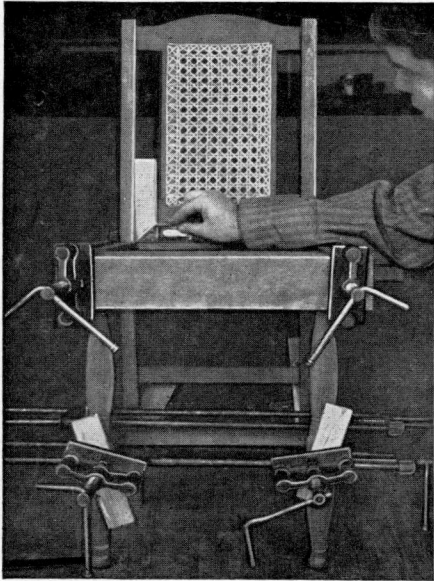

275. CHECKING A PROJECT after it has been temporarily clamped together, to make sure that the project is squared up.

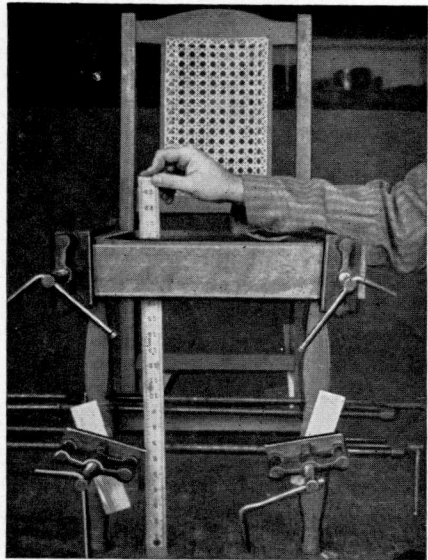

276. USING A RULE TO MEASURE THE HEIGHT of the project at various points. This is important. Without this check, the project may not be level after drying.

## Assembling with glue

If you do not have a special glue bench or gluing room, it is a very good idea to place a piece of wrapping paper over the bench or floor where the gluing is to be done. If the project is to be glued, carefully remove the clamps from top to bottom, laying the clamps on the bench in definite order so that you can pick them up easily. Place the scrap pieces of wood next to the clamps so that everything will be in order as you are ready for it.

If the project is one that must be assembled all at one time, such as a book shelf or hanging shelf, do it in that way. On the other hand, if the project is a desk, table, or stool, you may assemble and glue the end section one day and then assemble the rest the next.

In addition to your project parts, clamps, scrap pieces, and glue, have a rubber mallet ready, a rule or tape measure, and a square. If animal glue is used, heat the wood parts before assembling and work very rapidly, as the glue sets quickly. If casein or resin glue is used, you do not need to work quite so fast. (See page 74.)

Use a brush to apply the glue carefully to both parts of the joint. Do not use too much glue, since any excess is just a problem to remove later. Especially when working with animal glue, there is a tendency to dribble it around. As quickly as possible, fasten the joints.

Place the scrap pieces over the proper places and lightly screw up the clamps. Do this until all the clamps are in place. Then simultaneously turn up each clamp a little at a time, making the checks to see that the project is square and that it measures the same distance wherever there are parallels. You may need a rubber mallet to tap a joint in place or to change the position of a clamp.

As soon as the project is all clamped together, remove any of the excess glue with an old chisel or glue scraper. Be careful not to mar the surface of the project. Then put the project in a safe place where no one will bump it and allow it to dry from twelve to twenty-four hours. Carefully remove each of the clamps and the scrap pieces.

## Can You Answer These Questions on Fitting, Assembling, and Gluing Up the Parts?

1. Why should identification marks be kept on all pieces before they are assembled?

2. What things must be completed before a part of a project can be considered ready for assembly?

3. Should joints be checked again just before assembly? Why?

4. What should be a guide for determining how a project should be assembled?

5. Name the three things commonly used for fastening parts together permanently.

6. Why are protective wood pieces unnecessary when hand screws are chosen for assembly?

7. Think of several projects which require special-shaped protective pieces.

8. Why is it necessary first to make a trial assembly?

9. Would you always assemble a project completely in one operation?

10. Describe the checks that should be made when the project is temporarily assembled.

11. How much glue would you apply?

12. How would you tap the parts into place and what kind of mallet should be used? How should excess glue be removed?

13. How long should a project be allowed to dry?

## PREPARING THE PROJECT FOR FINISHING

After the project is assembled, it is very important to go over it carefully to get it ready for finishing. This is an important step and one that is frequently viewed too lightly, with the result that a poor finish is attained.

## Removing excess glue

First of all, remove all excess glue from around the joints and anywhere else, being especially careful not to gouge the wood **or** cut off a sliver of stock. It is very easy to do this when removing glue around a mortise-and-tenon joint, for example. To remove the glue, use a good, sharp chisel and carefully separate the glue from the wood surface. On flat areas, the glue may be removed with a hand scraper. Make sure that every fleck of glue has been completely removed, as glue will not take stain.

If casein glue has been used, it may be necessary to apply a bleach wherever there is glue, since one of the undesirable things about certain kinds of casein glue is that it darkens the wood, especially open, porous woods. There is a type of casein glue on the market that will not do this, but, if you think it necessary, bleach out these glue spots before staining. This can be done by mixing oxalic acid crystals in very hot water to form a solution. Add as many crystals as will dissolve in the hot water; then brush the solution on the areas and let them dry. These spots can then be sanded out. Commercial bleaching solutions can also be used effectively.

### Checking holes and cracks

Go over the entire project carefully to see if there are any holes, cracks, or irregularities that need filling. If there are, several types of fillers can be chosen. You can purchase plastic wood either in a neutral color or in mahogany, walnut, oak, or other colors. You can also

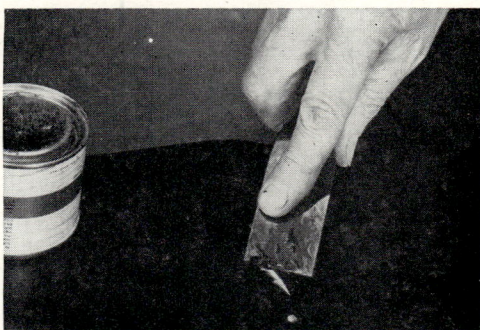

A
B

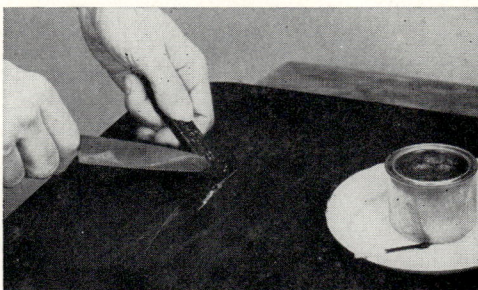

277. A. FILLING A CRACK WITH PLASTIC WOOD. B. Filling a crack with stick shellac and a warm putty knife.

purchase stick shellac in various colors. If necessary, you can make your own filler by mixing equal parts of cornstarch and wheat flour, to which you add linseed oil and a drier. This filler can be colored either with stain or with coloring mixed in oil to match the surface of the wood. Fig. 277A, B.

Of course, if the project is to be painted, the irregularities can be filled with putty.

If there are shallow dents in the

wood, these can be raised sometimes by applying some hot water to them and then placing a warm iron on the portion. Make sure that the iron is not so hot that it burns the surface.

## Scraping and sanding the project

After all of the irregularities and holes have been filled, use a hand scraper and sandpaper to go carefully over the entire project, scraping and sanding where necessary. When you sand, continue to use finer and finer paper until a very smooth surface is secured with No. 2/0 garnet paper. Before the final sanding, moisten the project slightly, allow it to dry, and then use a very fine sandpaper as a final finish. Wipe off any dust with a clean cloth and you will be ready to apply the finish.

## Can You Answer These Questions on Preparing the Article For Finishing?

1. Why is it necessary to remove every bit of glue from the article after it is dry? How would you do this?

2. When is it necessary to bleach glued surfaces? Name a simple bleach.

3. List four materials that can be used for filling holes, cracks, and irregularities.

4. How can shallow dents in wood be raised?

5. A project is moistened before the final sanding. Why is this done?

## INSTALLING CABINET HARDWARE

On many large projects such as chests, cabinets, and desks, cabinet hardware in the form of hinges, locks, pulls, and knobs is installed to complete the project.

## Kinds of cabinet hardware

There are many different types

278. KINDS OF HINGES: A. Butt hinge. B. Concealed hinges. These give flush doors a neat appearance. C. Semi-concealed loose-pin hinges. These offer the same advantages as the butt hinge. They are better for plywood doors because the screws go into flat grain.

B

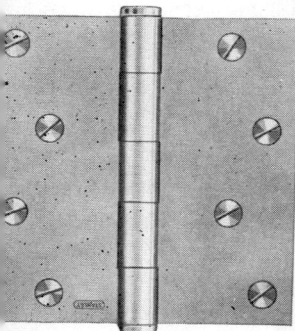

A

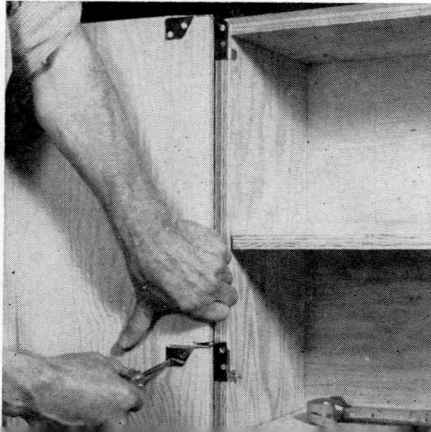

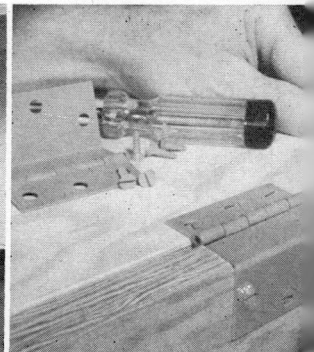

C

of cabinet hinges, three of which are shown in Fig. 278A, B, and C. The common type is the butt hinge. Fig. 278A. This hinge requires that a recess or gain be cut. In most cases, a gain is cut both in the door and in the frame on which the door is fastened. In other cases, a deeper gain is cut either in the frame or in the door so that the hinge is recessed in only one part of the two adjoining surfaces.

Fig. 279 illustrates many different types of drawer pulls and knobs suited to different furniture styles. The most common catches are friction, magnetic, elbow, and ball. The elbow catch holds one side of a double door closed when the other side is opened. Fig. 280.

## Installing a butt hinge

Select the proper size and kind of hinge for the door. The size of the hinge is indicated by its length. A 1-inch hinge would be for a cabinet door for a desk, while a 3½-inch hinge would be needed for a house door.

Fit the door into the opening and place a thin piece of wood un-

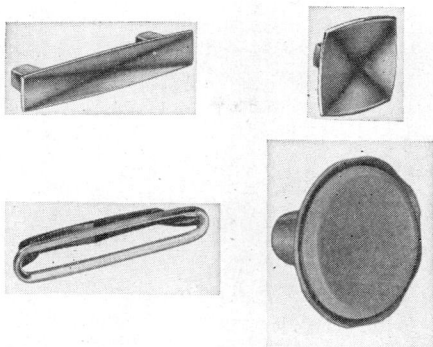

279. VARIOUS TYPES OF KNOBS AND PULLS. It is important to select the knob or pull that fits in with the design of your article.

der the door and on the side away from the hinges, to hold the door in place. Measure from the top of the door to the upper location of the top hinge and from the bottom to the lower point of the bottom hinge. The hinges should be located just inside the upper and lower rail. A mark should be made on both the door and the adjoining frame.

Remove the door and place it on the floor or bench with the hinge edge upward. Hold the hinge over the edge of the door with one end flush with the mark and draw an-

280. FOUR TYPES OF CATCHES: A. Friction. B. Magnetic. C. Elbow. D. Ball.

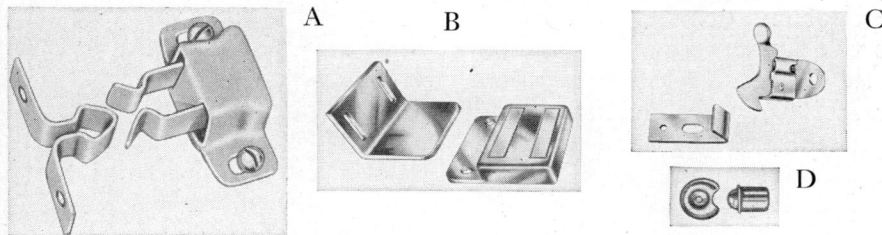

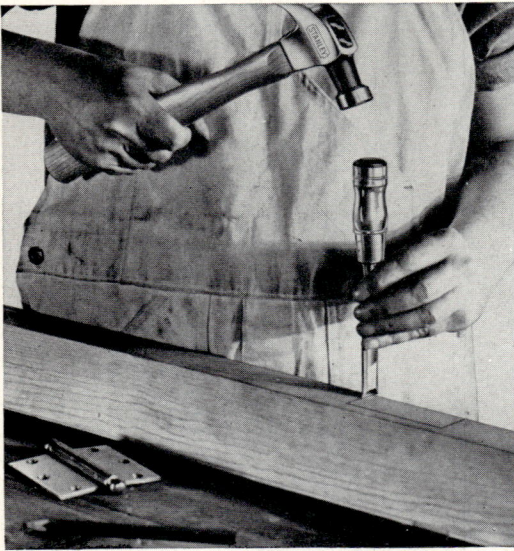

**281. HERE THE GAIN HAS BEEN LAID OUT** on the edge of the door and is being outlined with a chisel.

other line indicating the length of the hinge. Mark this length on the door frame also. Then, with a try square held against the face side of the door, square off these lines across the edge. Repeat on the door frame. Determine the distance the hinge will set in from the face of the door and set a marking gauge to this measurement. Hold the marking gauge against the face side of the door and mark a line between the two lines to show the position of the hinge. Repeat on the door frame. Then set a marking gauge to the thickness of one leaf of the hinge and from the edge mark a line indicating the depth to which the stock must be removed both on

the door and on the frame. This recess in the wood is called a gain.

With a chisel, outline the gain on the door as shown in Fig. 281. Then make several V cuts in the stock to be removed. Fig. 282A. Pare out the stock to the depth of the gain. Fig. 282B. Try the hinge in the recess to see whether it fits flush with the edge of the door.

Mark the location of the screw holes and drill the pilot holes as needed. Fasten half the hinge to the door section.

Cut out the gains in the frame of the door. Locate the position of the holes, drill, and insert one screw. Put the door in position and place the pins in the hinges. Try the door to see how it operates. It may be necessary to shift slightly the position of half the hinge. Sometimes it is necessary to cut the gain a little deeper or to raise it by putting a piece of paper under it. After any needed correction has been made, drill the other pilot holes and fasten the other half of the hinges securely.

## Installing drawer knobs and pulls

Draw two parallel lines horizontally across the face of the door to locate the upper and lower edge of the knob. Then measure in from either end to the outside of the knob. Draw two vertical lines to complete the outline of the knob. Measure inward from this outline to locate the positions of the holes. Drill a hole the same size as the ma-

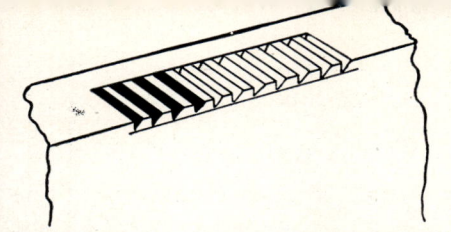

282A. CHISEL CUTS IN THE STOCK to be removed to form the gain.

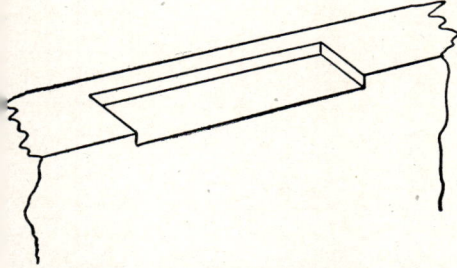

282B. THE GAIN IS CUT and ready to have the hinge installed.

chine screws used to fasten the knob. Insert the machine screws from the back side of the drawer front and tighten the knob. Pulls are installed in about the same way.

## Using Repair Plate

Repair and mending plates come in many sizes and shapes. Fig. 283. The *mending plate* is used to strengthen a butt or lap joint. The *flat-corner iron* is used to strengthen corners of frames such as a screen door or window. The *bent-corner iron* can be applied to shelves and

the inside corners of tables, chairs, and cabinets. It can also be used to hang cabinets and shelves. *T plates* are used to strengthen the center rail of a frame.

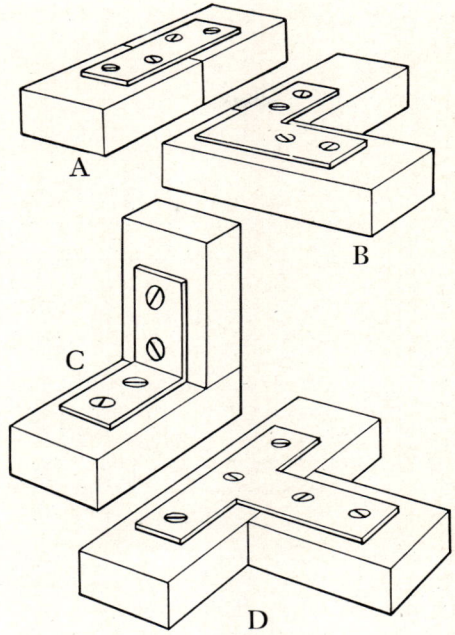

283. FOUR TYPES OF REPAIR PLATES: A. Mending. B. Flat corner. C. Bent corner. D. T plate.

## Can You Answer These Questions on Installing Cabinet Hardware?

1. Name some of the common types of hinges.

2. Define a gain.

3. What indicates the size of a hinge?

4. Sketch the position of hinges on a panel door.

5. Describe the method of laying out a gain.

6. A gain is trimmed out with what tool?

7. How can you test a hinge to make certain that it has been installed correctly?

8. What should you think about before selecting the drawer knobs or pulls?

9. What is the best practice to follow when installing locks?

# Section IX

# Finishing Projects

The ninth 8 steps in hand woodworking—what you must know and be able to do.

38. Finishing supplies: where they come from and how to use and keep them in good working condition; materials used in applying finishes; and different kinds of sandpaper and abrasives.

39. The kinds of stains which are applied to beautify or to imitate, what they are, and how to apply them to get the best results.

40. Using wood fillers of different kinds on open- and closed-grain woods.

41. The technique of applying shellac, what shellac is, and what makes it good for finishing.

42. Varnish finishes require a special technique, more time and better physical setup; method of application and steps in producing a varnish finish.

43. How a clear or colored lacquer finish differs from other finishes and how to apply lacquer.

44. How enamel differs from paint in its composition and application.

45. Painting a surface: mixing the paint and how to apply it with a brush.

A GOOD START deserves a good "finish"! If you apply a good finish, your work will carry the mark of the fine craftsman. Don't ruin your project by applying the wrong finish or by putting on the right finish carelessly. Remember, too, that, while it is convenient to have a separate finishing room, you don't need one to do a successful job. You do, however, need to carry your share of responsibility in taking care of the finishing area and supplies. No one in your class could achieve a proper finish if someone, for example, used the shellac brush and then let it dry out or opened a can of varnish and did not reseal it properly, or dripped enamel on someone else's project or on the finishing bench.

Before you begin to apply a finish, look around at some pieces of fine furniture. Notice the rich finish, which accounts greatly for its quality. You, too, will be proud of your work if you finish it well. For materials and methods, see "box" above. Further steps in woodworking are on pp. 12, 37, 53, 84, 97, 111, 119, 148, and 187.

## CARING FOR FINISHING SUPPLIES

Wood finishing is one of the most important steps in the completion of attractive and beautiful projects. In fact, the one thing about handmade articles that is often far inferior to commercially made ones is the finish.

An important part of securing a good finish in woodworking is to have the proper finishing supplies *in good condition*.

## Brushes

A variety of sizes should be available for all different types of finishes. Most brushes used for painting, varnishing, and enameling should be made from Chinese or Russian boar bristles set in rubber. Brushes you will need should vary in size from 1 to 4 inches. It is a wise practice to have a different brush with individual container for each different type of finishing material. A poor finish usually results when you use a shellac brush for varnish, for example.

## Caring for brushes

Whenever brushes are not in

use, they should be suspended in a solvent suited to the material used on the brush. Some means should be provided to hold the brushes so that the bristles will not be bent on the bottom of the container or pick up the impurities that settle on the bottom of the container.

The proper solvents for finishing materials are:

| Solvent | Finishing Material |
|---|---|
| Turpentine | Oil stain<br>Filler for varnish and shellac finish<br>Varnish<br>Enamel |
| Turpentine and linseed oil | Paint |
| Alcohol | Shellac |
| Lacquer thinner | Filler for lacquer finish<br>Lacquer |

## Finishing supplies

*Turpentine* is made from the resin drippings of pine trees. These drippings are distilled by boiling in large copper vats and then running the solution through a condensing coil to a collection barrel. Turpentine rises to the surface and is drained off.

*Linseed oil* is made from flaxseed. The oil is obtained by compressing the seed under high pressure to squeeze out the oil. The oil is used either in its raw state or is boiled to improve its drying qualities. Boiled linseed oil does not have the flexibility of raw oil but dries much faster.

Many times linseed oil is used by itself to finish certain types of furniture. The oil is applied with a rag and then rubbed into the surface. Several coats are applied in this manner. After the oil is dry a paste wax is applied and rubbed to a high polish.

The best *alcohol* for mixing shellac is made from grain. This, however, is not always available. The Government has established a standard alcohol mix that is called Formula Special No. 1 denatured alcohol, which is composed of ethyl alcohol and wood alcohol, 5 gallons of wood alcohol to 1000 gallons of ethyl alcohol.

*Benzine,* used as a solvent and a cleaning fluid, is made from coal tar.

*Waxes* are either liquid or paste for use in the woodshop. Both are made from a base of beeswax, paraffin, carnauba wax, and turpentine. Wax always provides a good waterproof surface that can be renewed periodically.

*Steel wool* is made of thin metal shavings. It comes in pads or rolls and can be purchased in grades from 000, very fine, to 3, coarse.

*Pumice* is a white-colored powder made from lava. It is available in several grades, but the most commonly used for woodworking finishing is FF and FFF. It is combined with water or oil to rub down the finish.

*Rottenstone* is a reddish brown or grayish black substance that is obtained from the decomposition of shale. It is much finer than pumice and is used with water or oil to produce a smoother finish after the surface has been rubbed with pumice.

*Oil* used for rubbing should be either petroleum or paraffin oil. If oil refined from petroleum is used, be sure of the grade.

*Sandpapers* needed are garnet finishing papers in grade No. 4/0 and No. 6/0. No. 4/0 is used for sanding after staining and after applying first coat of shellac and before applying the filler coat. No. 6/0 is used for final smoothing after shellac coats or other finish. These grades may be used dry or with oil.

*Waterproof abrasive paper* in grades of 240 and 320 grit are used with water for hand sanding between lacquer coats or for rubbing enamel or lacquer.

## Can You Answer These Questions on Caring for Finishing Supplies?

1. There is one way in which school projects prove inferior to commercially made projects all too often. What is this and how do you think it can be overcome?

2. What are the best bristles for most finishing brushes?

3. Tell what turpentine is.

4. What is linseed oil? What is the difference between raw and boiled linseed oil?

5. From what is the best alcohol made?

6. What are waxes made from?

7. What is pumice? Rottenstone? Which is finer?

## APPLYING STAINS

Stain is transparent color that is applied to the surface of wood to improve its appearance, to bring out the grain, to preserve the wood, and sometimes to imitate the more expensive woods. There are three kinds of stains—oil, water, and spirit. However, only the oil and water stains are commonly used.

## Oil stain

Oil stain is coloring that has been mixed in an oil base. You can mix your own oil stain by adding such pigments as raw and burnt umber, raw and burnt sienna, Venetian red, black drop, and Vandyke brown to linseed oil and turpentine. However, it is much simpler and easier to buy commercially prepared oil stains. They are available in all ranges of colors—walnut, light, medium, and dark oak, various shades of mahogany, cherry, rosewood, and many others.

## Water stain

A water stain is made by mixing aniline dye in hot water. The dye usually comes in a powdered form and it is possible for you to mix it yourself. The strength of the stain can be changed by increasing or decreasing the amount of dye.

Water stains are also available in ready-mixed form. Water stain has the advantage of being cheaper than other stains, having a more uniform color, and being less likely to fade.

It has the disadvantage of raising the surface of the wood.

Stains are usually applied with a brush, sponge, or rag and then wiped off with a clean piece of cheesecloth or pad of cotton waste. It is easiest to use a 1½- to 2-inch brush set in rubber, especially for applying water stains. Before applying the stain to the finished project, a small scrap piece of the same kind of wood should be stained first. If you are closely matching the color of another piece of furniture, it is necessary to complete the entire finishing process on the scrap piece to make sure that you have duplicated the finish you want. However, if matching is not important, you can get a very good idea of the stain merely by applying a little to a scrap piece and letting it dry.

## Applying oil stain

Select the color stain you want and test it on a scrap piece. When you find the color you want, mix up enough to complete the whole job. For example, it will take about one pint of stain to cover about 25 square feet of porous wood such as oak. Pour out about one third cup into a porcelain, glass, or enamel container. Use a good-grade brush. A rag or sponge can be substituted, although they are not so easy to use.

End grain of wood absorbs stain much more readily than the surface grain and therefore appears darker. To prevent this, soak a rag in some linseed oil and rub the end grain before applying the stain. Now you are ready to apply the stain to the surface.

If it is possible, try to apply the stain with the wood held in a horizontal position. Always stain the lower surfaces first, beginning at the corner and working out. To stain a large, flat surface, dip about one third of the brush into the liquid, wipe off the excess stain on the side of the jar, and begin at the center of the surface. Fig. 284. With light strokes, work out toward the edges, brushing on the stain evenly. With each new brushful of stain, begin on the unfinished surface and stroke toward the stained surface. As you near the edges and ends of the wood, brush carefully to keep from spattering the stain. Apply the stain to one small area at a time, wiping off the excess with a clean, dry cloth.

One reason oil stains are so satisfactory to use is that they are slow in drying. Make sure that you cover and wipe off the total surface evenly. Allow the work to dry from twelve to twenty-four hours before proceeding with the rest of the finishing operation.

284. STAINING A SURFACE. The stain is being applied from the center toward the outside edges.

## Applying water stain

Before applying a water stain, sponge the surface of the wood lightly with water. After the surface is dry, sand with No. 2/0 sandpaper. This will help the stain to flow on evenly and to achieve a clear, transparent color. Apply the water stain in the same general manner as the oil stain, wiping off the excess with a cloth. After it has dried from twelve to twenty-four hours, use a small piece of No. 2/0 sandpaper to sand the surface lightly, removing the high surfaces of the wood. Then proceed.

## Can You Answer These Questions on Applying Stains?

1. Name the two common types of stains?
2. What pigments are found in oil stain?
3. What is the advantage of buying commercially prepared oil stain?
4. How can the strength of water stain be varied?

5. What advantage has water stain? What disadvantage?
6. Tell how stains are applied.
7. How can you judge the amount of oil stain needed?
8. How can you prevent the end grain of wood from taking up too much stain?

9. Describe the brushing technique for
10. How should the wood surface be
prepared before water stain is applied?

## APPLYING WOOD FILLER

Fillers are used to seal the pores
of wood and to add beauty to the
finish. On open-grained woods such
as oak, walnut, and mahogany, a
paste filler is usually best, while on
closed-grained woods like birch,
fir, and pine, the most suitable filler
is a liquid type such as shellac.

*Paste filler* is made primarily
from ground silicon, linseed oil,
turpentine, drier, and coloring. You
can buy paste filler in cans in either
natural color or in various colors to
match wood stains. The paste is
thinned with turpentine to the right
consistency. If fillers are used under lacquer finishes, the filler must
be thinned with a lacquer thinner.
On modern bleach finishes, white
lead or pure zinc paste sometimes is
the filler. Fig. 391. Either of these
can be colored to match any desired
finish by adding some burnt umber,
raw sienna, or other pigment. In
preparing for use, add turpentine
until the paste becomes a thin cream
in consistency. The filler should be
of a heavier consistency on woods
that have larger pores such as oak,
elm, or chestnut. If the filler is to

be applied over a stained surface, a
wash coat of shellac (1 part shellac
to 10 parts alcohol) should be applied over the stain to prevent any
bleeding of the finishes. Then the
surface should be sanded with No.
4/0 paper before applying the filler.

Apply the paste filler with a stiff
brush, thoroughly covering the surface. Brush first with the grain, then
across it. Do not cover too large an
area at one time, as the filler dries
very rapidly. Rub in the paste filler
with the palm of your hand, going
over the entire surface in a circular
motion. Allow the filler to dry until
the surface loses its glossy appearance. This will take anywhere up
to 20 minutes. Then use a piece
of burlap or rough cloth to wipe
across the grain to remove the
excess filler. After most of the
filler has been removed, you can use
a thin, clean cloth (cheesecloth or
cotton) to go over the surface
lightly *with* the grain to remove
the remainder of the surface filler.
Do not press too hard, though, or
you will rub out some of the filler
from the pores. If necessary, you
can add another coat of filler in the
same way as the first one. After the
filler has dried from six to eight
hours, proceed with shellac, lacquer, or varnish finish.

## Can You Answer These Questions on Applying Wood Filler?

1. Name the two kinds of wood filler.
2. What kind is applied to open-grained
woods?

3. Filler is thinned with what solvent?
Can this solvent be used for all types of
finishes?

4. What filler is chosen for modern bleached finishes?

5. How can you make a wash coat of shellac?

6. How long should a filler remain on the surface before it is wiped off?

7. What is the purpose of filler?

## SHELLAC FINISH

Shellac is a good finish for many projects because it is easy to apply, dries quickly, and produces a hard surface. It is not desirable, however, if the wood is to be exposed to moisture, since shellac will turn a cloudy color under such conditions. Shellac is frequently used as a finish by itself, or it is sometimes used as a sealer over a stain or filler coat before varnish is applied. (See Fig. 432.)

## Shellac

The shellac itself is a resinous substance which is the product of the lac bug. Most of our supply comes from India and Siam, where these bugs feed on resinous material and deposit the lac on trees. This is removed twice yearly and heated, purified, and laid out in strips to dry. The lac is then ground and held in solution by mixing it in denatured alcohol. The standard shellac is a mixture of four pounds to a gallon of alcohol and is called a four-pound cut. The natural shellac is orange in color and is a good, tough finish. However, on many of the lighter woods, this natural shellac produces an unattractive yellowish cast.

Shellac is therefore also available in a bleached form, called white shellac. This is more satisfactory for general use, especially for work with lighter wood finishes.

## Applying shellac

The wood must first be clean and dry. The surface should be wiped clean with a lint-free cloth that has been dipped in alcohol. Pour a small amount of shellac into a glass or porcelain container and add an equal amount of alcohol to thin it.

It is far better to apply several thin coats than fewer, heavier coats. The thinned shellac can penetrate the surface of the wood better, providing a smoother finish. Use a clean brush that is about $1\frac{1}{2}$ to 3 inches wide with bristles set in rubber. To apply the shellac, dip the brush about one third of the brush length into the shellac, wipe off the sides of the brush on the container, and begin at the center of a flat surface or near the top of a vertical surface to work out toward the edges. Work quickly and evenly, taking light, long strokes. Do not attempt to brush over the same surface several times as shellac dries very rapidly and becomes sticky. The tendency for a beginner is to put shellac on thick, producing a yellowish cast. On the edges of your project, be careful to keep the shellac from piling up and running. After the entire surface has been covered, soak the brush in pure alcohol and allow the project to dry from two to four hours.

## Applying a shellac finish

After the surface is dry, go over it with steel wool or 5/0 sandpaper. Rub *with* the grain of the wood. Steel wool has the advantage of following the wood better and covering better both the high and low spots. If you use sandpaper, do not use a sanding block but hold the paper in your fingers.

Wipe the surface with a clean rag to remove all dust and dirt before applying the second coat. This coat is applied in the same way as the first coat but may have only about 40 per cent alcohol. Again go over the surface with steel wool or sandpaper. Then apply a third coat with even less alcohol added, perhaps 25 per cent. After the last coat, rub the surface lightly with sandpaper or, to produce an even smoother surface, mix some ground pumice in oil and rub down the surface with a felt pad. After this, a still smoother surface can be produced by mixing rottenstone with oil and rubbing the surface with it.

Clean off the surface with a clean cloth dipped in benzine. Allow it to dry about one-half hour. Then apply a good coat of wax to the surface and allow it to dry thoroughly. Rub briskly with a soft cloth for a good polish.

The shellac brush should be cleaned with alcohol.

## Can You Answer These Questions on Applying Shellac?

1. What is the source of shellac? What countries supply it?
2. How is shellac made?
3. What is meant by a four-pound cut?
4. Shellac is what color naturally?
5. Shellac is available bleached. Why?
6. What good rule should be followed in applying shellac?
7. Describe the special brushing technique for applying shellac.
8. What is the common error made by the beginner in applying shellac?
9. List the steps that must be followed in applying a shellac finish.

### VARNISH FINISH

Varnish is a very fine finish and if done correctly will produce the most desirable and practical surface. However, it is difficult to obtain a good varnish finish anywhere but in a dust-free room. The objection to using varnish in the small shop is that it dries so slowly that the surface becomes marred with tiny dust particles. Fig. 423.

## Varnishes

Varnish is a liquid that can be spread on a surface in a thin film, giving the wood an even, transparent coating. It protects the surface of the wood and adds brilliance to the color of the stain. Varnishes are made by mixing various gum resins with vegetable oils that are combined through heating and by adding the necessary thinners and driers. Natural varnish takes from twenty-four to forty-eight hours to dry and therefore has the disadvantage of giving the dust extra time to collect and mar the surface. In recent years there have been developed quick-drying varnishes that dry overnight and are dust free in two hours after applying. For most uses, one should select a quick-drying varnish, as it is easier to apply and gives a better chance for a satisfactory finish.

For outside finishes subject to moisture and for the tops of tables, cabinets, and other pieces that will have hard wear, the best type of varnish is spar varnish. This is made by adding China wood oil to varnish, making it water repellent and heat resistant.

In the small shop, it is a wise practice to buy varnish in small cans, since, once the can has been opened, a scum forms on the surface which is difficult to prevent and hard to remove and interferes with a good finish. If necessary, the varnish can be strained through a silk or fine muslin cloth to remove any scum.

## Applying varnish

Find a dust-free place. If no finishing room is available, wait to do your varnishing until no woodworking machines or tools have been used for some time. Then sprinkle the floor with water to settle the dust. Also, do not varnish anything on cold and damp or hot and humid days. Make sure that the temperature is between 70 and 80 degrees.

Open a small can of quick-drying (synthetic-resin) varnish and pour some into a porcelain or glass container. For a first coat, add about 25 per cent turpentine. Select a 2- to 3-inch brush with long bristles. Wipe the surface with a clean cloth dipped in benzine.

Dip the brush in the varnish to about one third the length of the brush but do not overload it. Do not wipe the brush on the side of the can. Begin to apply the varnish with long, easy strokes. Brush first with the grain and then across the grain. After the brush is empty, brush out the varnish with the grain, using only the tip of the brush. You can do more brushing out of varnish than you can of shellac. Continue to work from the center toward the outside edges. As you near the edges, use very little varnish on the brush to keep it from running over the edges or from piling up along the arrises. Never put your brush down where it may pick up dust.

After applying the first coat, dip the brush immediately in a can of turpentine. Also, cover the varnish left in the can to keep the scum from forming. Allow the varnish to dry about twelve to twenty-four hours, or until all "tackiness" has gone. After it is dry, rub the surface with the grain, using No. 5/0 sandpaper.

## Applying a varnish finish

Make sure that the varnish is perfectly dry before applying another coat. Most of the trouble that can arise when applying a varnish finish comes from being too quick to apply the second and third coats. When applying the second coat, use the varnish in its regular consistency. Observe the same brushing techniques as for the first coat. Allow it to dry and rub down the surface with No. 6/0 sandpaper. If you want a dull, rubbed appearance, you can either apply a dull finish

varnish as a third coat or rub down the regular varnish with pumice and oil and rottenstone and oil.

After the varnish coats have dried thoroughly, apply a good paste wax and polish with a clean piece of cheesecloth.

## Varnish stains

A simple finish to use on many projects is a varnish stain which will provide the desired color and finish in one coat. This finish is especially satisfactory for simple woodworking projects on which the time and energy cannot be given to applying many coats of regular varnish. Varnish stains can be purchased in different colors. Applied the same as varnish; dry in two to eight hours.

## Can You Answer These Questions on Applying Varnish?

1. Why is it difficult to obtain a good varnished surface?
2. Tell from what and how varnishes are made.
3. When buying varnish, what considerations should be taken into account?
4. How and why is varnish strained?
5. What conditions must prevail to obtain a good varnished surface?
6. Describe the technique for applying varnish. How does it differ from the technique for applying shellac?
7. Should the first varnish coat be applied full strength?
8. List the steps to be followed in applying a varnish finish.
9. Name the most common mistake made.
10. How can a dull finish be obtained?
11. What is a varnish stain? Why is it commonly used by beginners?

## APPLYING LACQUER

Lacquer is a chemical composition of nitrocellulose, resins, and solvents. Lacquers have come into common use in recent years in both clear and colored forms for wood

surfaces because they dry quickly and produce a hard finish. While most commercial lacquer finishes are applied by spraying, the brush finish is usually done in most small shops. Because lacquer contains substances that are similar to paint and varnish remover, it is not possible to lacquer directly over painted or varnished surfaces. Fig. 434.

## Applying a clear lacquer finish

Apply the stain and filler coat as for shellac and varnish finishes. It is better to use a water stain than an oil stain in a lacquer finish, since this does not "bleed" so much. In any case it is well to apply a thin coat of shellac as a sealer before applying the lacquer.

Open a can of clear brushing lacquer and stir it thoroughly. (Ordinarily, lacquer does not have to be thinned but, if it does, use a commercial lacquer thinner. Also use this for cleaning the brushes after applying the lacquer.) Select a brush with soft bristles, such as a camel's-hair brush. Dip the brush about one third of the way into the lacquer but do not wipe any off on the side of the container. Flow on the lacquer with long, easy strokes, but do not attempt to brush it in as you would a paint or varnish. Lacquer dries very quickly and gives a smooth, tough surface. Allow the lacquer to dry about two hours. Then go over the surface lightly with No. 6/0 sandpaper.

Apply a second and third coat in the manner previously described. After the third coat is dry, the surface can be rubbed with rottenstone and oil and pumice stone and oil.

## Applying colored lacquer finish

Sand the surface of the wood with No. 2/0 sandpaper. Then apply a thin coat of shellac to the wood to provide a base for the lacquer. Apply two or three coats of the colored lacquer in the same way as clear lacquer is applied. To finish the surface, rub it down with rottenstone and oil after the lacquer is dry.

## Can You Answer These Questions on Applying Lacquer?

1. What is lacquer? Can it be applied over a painted or varnished surface?

2. How is lacquer most often applied commercially?

3. Describe the correct brushing technique for applying lacquer.

4. What is the principal advantage of a lacquer finish?

5. How many coats of lacquer are usually needed to obtain a good finish?

## APPLYING ENAMEL

An enamel is a colored varnish that differs from a paint in that it does not have an oil base, and contains varnish to give a gloss finish. Enamel is also only semiopaque, and therefore the primer coat must be opaque to be suitable. Enamels dry with either a high gloss or semigloss, depending on the percentage of varnish. It is an extremely satisfactory type of finish for small projects on which a colored finish is desired. Fig. 414.

**285. RUBBING DOWN AN ENAMELED SURFACE. It** is especially important **to rub** down an enameled surface with pumice stone to secure a smooth finish.

## Applying enamel finish

Sand the surface of the wood with No. 2/0 sandpaper. Cover all knots and sap streaks with a coat of thin shellac. Select a can of enamel undercoat and mix it thoroughly. Use a 2- to 3-inch brush and apply the undercoat in a manner similar to that used to apply varnish. In other words, do not brush in the enamel as you would paint.

After the surface has thoroughly dried, sand lightly with No. 2/0 sandpaper. Then apply a second undercoat. Select quick-drying finish enamel of the desired color and apply one or two coats of this enamel the same way as the undercoat. If a dull finish is desired, allow the final coat to dry for a day or two and then rub down the surface with pumice stone and water. Fig. 285.

## Can You Answer These Questions on Applying Enamel?

1. In what ways does enamel differ from paint?
2. Why is a primer coat put on first?
3. Why is enamel a desirable finish for small projects?

4. What things should be done before the first coat of enamel is applied?
5. How does the brushing technique differ from that for applying paint?
6. How can a dull finish be secured?

## APPLYING PAINT

Painting is a good way to finish inexpensive pieces of furniture and cabinetwork. Paints are usually made from white lead and zinc, or other oxides, linseed oil, turpentine, drier, and coloring. Paints are available either in outside or inside type. In applying paint to a surface, usually three coats are given; namely, the primer, undercoat, and finishing coat. Fig. 396.

### Applying a paint finish

Sand the surface of the wood with No. 1 or No. 0 sandpaper. Apply a light coat of shellac to wood that is porous or that contains knots and sap streaks. Open a can of the primer paint and pour off the light liquid on the top into a second container. Thoroughly stir the primer and then gradually add the liquid until it is mixed. For the first coat, it is well to add some turpentine and/or linseed oil to thin it. Sometimes a small amount of yellow ochre is added to provide a better coverage for the primer coat. Use a good brush of the right size for the project and apply a thin coat of the primer.

When applying paint, use a small amount on the brush and brush it into the surface. The difficulty for beginners is that they apply paint too thick and do not brush it in thoroughly. Allow the paint to dry from twelve to twenty-four hours and then go over the surface with No. 1 sandpaper. Then apply the undercoat of the color desired. This coat should be thinned somewhat with turpentine. Go over the surface thoroughly, covering all parts of the project. Apply the final coat in the same consistency as it comes from the can and thoroughly brush the paint in, making sure that a smooth, even coat is applied.

## Can You Answer These Questions on Applying Paint?

1. From what are paints made?
2. How many coats are usually applied to obtain a good surface?
3. Describe the proper method of mixing a primer paint.
4. Should anything be added to the first coat? Explain.
5. What material can be added to the primer which will provide better coverage?
6. Beginners usually encounter difficulties in learning to paint correctly. How can these difficulties be overcome?
7. List the steps followed in painting a wood surface, beginning with the primer coat and continuing until the final coat is applied.

# Section X

# Sharpening Tools

The final step in hand woodworking—what you must know
and be able to do.

46. Single-edge cutting tools: all steps in accomplishing a good, new cutting edge such as removing the old edge, grinding the angle, and whetting the edge; special problems in sharpening a hand scraper, grinding a screw driver and sharpening a handsaw.

IF IT would be possible to choose one rule which was more important than any other in woodworking, it might be this:

*Successful woodwork depends upon sharp cutting edges.*

If you are using a plane that digs in, sticks, is hard to push, and leaves grooves in the work, you will understand why sharp cutting-tool edges are so important. After you have sharpened the plane and it glides smoothly over the wood surface, taking off a thin, feathery shaving and leaving the surface smooth, you will then be sure of the importance of this difference between dull and sharp tools. Time spent on sharpening tools will be well rewarded in better and easier work.

Nothing is so important to good workmanship as sharp tools. With tools that are correctly ground, woodworking can be interesting and pleasant. Dull tools, on the other hand, cause accidents or bad temper and always result in poor workmanship. Time spent in sharpening and maintaining tools is time well spent and time repaid with good workmanship and the satisfaction that always comes from a job well done.

## Sharpening single-edged tools

There are several single-edged tools such as plane irons, chisels, or spokeshave blades that are sharpened in the same general manner. A description of sharpening a plane iron will illustrate the procedure for sharpening all of these tools.

Determine if the plane iron needs to be ground. The plane iron

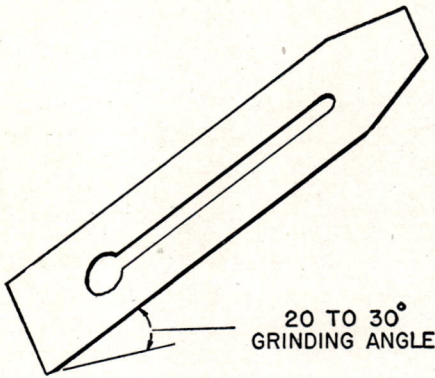

286. A PLANE IRON BLADE should be ground at an angle of 20 to 30 degrees, or the length of the bevel should be about 2 to 2½ times the thickness of the blade.

the old cutting edge until all nicks are removed and until the edge is square with the sides of the plane iron. This reshaping of the plane iron needs to be done only when the plane iron is in very poor condition. Check the edge for squareness by using a try square with the handle held against the side of the plane iron. After the edge is square, remove the plane iron cap.

## Grind the plane iron

The plane iron, chisel, and other single-edge tools are usually ground with a bevel that is two to two and one half times longer than the thickness of the blade. Fig. 286. The smaller angle, about 20 degrees, is used on softwoods and the more blunt angle, about 25 to 30 degrees, on hardwoods. Before grinding the bevel, the wheel should be checked to make sure that it is true and that the face is square. Also, make sure that the wheel is turning towards the cutting edge.

Use a grinding attachment to hold the plane iron, if one is available, since this will assure that the correct bevel will be ground. Fig. 287. If one is not available, hold the plane iron in both hands as in Fig. 288.

Carefully move the plane iron back and forth across the grinding wheel. Fig. 289. Apply just enough pressure to assure grinding action. Do not apply too much pressure, as this will tend to overheat the edge.

needs to be reground if it is badly nicked, untrue, or if the bevel is rounded, too blunt, or too thin. Before regrinding the plane iron, determine what the shape of the cutting edge should be. For most work of a general nature, the cutting edge should be straight with the corners slightly rounded to prevent them from digging into the wood. For rough planing, the whole edge should be slightly rounded, with the center of the cutting edge about 1/32 inch higher than the corners.

## Remove the old edge

With the plane iron cap still fastened to the plane iron to act as a guide, hold the plane iron at right angles to the grinding wheel and move it back and forth to grind off

287. GRINDING A PLANE IRON BLADE HELD IN AN ATTACHMENT. This is the simplest method of grinding a plane iron blade since, once the angle has been set, it is easy to keep the bevel even. Care must be taken, however, not to burn the cutting edge, especially when using a dry grinder as is shown here. COURTESY THE JAM HANDY ORGANIZATION.

At frequent intervals, remove the blade and dip it in water to cool it and to prevent the temper from being drawn from the steel. If you are grinding it by the freehand method, as you bring the tool back to the grinding wheel after cooling, move slowly to get the "feel" of the angle, to be sure that you will continue grinding at the same angle as before.

As the cutting edge is formed, a slight burr may appear but this will be removed in whetting. Make sure that, as the final grinding is done, you have a single surface on the bevel and that the bevel is at the correct angle. This can be checked with a sliding T bevel or a protractor head of a combination set.

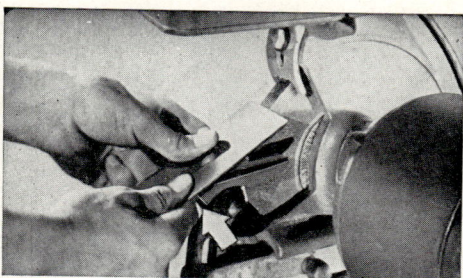

288. GRINDING A PLANE IRON BLADE WITHOUT THE USE OF A GUIDE. In using this method, the plane iron should be moved from right to left constantly and should be cooled frequently in water. It takes considerable skill to keep the bevel even when grinding in this manner. COURTESY JAM HANDY ORGANIZATION.

289. GRINDING A CHISEL. Notice especially that safety glasses are being worn and that the eye shield is in place. COURTESY THE JAM HANDY ORGANIZATION.

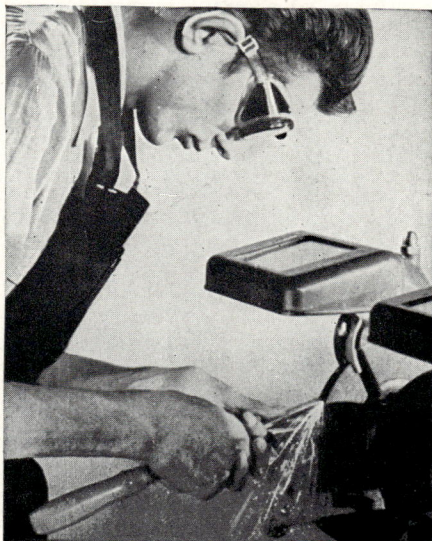

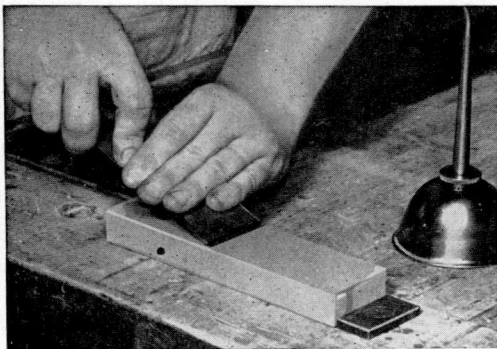

290. WHETTING A PLANE IRON.
Hold the plane iron with the bevel
side down at a slightly greater angle
than that at which it is ground. Apply
oil to the stone and move the plane
iron back and forth or in a circle-8
movement.

## Whetting or Honing the edge

Select an oilstone the surface of
which is flat and true. There are
two classes of oilstone for this purpose. The natural stones, such as the
Arkansas and Washita, are white in
color; the artificial oilstones are
made either of aluminum oxide,
which is brownish in color, or silicon carbide, which is grayish in
color. A combination artificial oilstone is best, since one surface is
coarse and the other surface is fine.

Wipe off the stone and then
apply a mixture of half kerosene
and half machine oil to the surface.
Hold the plane iron on the oilstone
with the bevel side down, first applying pressure on the heel of the
bevel, then slowly raising the plane
iron until the bevel is in contact with

the surface of the oilstone. Fig.
290.

The whetting angle should be
between 30 and 35 degrees. Move
the tool back and forth on the face
of the oilstone or in a circular motion to form a figure 8. Fig. 291.
A wire or feather edge will form on
the cutting edge. To remove this,
turn the plane iron around with the
side opposite the bevel flat against
the oilstone and move it back and
forth a few times. Make sure that
you hold the tool *flat*, since the
slightest bevel on this side will prevent the plane iron cap from fitting
properly, with the result that chips
will get between the cap and the
plane iron.

If the wire edge is not completely removed, the cutting edge
should be pushed across the corner

291. WHETTING A CHISEL. It is extremely important to keep the bevel
flat.

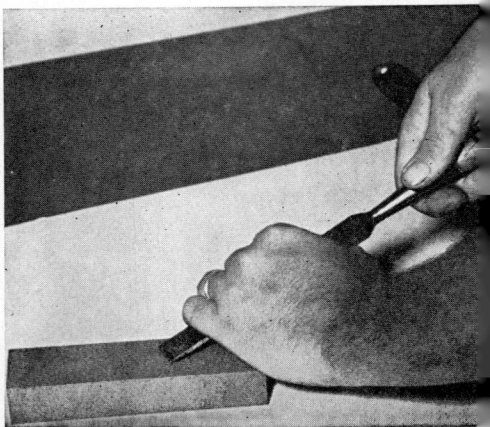

**292. DRAW FILING THE HAND SCRAPER.** Hold a fine file in the manner shown and draw-file the edge until it is square with the sides of the scraper.

**293. WHETTING THE EDGE OF THE SCRAPER.** Hold the scraper at right angles to the stone and move it back and forth.

of a piece of softwood. If desired, the finer side of the oilstone can be used to get a keener edge on the plane iron.

### Test the plane iron for sharpness

One method is to hold the plane iron with the cutting edge down and allow the edge to rest lightly on the thumbnail. Then, as the tool is moved, it will tend to "bite" into the nail, if it is sharp, or it will slide across easily, if it is dull.

Another check is to observe the edge. If it is sharp, the edge cannot be seen. If it is dull, a thin, white line can be seen. Be careful when assembling the plane iron and cap and when inserting them into the plane, so as not to nick the cutting edge.

### Sharpening a hand scraper

A hand scraper must be sharpened frequently, and the good worker frequently does it every time the hand scraper is used. Place the tool in a vise with the cutting edge exposed. To remove the old cutting edge, hold a file flat against

the side of the scraper and take a few strokes. Then use a fine file to drawfile the edge until it is square with the sides of the scraper. Fig. 292.

Whet the cutting edge by moving it back and forth across an oilstone, holding the blade at right angles to the surface. Fig. 293. Then hold the sides of the blade flat against the stone, working it back and forth to remove the wire edge. Fig. 294.

**294. HOLD THE SCRAPER FLAT** against the stone on both sides to remove any burr.

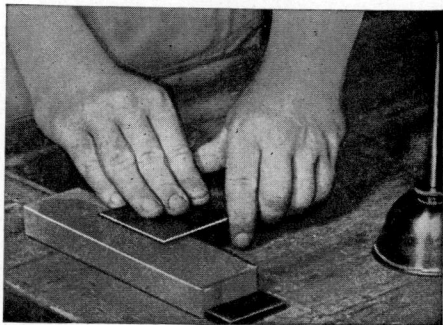

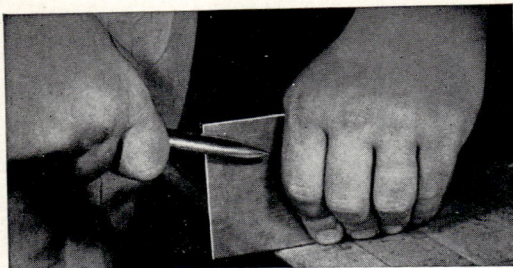

295. DRAWING OUT THE EDGE. Use a burnishing tool. Hold the scraper on the bench top to draw out the edge, as shown.

Place the scraper flat on the bench with the cutting edge extending slightly over the edge of the bench. Hold a burnisher flat on the side of the scraper and take a few, firm strokes toward you to draw the edge.

Then hold the scraper on edge as shown in Fig. 295 and use the burnishing tool held at an angle of about 85 degrees to turn the edge of the scraper. Fig. 296. This is done by drawing the burnisher up with a firm brisk stroke. The edge is correct when it will just catch your thumb as it is drawn across it.

## Sharpening an auger bit

The auger bit must be kept sharp to obtain best results in boring. This is done by filing the spur and the lip with a small half-round or three-cornered file. Fig. 172b. Sharpen the spur by filing it on the inside to retain the same general contour. Never file the outside. File the lip on the underside or the side

toward the shank until it attains a sharp cutting edge. Keep the bits in good condition by cleaning off the pitch with a solvent and using steel wool to polish the surface.

## Sharpening a drawknife

The drawknife can be sharpened on the grinding wheel in the same general manner as the plane iron. To whet the edge of the blade, hold the drawknife with one handle against the top of the bench and the other handle in your hand. Use a small oilstone in the other hand and move it along the bevel back and forth to produce a keen edge.

## Sharpening a screw driver

The screw driver is one of the most misused tools in the woodshop and very frequently is not ground properly, with the result that a burr is formed in the groove of screws when they are set. These burrs are both dangerous and unsightly. The screw driver should be ground with

296. TURNING THE EDGE OF A HAND SCRAPER. After the edge is drawn out, hold the burnishing tool at an angle of about 85 degrees to the side of the scraper and turn the edge.

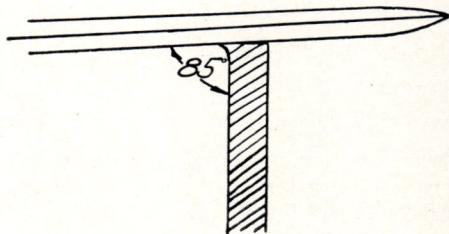

a slight taper on either side and the end flat, as shown in Fig. 297A.

## Sharpening a saw

Sharpening and setting a hand-saw is an extremely difficult procedure and should not be attempted by anyone who does not perform the job frequently. To resharpen a saw successfully, it is necessary to file off the teeth until they are all the same height, then reshape the teeth by filing, and finally to set the teeth by bending them alternately, to left and right. In using a saw, therefore, one should appreciate the difficulty of this operation and realize that the necessity for sharpening can be greatly reduced by

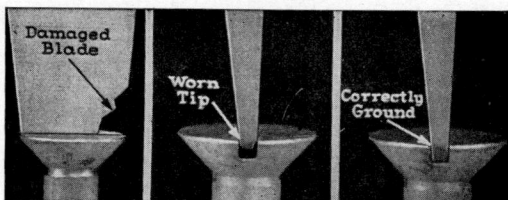

297A. BAD AND GOOD BLADES: a damaged blade that needs regrinding; a worn tip that should be reground; and a correctly ground screw driver. COURTESY THE JAM HANDY ORGANIZATION.

proper use of the saw at all times.

## Sharpening Turning Tools

Grinding angles for wood-turning tools are shown in Fig. 297B. The sharpening is done the same as for a chisel.

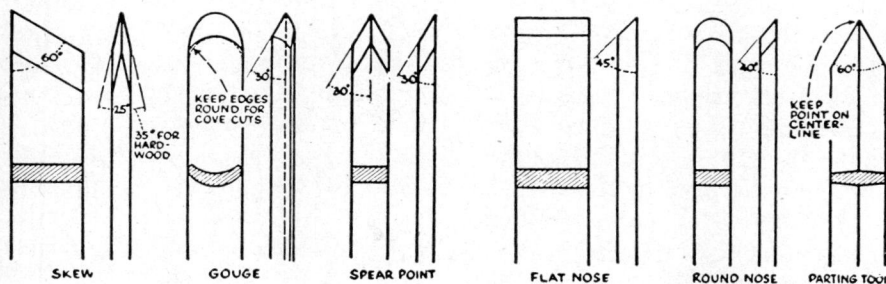

297B. GRINDING ANGLES for wood-turning tools.

# Can You Answer These Questions on Sharpening Hand Tools?

1. Why is it important to keep the tools sharp?

2. What can be done to correct a badly nicked cutting edge?

3. At what angle should a plane iron be ground for softwood? For hardwood?

4. At what angle should a plane iron be whetted?

5. Tell how to test a plane iron for sharpness.

6. How is the edge of a hand scraper shaped? At what angle should the burnishing tool be held?

7. Describe the correct way to grind a screw driver.

8. Are saws commonly sharpened by beginners in woodworking? Explain your answer.

# Section XI

# Machine Woodworking

## THE CIRCULAR SAW

THE CIRCULAR saw is the most commonly used machine tool in the woodshop. It consists of a frame, an arbor to hold the saw blade, the saw blade, a table, a ripping fence, and a crosscutting or mitering gauge. In addition, the machine should be equipped with a guard and slitter to protect the operator from injury. Fig. 298. The size of the circular saw is indicated by the largest diameter of saw blade that can be used on the machine. The most common sizes for small shops are the 8 and 10-inch machines. Another way in which saws are designated is by whether the table or the saw blade tilts to do beveling, chamfering, etc. The first is called a tilt *table* saw and the other a tilt *arbor* saw.

The two adjusting levers most frequently used are the raising handle, usually located under the front of the table, which is used to raise and lower the saw blade, and the tilting handle, usually on the left side, which is used to tilt the arbor or table. There are three types of saw blades: the ripsaw, the cross-cut, and the combination blade. Fig. 299. In the small shop in which a variety of operations are done consecutively, it is a good idea to keep a combination saw blade in the machine, since it can be used for ripping, crosscutting, beveling, rabbeting, and a variety of other operations.

### Safety

The circular saw is undoubtedly one of the most dangerous tools in the woodshop, especially when in the hands of an inexperienced operator. Therefore it is suggested that the following safety practices be observed when using a circular saw:

1. Make sure that the saw is equipped with a guard and a slitter. The slitter holds the stock open after it has been cut so that it won't tend to bind and kick back.

2. Always stand to one side of the saw blade, never directly back of it, so that if the piece does kick back it will not strike you.

3. Make sure that the saw blade is sharpened properly. A dull saw

194

is frequently the cause of kick-back.

4. Always set the saw so that it is about ⅛ inch higher than the thickness of the stock to be cut.

5. Never reach over the saw with your hand.

6. When ripping stock to narrow widths, always use a push stick to complete the ripping. Never place your hand between the saw and the ripping fence.

7. Never saw freehand on a circular saw. Always use the guide intended for this purpose.

8. Pay attention to business when using the circular saw. One small lapse in your attention could cost you a finger or hand.

## Ripping

Before attempting to rip stock to the specified width on the circular saw, make sure that one edge of the stock is true. If it is not, plane one edge. Then with the power off, adjust the saw blade to a height of

298. A 10-INCH, FLOOR-TYPE, CIRCULAR SAW of the kind most suited to school and home workshops. Notice the names of the parts. You should familiarize yourself with them.

⅛ to ¼ inch more than the thickness of the stock. Adjust the ripping fence to the correct width by

299. THREE TYPES OF SAW BLADES: crosscut, rip, and combination. The combination saw should be chosen when a variety of cutting operations must be done at one time.

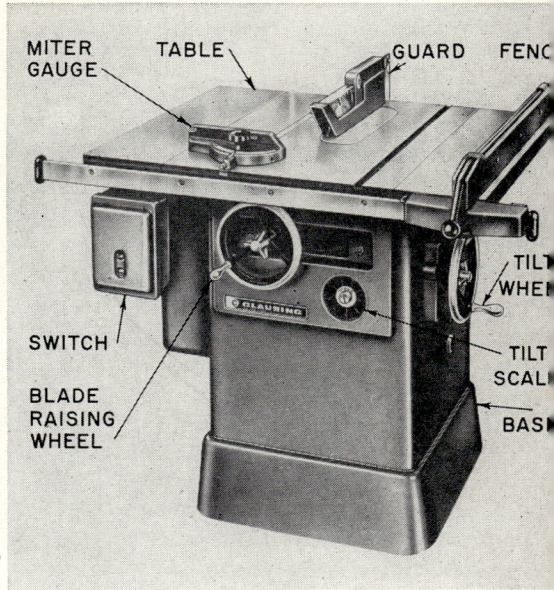

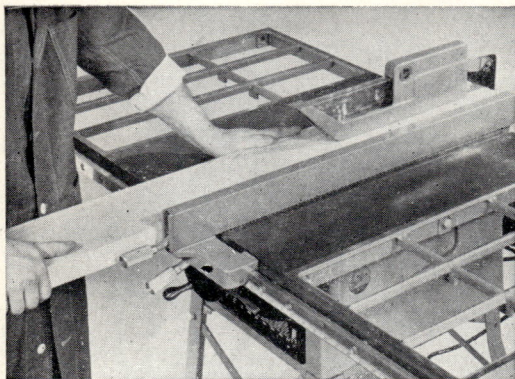

300. RIPPING STOCK ON A CIRCU-
LAR SAW. The left hand guides and
holds the stock against the fence, and
the right hand applies forward pressure. The saw is protected with a guard.

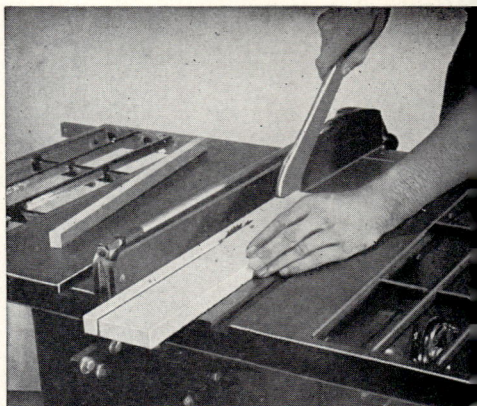

301. CUTTING STOCK TO NARROW
WIDTHS. A push stick is used to
apply the forward pressure. Never
run your right hand between the revolving saw and the fence if narrow
widths are being ripped.

holding a rule or try square against the ripping fence and measuring the distance to the saw blade. On many machines, the width for ripping is found directly on a scale that is mounted on the front edge of the saw table. Fig. 298. Lock the ripping fence securely. Turn on the power. Place the stock on the table. Stand to one side but not directly back of the saw blade. To start the cut, apply forward pressure with your right hand as you hold the stock with your left. Fig. 300. Do not apply too much forward pressure on a small saw, as this will make the saw burn or stop altogether. Continue to feed the work into the saw easily.

If the stock is hardwood and quite thick, it may be necessary to begin with the saw set at less than the total thickness and run it through several times rather than to try to cut through the thickness in one cut.

When you are cutting to narrow widths, pick up a push stick with your right hand and, as the rear edge of the stock clears the table, apply the forward pressure with the push stick until the cut is completed. Fig. 301.

## Crosscutting

The mitering or crosscutting gauge fits into either groove of the table but is most often placed in the left groove. Some operators attach a squared piece of stock the same width as the miter gauge to its face to provide better support for the work. To make a square cut, set the gauge at a 90-degree angle. This can be checked by holding a try square against the gauge and the saw blade. Carefully mark the location of the cut, making the mark very clear on the front edge or face of the stock. Set the blade to the correct height. Hold the stock firmly against the gauge and slide

196

both the work and gauge along the table to complete the cut. Fig. 302. If you must cut several pieces to the same length, one of the following methods can be followed:

1. Set the stop rod that is attached to the miter gauge to the correct length. Fig. 305.

2. Clamp a small block of wood to the ripping fence just in front of the saw blade. The fence with block attached acts as a length guide. Fig. 303. Never use the ripping fence only as a length guide because if you do the piece will become lodged between the revolving saw and the ripping fence and may kick back with terrific force.

3. Clamp a small piece of wood directly to the saw table to act as a length guide.

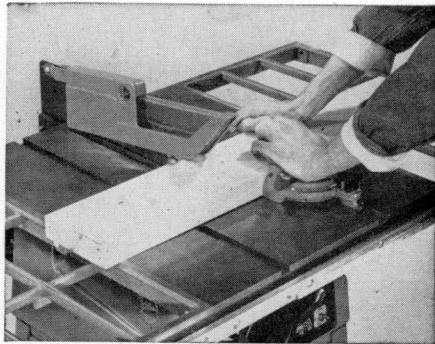

302. CROSSCUTTING. The miter gauge is set at right angles to the saw blade. Even, forward pressure should be applied to the stock and the gauge.

## Mitering

To make a miter cut, adjust the miter gauge to the correct angle and then proceed as in crosscutting.

303. CUTTING STOCK TO LENGTH with a block attached to the ripping fence. This is one of the simplest methods of cutting many pieces of stock to the same length. Note that as the stock is cut off, there is plenty of clearance between the saw blade and the fence, so that there is never danger of a kick back.

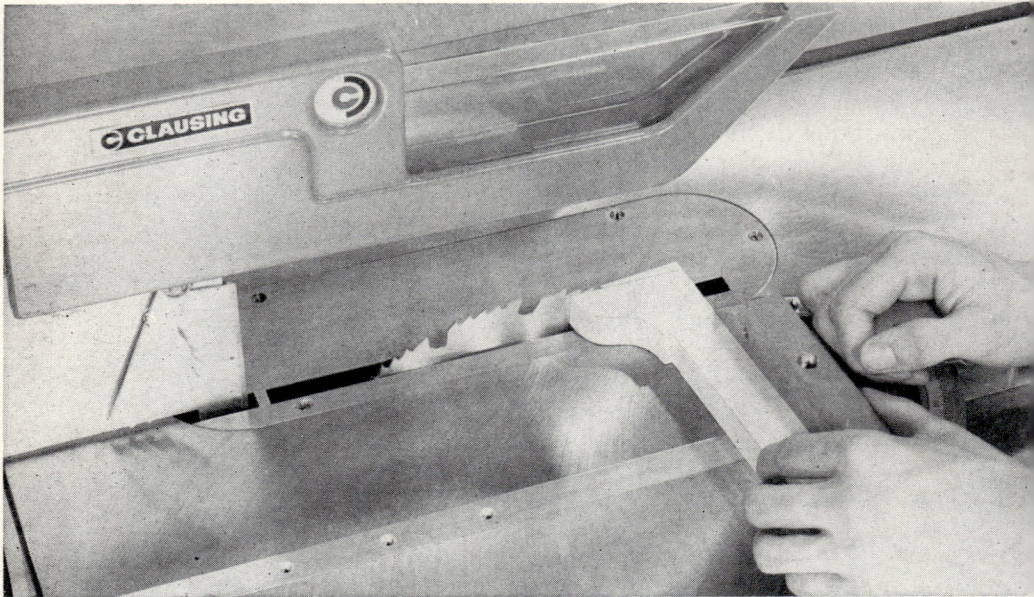

304. MAKING A MITER CUT. Adjust the miter gauge to the correct angle. Hold the stock firmly against the gauge as the cut is made. The guard is raised to show the action.

Make sure that you hold the stock firmly against the miter gauge, as it tends to creep toward the revolving saw as the cut is made. Fig. 304. To make a compound miter cut, the gauge must be set to the correct angle and the blade tilted to the desired amount. Fig. 305.

305. MAKING A COMPOUND MITER CUT. The miter gauge is set at an angle and the blade is tilted. The stop rod on the miter gauge is to control the length of the cut. This type of saw cut would be extremely difficult to make except on a circular saw.

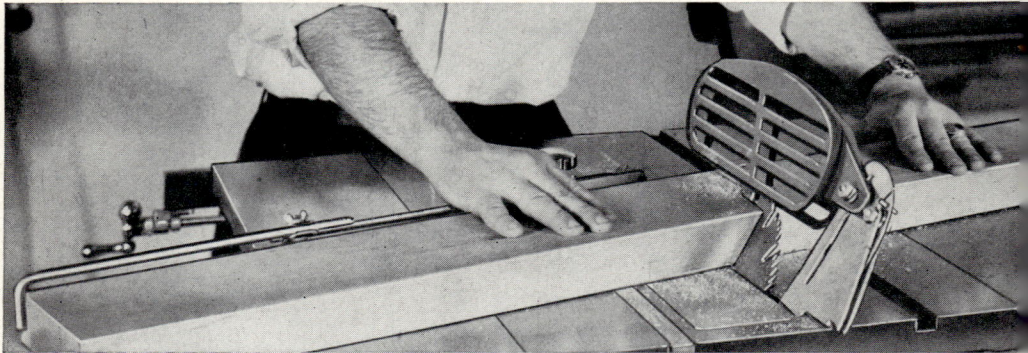

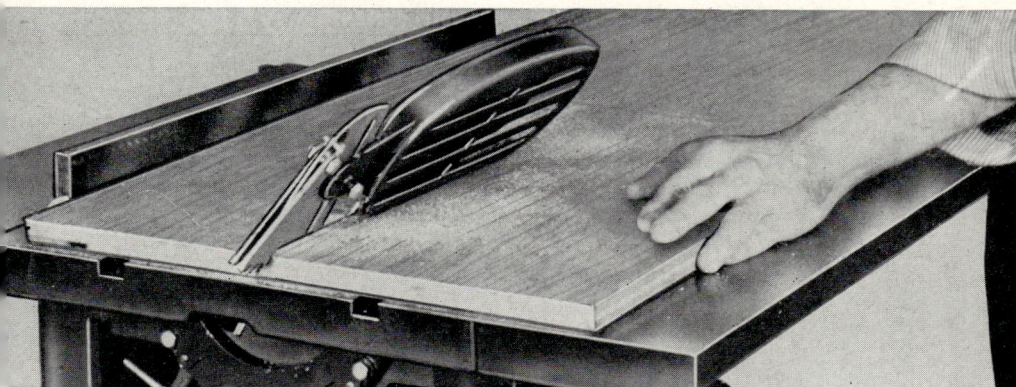

**306. CUTTING A BEVEL WITH THE GRAIN.** The saw blade has been tilted to the correct angle and a fence attached to control the width of the cut. On other types of saws, the table would be tilted to make this kind of cut, but the procedure would be the same.

## Beveling and chamfering

To cut a bevel or chamfer when you are either ripping or crosscutting, you must tilt the saw blade to the correct angle for the cut. The gauge that you will use to indicate the angle at which the saw blade is tilted is found on the front of the saw just below the table. Fig. 306. After the adjustment is made, check

**307. CUTTING A CHAMFER ON A CIRCULAR SAW.** Here a chamfer is being cut on the end grain of a piece of stock. The saw table is tilted to the correct angle (usually 45 degrees) and the stock is held against the miter gauge. The saw guard is removed, since it is difficult to see how to make this cut if it is used. However, whenever the guard is removed, greater care must be exercised.

**308. CUTTING A TENON ON A CIRCULAR SAW.** The saw blade has been set to a height equal to the amount of stock that must be removed from one side of the tenon. This is called the cheek cut. When the stock is held flat, the shoulder cut is made. Notice the feather board used as a guard.

the angle by holding a sliding **T** bevel against the table top and saw blade. After the correct angle has been secured, you can proceed as for ripping or crosscutting. Fig. 307.

## Grooving

Cutting a groove on the circular saw will simplify the making of a spline joint. Lay out the groove on the edge of the stock. Set the circular saw to a height equal to the depth of the groove. Adjust the ripping fence to allow the cut to be made just inside the layout line. Hold one surface of the stock firmly against the fence and make a cut. Reverse the stock and make a second cut. If necessary, you can

make several cuts in the waste stock of the groove. Clean out the groove with a sharp chisel.

## Rabbeting

A rabbet can easily be cut on the end or edge of the piece of stock with a circular saw. Lay out the rabbet joint (see the unit on making a rabbet joint). Set the saw blade to a height equal to the depth of the rabbet. If the rabbet is cut at the end of the board, hold the stock against a miter gauge and make the shoulder cut. Then set the saw blade to a height equal to the width of the rabbet. Set the ripping fence to a position that will permit the saw kerf to be just inside the layout line. Hold the stock on end

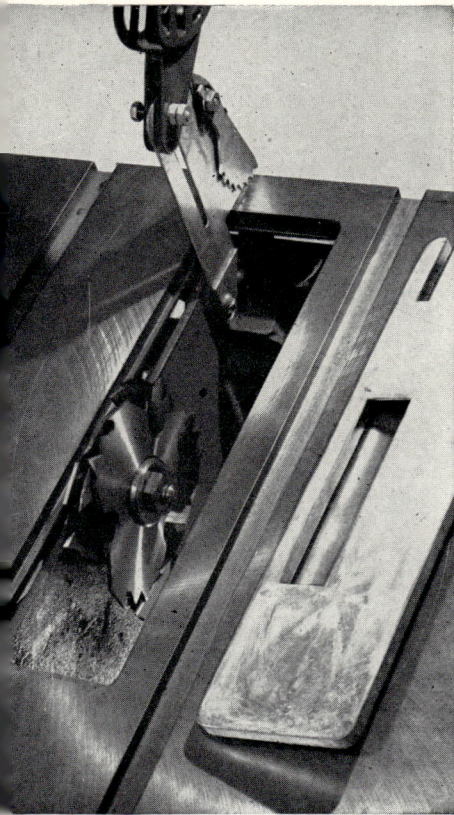

309. A DADO HEAD ATTACHED TO THE SAW ARBOR in preparation for use. The plate that must be used over the dado head has a wider opening than that used with the regular saw blade.

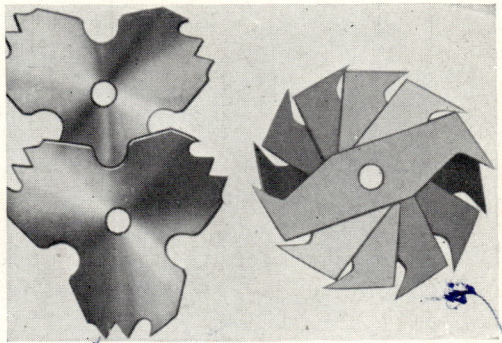

310. DADO BLADES WITH CUTTERS. Here are the two dado blades with the cutters that can be placed between them to provide the proper width of cut.

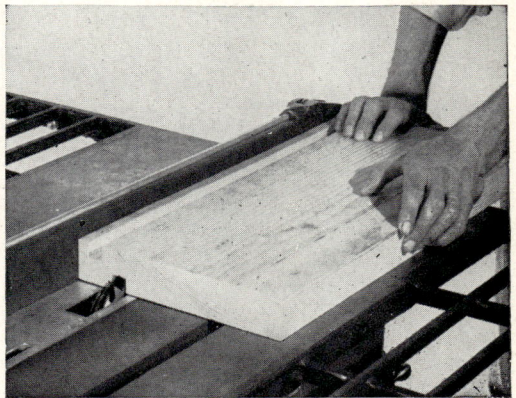

311. CUTTING A GROOVE WITH A DADO HEAD. Note how simple it is to cut a groove of any desired width and depth with this attachment. When the groove is cut across grain, it is called a dado and is a common type of joint construction.

with the surface opposite the rabbet firmly against the ripping fence and make the second cut.

An edge rabbet is cut in the same way except that the ripping fence is used for making both cuts.

## Tenoning

Making mortise-and-tenon joints is greatly simplified if the tenon is cut on the circular saw. Lay out the tenon (see the unit on making a mortise-and-tenon joint). Set the saw blade to a height equal to the thickness of stock to be removed from one side of the tenon. Hold the stock against the miter gauge and make the shoulder cuts. After this is done, set the saw blade to a height equal to the length of the tenon. Adjust the ripping fence to make a cut that will remove the

201

waste stock from the side of the tenon. Hold the tenon on end and make the check cut. Do not follow this method of cutting a tenon if the rail is less than 4 inches in width. Fig. 308.

## Using a dado head

A dado head (Figs. 309 and 310) can be purchased that will cut grooves or dadoes from ⅛ to 2 inches in width and is equally adapted to cutting with or across the grain. One dado blade will cut a groove ⅛ inch thick and two will make a cut ¼ inch thick. Cutters of different widths can be inserted between these two dado cutters to cut a groove of any width desired. This attachment is especially useful for cutting grooves, Fig. 311, tenons, dado joints, and lap joints.

## Can You Answer These Questions on the Circular Saw?

1. Sketch a circular saw and name the parts.
2. Name the two types of circular saws.
3. What are the three types of saw blades? Which is best for use in the average shop?
4. List the safety precautions to observe when using a circular saw.
5. At what height should the saw blade be set for ripping?
6. Tell how to make a cut on hardwood that is quite thick.
7. At what times should a push stick be used?
8. Name the gauge employed for doing crosscutting.
9. Relate the three methods of cutting several pieces to the same length.
10. What is the difficulty frequently encountered when making a miter cut?
11. How can a compound miter cut be made?
12. Point out the difference between a bevel and a chamfer.
13. How can a groove be cut?
14. What difference is there between cutting a rabbet on the end and on the edge of a piece of stock?
15. Tell how to make the cheek cut in tenoning.
16. What is a dado head? What is it used for?
17. What is the difference between a dado blade and cutter?

## THE BAND SAW

A band saw consists of two wheels mounted on a frame, a table, guides, a saw blade, and guards. Fig. 312. In addition, a ripping fence and miter gauge are sometimes used. The table can be tilted at various angles. The size of the band saw is indicated by the diameter of the wheels. The band saw is used primarily for cutting curves, circles, and irregular designs. It can also be used for crosscutting, ripping, and resawing.

To install a saw blade, the guards over the wheel are removed, the top wheel loosened, and the throat plate removed. Then, grasping the blade in both hands, slip it through the slot in the table and then over the wheels. Fig. 313. Then tighten the upper wheel to

312. A SMALL TYPE, 14-INCH BAND SAW that can be mounted on a table or bench. It has all the features of a larger machine—such as a tilting table, ball-bearing guides, and an adjustable upper wheel. It differs only in that it has a smaller capacity.

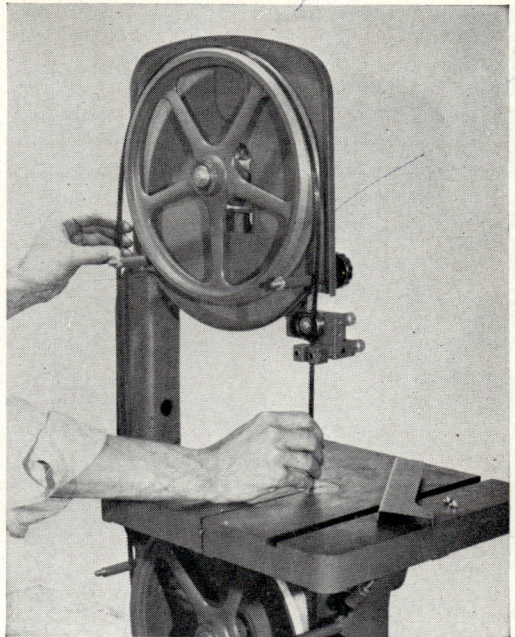

313. INSTALLING A BAND-SAW BLADE. The guards have been removed and the upper wheel released to permit the new band-saw blade to be slipped over the two wheels. There are adjustments on the reverse side of the upper wheel for tension and for tilting the wheel back and forth. This will, of course, also move the blade.

apply tension to the blade. The upper wheel can be tilted to move the blade forward or backward on the wheel. Replace the little throat plate around the blade and look to see if the blade is running in the guide properly. Turn the wheels over by hand once or twice to check the operation of the blade.

## Cutting with a band saw

Adjust the upper saw guide just to clear the stock. Fig. 314. Stand slightly to the left and in front of the table. Guide the stock with your left hand and apply forward pressure with the right hand. Do not force the work into the saw.

## Cutting curves

Select a band-saw blade for cutting curves, using the following general rule: A ⅛-inch blade will cut down to about a 1-inch circle, while a ⅜-inch blade will cut down to about a 2½-inch circle. The width of the blade to be used should be determined by the thickness and kind of wood to be cut, as well as by the sharpness of the curve.

In cutting curves, apply even forward pressure and carefully guide the work with your left hand,

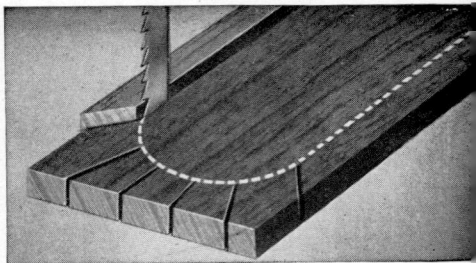

**316. CUTTING SHARP CURVES.** When the blade on the band saw is slightly wider than desired, a rather sharp cut can be made by first making many relief cuts.

**314. THE BAND SAW WITH THE GUIDE PROPERLY ADJUSTED.** The stock, which just clears the guide, is being held with the thumbs and forefingers of both hands.

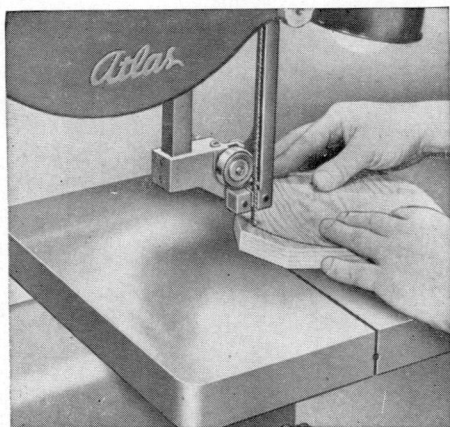

**317. RESAWING STOCK.** A pivot block is fastened to the table with a C clamp to control the thickness of the cut. A band saw is better for resawing than a circular saw because less stock is wasted with the thinner blade and because the exposed blade is longer. Notice the tension nut for tightening the upper wheel and the adjustment for tilting the upper wheel.

**315. CUTTING A CURVE ON A BAND SAW.** The stock is carefully guided along the layout line.

to keep the cut just outside the layout line. Fig. 315. If you are cutting quite sharp curves, you should make many relief cuts from the out-

side edge to within less than the thickness of the blade from the layout line. Fig. 316. Then, as you cut along the layout line, the waste stock will fall away freely.

## Resawing

When stock is much thicker than is needed, it is resawed. This can be done on the band saw. The widest possible blade should be selected and a fence or pivot block attached to the table. A layout line across the end and edge of the board is helpful. Hold the stock against the fence or block and slowly feed the work against the blade. Fig. 317.

## Ripping

If a circular saw is not avail-

able, stock can be ripped to width by fastening a fence or pivot block to the table and proceeding in the same manner as with a circular saw.

## Crosscutting and mitering

The table of the band saw has a groove into which a miter gauge will fit. Stock can be held against this miter gauge to do accurate crosscutting or miter cutting on the band saw.

## Tilt-table work

The table can be tilted to do many jobs such as beveling and chamfering on curves and irregular designs.

## Can You Answer These Questions on the Band Saw?

1. Name the parts of the band saw.
2. How is the size of the band saw determined?
3. Describe the method followed for installing a saw blade.
4. Where should you stand when cutting with a band saw?
5. There is a rule for selecting a band-

saw blade for cutting curves. What is it?
6. How can a sharp curve be cut?
7. What is resawing?
8. What is the advantage of resawing on a band saw over resawing on a circular saw?
9. How can ripping be done on the band saw?

## THE JIGSAW OR SCROLL SAW

The jigsaw or scroll saw is mechanically operated so that the saw moves up and down to do the same type of work that can be done by hand with a coping or compass saw. It will cut curves or irregular designs both externally and internally. Fig. 318. The saw consists of a frame with overarm and base, a driving mechanism to convert rotating action into up-and-down ac-

tion, a table, guide, and saw blade. Figs. 319-320. A tension sleeve is mounted in the end of the overarm, through which a plunger moves. The size of a jig saw is indicated by the distance between the blade and the overarm measured horizontally. The speed of the jig saw can be adjusted by shifting a belt to various positions. There are three types of blades. *Power jig saw blades* are used for all kinds of cutting on

**318. CUTTING AN INTRICATE LAYOUT ON THE JIG SAW.** This saw greatly simplifies making irregular designs. The saw can cut stock up to 2 inches in thickness.

wood. The *saber blade* is fastened only in the lower chuck. *Jeweler's piercing blades* are used to cut thin metal, Figs. 321-322, while the saber blade is for heavier stock.

## Cutting with a jigsaw

Cutting with the jigsaw requires the same care and attention as does cutting with a coping saw. Adjust the guide so that the small spring tension holds the stock firmly against the table. Fig. 323. If it is a small piece of stock, hold it with the thumb and forefinger of both hands. Apply even, forward pressure. Do not force the stock into the work. Turn the stock

**319. A JIG OR SCROLL SAW,** with the names of the major parts.

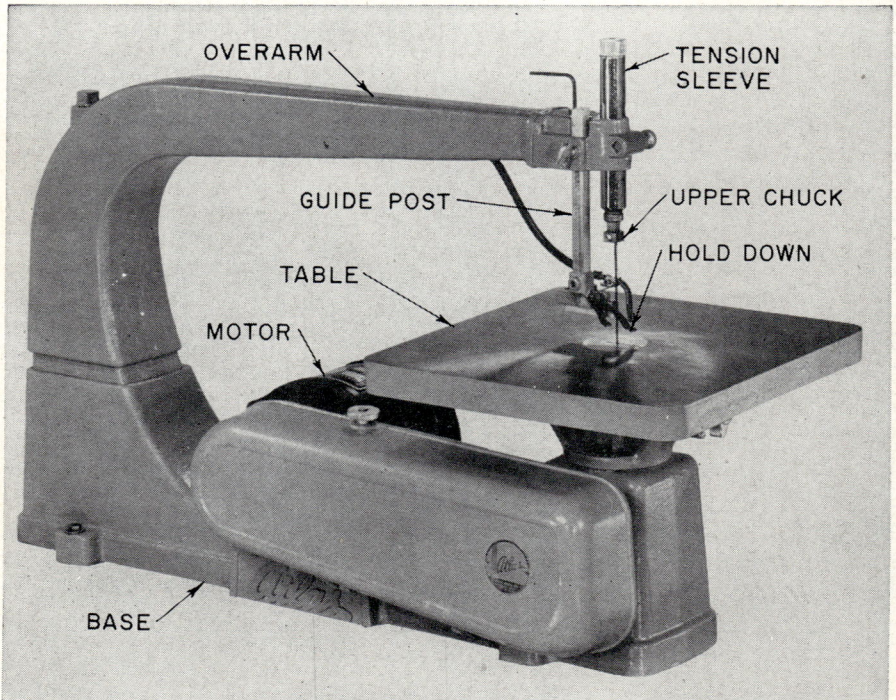

OVERARM · TENSION SLEEVE · GUIDE POST · UPPER CHUCK · TABLE · HOLD DOWN · MOTOR · BASE

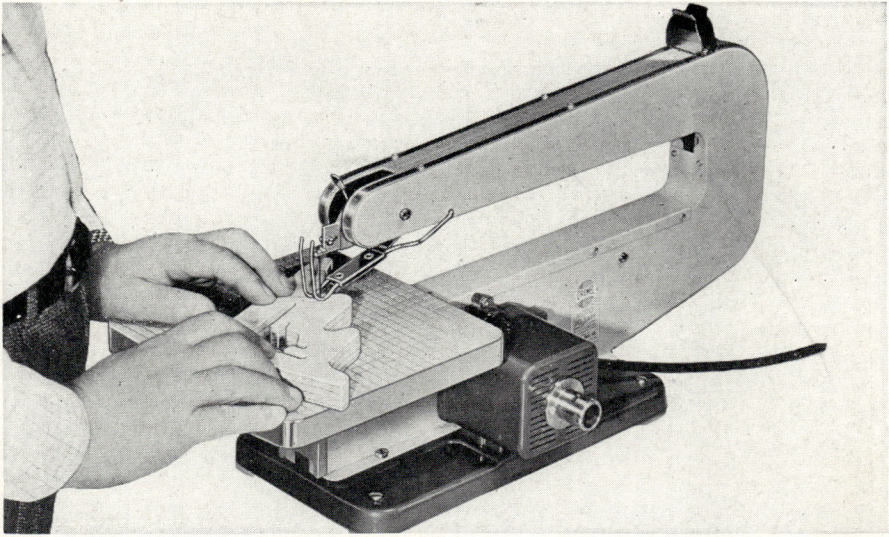

320. THIS ROCKER-ACTION JIG SAW has a smooth, even cutting action. The 3-inch blades have pins on either end and are easily installed.

321. THE PROPER METHOD OF FASTENING A JEWELER'S BLADE in the upper and lower chuck of a jig saw.

322. FASTENING A SABER BLADE in the lower chuck. The blade is held in the V-shaped jaw. The table is cut away to show the construction.

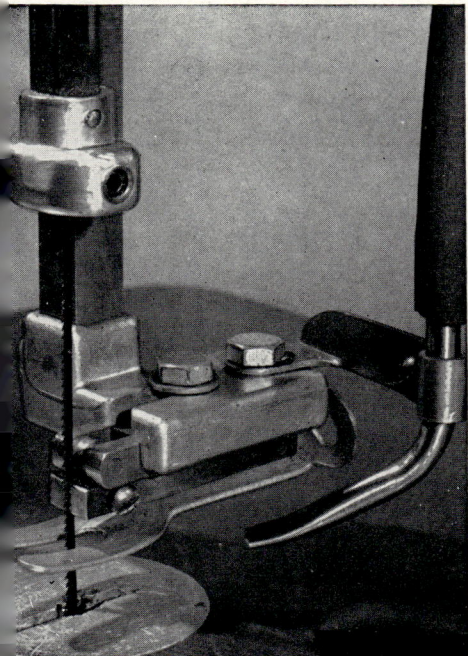

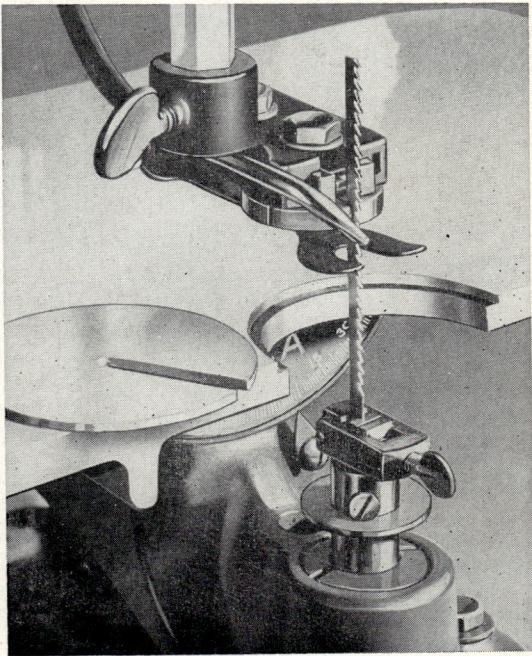

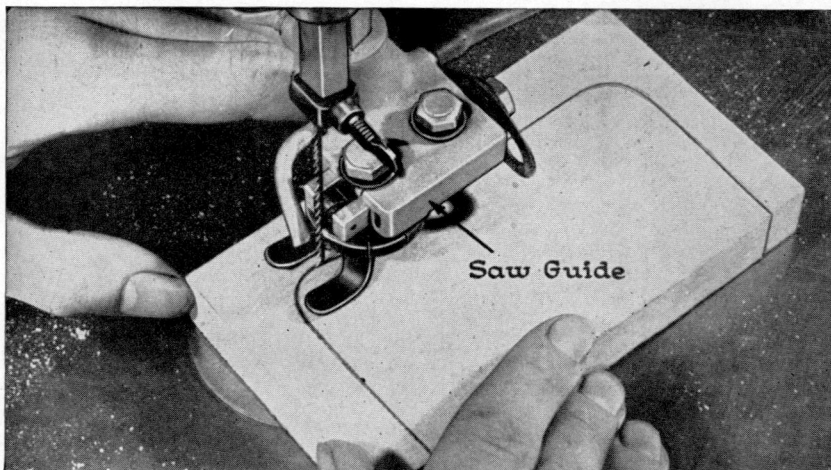

**323.** THE SAW GUIDE PROPERLY ADJUSTED. The small spring tension in the bottom of the saw guide holds the stock firmly against the table of the saw.

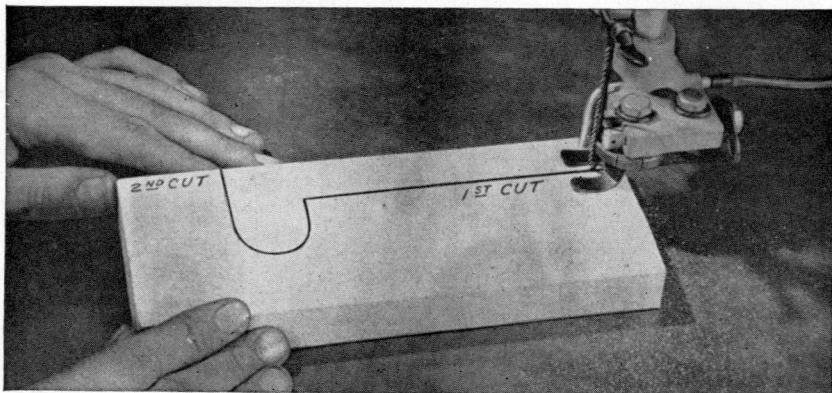

**324.** THE PROPER METHOD OF MAKING COMPLICATED CUTS on the jig saw. In cutting out this design, a straight cut is first made. Then the stock is backed off the saw and a curved cut made until it joins the straight cut. This eliminates the necessity for trying to cut a sharp corner.

slowly when cutting a curve. If the stock is turned too abruptly, it will break the blade. If rather complicated cuts must be made, determine the best method. Fig. 324.

**Cutting internal curves and designs**

Drill a relief hole in the center of the waste stock. If a jeweler's blade is to be used, remove the

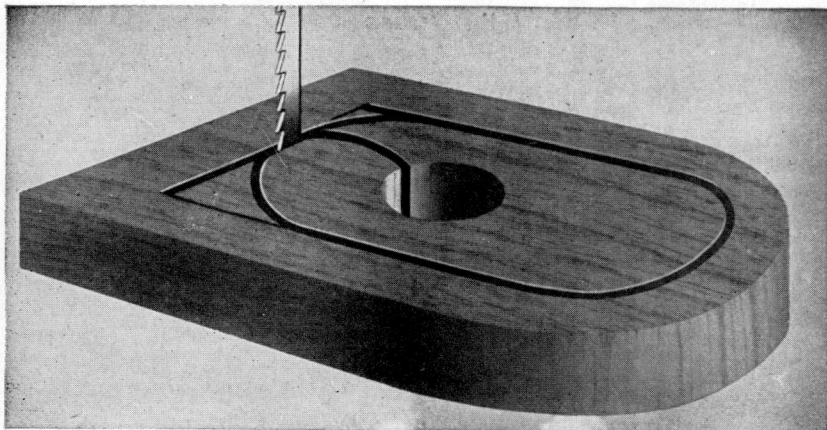

**325. MAKING AN INTERNAL CUT ON THE JIG SAW.** The relief hole has been drilled in the center of the waste stock and the cut made to the layout line.

throat plate. After the blade is fastened in the lower chuck, insert the stock over the blade, fasten the other end of the blade to the plunger chuck, and then replace the throat plate. Adjust the guide to the correct height. Then make a circular cut from the relief hole to the layout line. Fig. 325.

## Tilt-table work

The table of the jigsaw can be tilted to cut a bevel on circular or irregular designs. Fig. 326.

## Can You Answer These Questions on the Jigsaw or Scroll Saw?

1. Sketch a jigsaw and locate its parts.
2. How is the size of the jigsaw indicated?
3. Name the two types of blades.

4. What is the most common cause of blade breakage?
5. How can internal cutting be done?

## THE JOINTER

The jointer is used for surfacing, jointing an edge, beveling, chamfering, and rabbeting. It consists of a base, two tables—the front or in-feed table and the rear or out-feed table—a cutterhead, a fence, and a guard. Fig. 327.

The circular cutterhead usually holds three blades firmly mounted with wedges and set screws. The size of the jointer is determined by

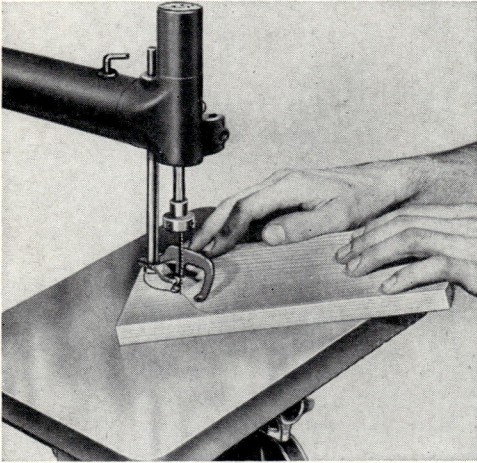

326. TILT THE TABLE only 2 or 3 degrees when cutting draft on a pattern.

the width of these blades, the most common size for the small shop being the 6 or 8-inch machine.

The in-feed and out-feed tables are mounted on sliding ways so that they may be raised and lowered to make adjustments. The out-feed table supports the work after it has been cut and therefore should be the same height as the cutting blade at its highest point. The in-feed table supports the work before it is cut, and therefore the height of this table determines the thickness of the cut to be taken. Once the out-feed table has been adjusted to the proper height, it can be locked in position and does not need to be changed. Only the in-feed table should be moved up or down to change the

327. A JOINTER WITH FENCE AND GUARD. The parts include a base, the cutter head, the in-feed or front table and the out-feed or rear table. This is a 6 inch jointer.

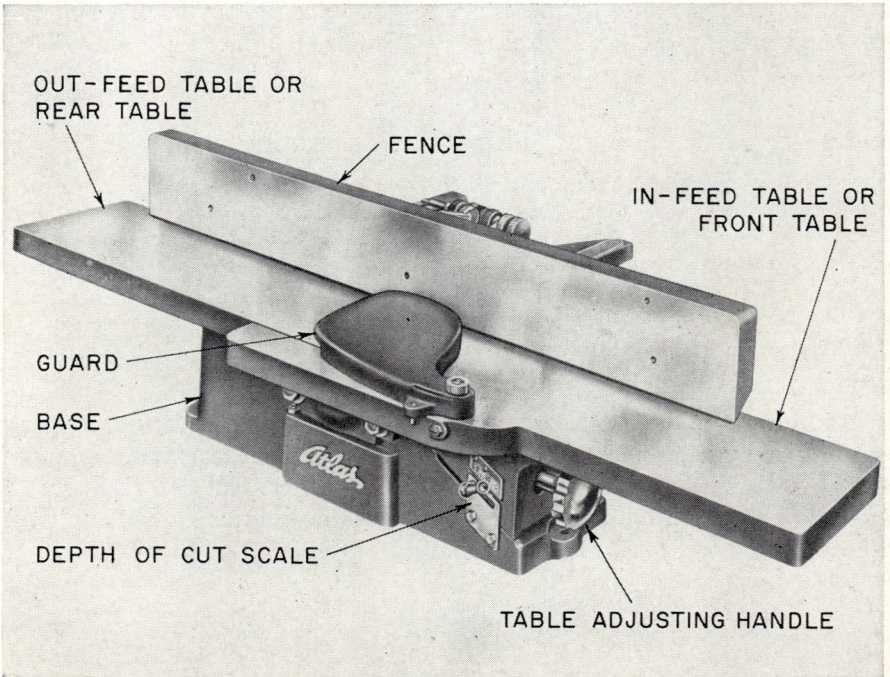

OUT-FEED TABLE OR REAR TABLE

FENCE

IN-FEED TABLE OR FRONT TABLE

GUARD

BASE

DEPTH OF CUT SCALE

TABLE ADJUSTING HANDLE

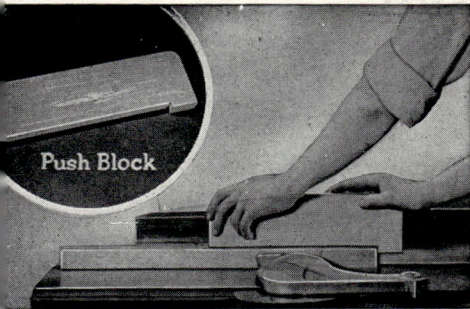

Push Block

**328. USING A PUSH BLOCK. Never at-**
tempt to surface thin stock or to joint
the edge of narrow pieces without
using a push block to keep your fingers
away from the revolving cutter.

thickness of the cut. The fence of
a jointer is usually set at right angles to the table but it can be adjusted at any angle when you want
to plane a bevel or chamfer.

## Safety

The jointer is not dangerous, if
used correctly. It can be a hazard
to safety, however, if the following
rules are not observed:

**329. THE CORRECT WAY TO FEED**
**STOCK INTO A JOINTER.** The
stock is fed into a jointer opposite the
grain direction, with the result that
the cutting action is the same as when
planing with a hand plane with the
grain.

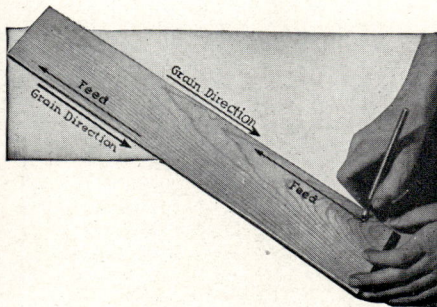

Danger Zone

**330. THE DANGER ZONE OF A**
**JOINTER** is the area directly over
the revolving cutter. This is the area
you must guard against.

1. Always make sure that the
jointer is equipped with a guard
over the cutterhead.

2. Use a push block when surfacing thin stock. Fig. 328.

3. Feed the stock with the
grain. Fig. 329.

4. Keep your hands clear of the
danger zone. Fig. 330.

5. Never attempt to surface
stock that is less than 10 inches in
length.

6. Stand to the left of the jointer, never directly in back of it.

7. Do not attempt to take too
heavy a cut.

## Face planing or surfacing

Face planing or surfacing means
planing the surface of stock true.
Only stock that is less in width than
the blades of the jointer should be
face planed. Generally speaking,
the jointer is not used for face planing. If it is done, set the in-feed
table to take a very thin cut. Hold
the stock firmly against the in-feed
table and push the stock with a push
block as the left hand holds the
front of the stock down. Slowly
push the board through the cutters.
As in hand planing, most pressure
should be applied to the front of the

211

331. SURFACING OR FACE-PLANING THIN STOCK. A push block is being used to hold the stock firmly against the table.

board as the cutting is started, then equal pressure applied to both front and back as the board passes across the cutter, and finally more pressure applied to the rear of the board as the major portion of it has passed the out-feed table. Fig. 331.

## Jointing an edge

The most common use of the jointer is to square an edge true with the face surface. To do this, make sure that the fence is at right angles to the table. Check this with a try square. Hold the stock on the in-feed table with the face surface against the fence. Use your left hand to guide the stock and your right hand to apply forward pressure. Fig. 332. Do not push the stock through the jointer too fast, as this will cause little ripples to be formed by the revolving cutter.

## Beveling and chamfering

To cut a bevel or chamfer on an edge with a jointer, set the fence at the proper angle to the table. The

332. JOINTING AN EDGE. The stock is held firmly against the in-feed table at the beginning of the cut; then even pressure is applied; and, finally, pressure is applied on the out-feed table.

333. CUTTING A BEVEL OR CHAMFER. The fence of the jointer has been tilted to cut a bevel or chamfer.

fence may be tilted in or out. Fig. 333. Check this angle with a sliding

T bevel, then proceed as in jointing an edge.

## Can You Answer These Questions on the Jointer?

1. Name the parts of a jointer.
2. How can you tell what size it is?
3. What two types of blades are used on the jointer?
4. How is the depth of cut controlled?
5. List the safety precautions to be observed in operating the jointer.
6. Is the jointer commonly used for face

planing? Explain.
7. How can the fence of the jointer be checked for squareness?
8. What causes ripples to be formed on a board when it is run through the jointer?
9. How can you check the fence for cutting a bevel or chamfer?

### THE DRILL PRESS

The drill press, although not used so often as the circular saw, is one of the most valuable tools to have in a small shop. It is very versatile and can be used not only for drilling, but for such common operations as shaping, routing, carving, sanding, and mortising. Because of this and because the drill press is

relatively inexpensive, it should be one of the first additions to a small shop. A bench-type drill press, showing the major parts, is seen in Fig. 334.

The drill press in the woodworking shop should have an auxiliary arrangement for varying the spindle speed from a low speed of 400 to 500 r.p.m., for such work as drilling and mortising, to a high speed of 5,000 to 7,000 r.p.m., for shaping and routing. Fig. 335.

334. A BENCH-TYPE DRILL PRESS, SHOWING THE MAJOR PARTS.

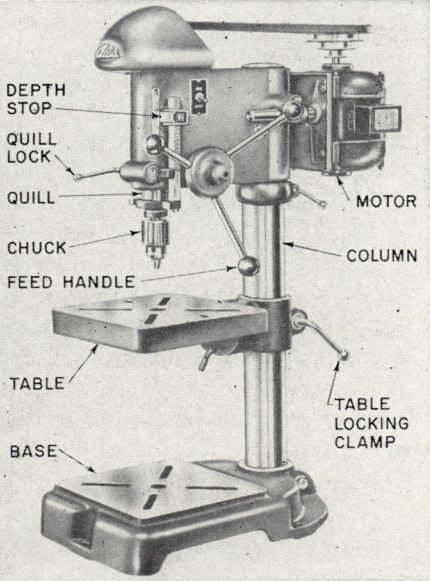

335. AN AUXILIARY ARRANGEMENT FOR ADJUSTING THE SPINDLE SPEED. If one of these is not available, a drill press can be equipped with a high-speed motor and large pulleys to do shaper and router work.

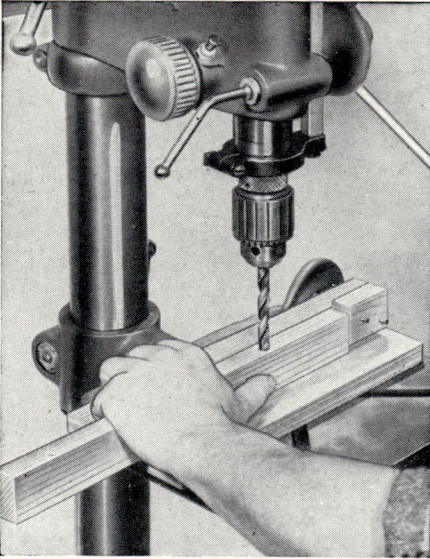

**336. DRILLING WOOD WITH A TWIST DRILL.** Make sure that you hold the stock firmly against the table of the drill press when drilling in this way.

**337. BORING STOCK WITH AN AUGER BIT.** The stock is clamped to the bed with a C clamp. An auger bit must have a straight shank to be used in a three-jaw chuck.

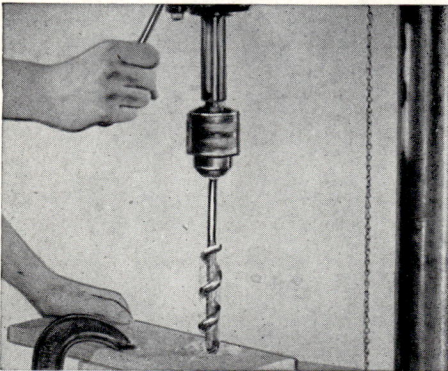

**338. DRILLING HOLES IN A CYLINDRICAL PIECE OF STOCK,** using a V block. The table has been turned at a 90 degree angle to its original position and a V block clamped to the table with two C clamps.

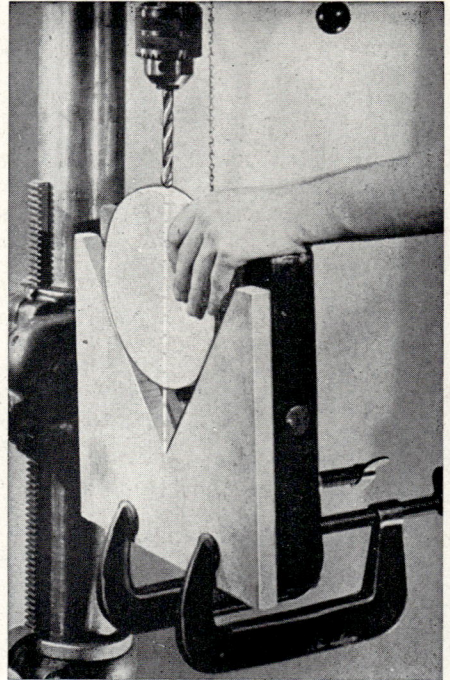

## Drilling

Drill presses are usually equipped with a Jacob's chuck to hold drills, auger bits, and other cutting tools. To drill or bore holes, locate and punch the center of the hole. Select a drill or auger bit of the correct size and fasten it in the chuck. An auger bit must have a straight shank and brad point. Adjust the spindle speed to a slower speed for larger drills and auger bits and a faster speed for smaller ones. Adjust the table to the correct height. Make sure that the hole in the table is directly under the drill, or place a piece of scrap stock on the table under the piece to be drilled or bored. Hold the piece securely and

339. USING A MORTISING ATTACH-
MENT. The part for holding the
chisel is locked to the quill of the
drill press, and the auger bit is fastened
in the chuck. A fence is locked to the
table and clamps are attached to hold
the stock in place.

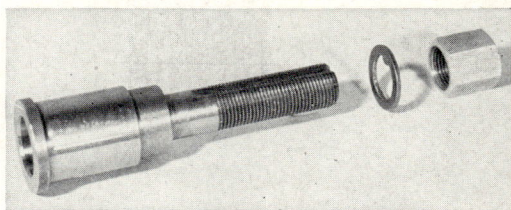

340. AN ADAPTER FOR HOLDING
SHAPER CUTTERS. This adapter is
fastened in the spindle of the drill
press.

just after the revolving bit and cut
the square opening after the bit has
removed most of the stock. On
most mortising attachments, the
chisel is fastened to the quill of the
drill press and a straight-shank auger
bit fastened in the chuck. Of course,
the chisel should be the same width
as the width of the mortise to be
cut and a fence attached to the
table to guide the stock as the mortise is cut. Fig. 339.

## Shaping

To do shaping it is necessary to
have a spindle speed of 5,000 r.p.m.
This speed can be attained by using
the auxiliary pulley arrangement or
a high-speed motor. It is also necessary to have a special adapter that
will hold the shaper cutter. Fig.
340. This adapter can be attached
to the spindle of the drill press.
Then an inexpensive set of shaper
cutters should be secured that will
enable you to construct setups that
make a variety of shapes. Select the
shaper cutters for the particular
shape you want to make. Fig. 341.

The depth of the cut can be
controlled by placing a collar of the
correct diameter just above or be-

apply even pressure to feed the drill
into the wood slowly. Figs. 336 and
337. Never force a drill or auger
bit into the wood. Drilling or boring holes in round stock can be
done by holding the work in a V
block. Fig. 338.

## Mortising

If considerable furniture construction is being done, a mortising
attachment should be available, as it
greatly simplifies cutting a mortise-
and-tenon joint. A mortising attachment consists of a hollow,
square mortising chisel in which an
auger bit revolves. The chisel itself
is ground to a sharp point at each
corner. These points enter the wood

**341. SHAPER CUTTERS.** Various shapes of cutters are needed to make the designs, in shaper operation.

## Can You Answer These Questions on the Drill Press?

1. Drilling is not the only operation performed on the drill press. Name several other operations.

2. About what speed is necessary for shaping and routing?

3. What kind of auger bits can be fastened in the drill press?

4. Name the parts of a mortising attachment and describe how it is used.

5. What two machines are most commonly used for making mortise-and-tenon joints?

6. What is meant by shaping an edge?

7. How do you control the depth of cut for shaping?

low the cutter or by using a fence. Fasten the cutter and collar to the special adapter. Raise the table to the correct position and lock it in place. Secure a piece of scrap stock of the same thickness as the finished pieces and make a trial cut. In using a shaper attachment, force the wood into the cutter very slowly. Sometimes it is desirable to cut the design to partial depth and then to go over it again. If the design is cut on three or four edges, finish the ends first and then the sides. If the trial cut is satisfactory, cut the edge. Fig. 342.

## Routing

A routing tool is fastened either in a chuck or in a special router attachment. The spindle speed must be about 6,000 to 7,000 r.p.m. Various types of routing work, such as cutting the opening for the pins and cards of the cribbage board (Fig. 404), can be done on the drill press. Fig. 343.

343. **DOING ROUTER WORK ON A DRILL PRESS.** The router cutters are fastened either in the chuck or in special adapters. Make sure that the stock is held firmly against the table in roing the cutting. Notice the guides that have been clamped to the table.

342. **USING THE DRILL PRESS AS A SHAPER.** When doing shaper operations on the drill press, a high spindle speed is required. If considerable work of this sort must be done, it would be better to have a shaper.

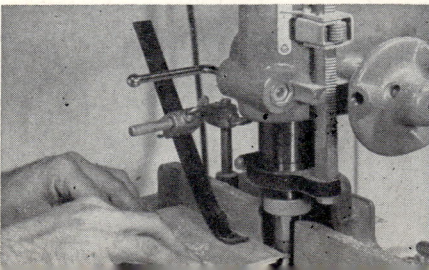

344. A COMBINATION DISK-AND-BELT SANDER. While these can be separate machines, the combination sander works very well.

## SANDERS

The most common power sanders are the combination disk-and-belt sander, the portable finishing (pad) sander, and the portable continuous-belt sander. With the correct sander, you can save many hours of tedious work, yet give the project a smooth finish. The bench or floor combination disk-and-belt sander is used when the work can be brought to the sander. Fig. 344. It is especially good for sanding parts. The continuous-belt portable sander is designed for heavy-duty sanding of projects already assembled. Fig. 345. The finishing, or pad, sander is designed for light sanding. The kind of abrasive cloth or paper used and the grip determine the quality of the wood surface—rough or finished. Fig. 346. The combination disk-and-belt sander has a rather violent action

### Can You Answer These Questions on Sanders?

1. Name four sanders commonly found in the shop.
2. What determines the quality of smoothness or roughness of the wood surface after sanding?
3. What is the best sander to use for a light finishing sanding after the project is assembled?
4. Describe the way to use a portable continuous-belt sander.

346. FINISHING, OR PAD, SANDER. This kind is best to use after the project is assembled.

345. PORTABLE BELT SANDER. This machine will sand large surfaces such as a table top.

and is good for fast, rough work. However, it will not always do a good job of fine sanding around corners and on thin plywood.

Sanders should never be used in place of cutting tools. When using the disk-and-belt sander, hold the work square with the abrasive paper. Fig. 347. Whenever possible, use a fence or table to guide the sanding. When using a portable continuous-belt sander, always grip the sander firmly with both hands. Then move it evenly in a straight line with the wood grain. Never allow it to rest in one place, as this cuts a deep groove in the wood surface. Also be careful that you do not round the edges. When using a finishing sander, apply it lightly to the surface. Guide it from one end of your work to the opposite end, moving it from one side to the other.

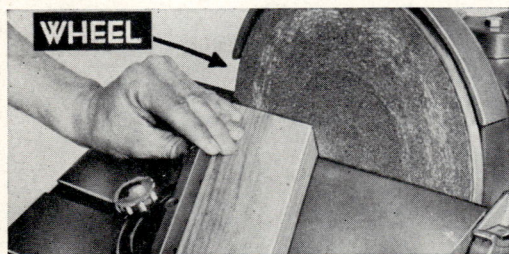

347. SANDING STOCK WITH A DISK
SANDER. The table has been set at
an angle and a miter gauge adjusted to
the correct angle to sand a miter cut.
It is as important to sand a surface accurately as it is to cut it accurately.

## PORTABLE ROUTER

The portable router is a versatile
tool that can do many cutting and
shaping jobs. Fig. 348. It consists of
a powerful motor mounted in an
adjustable base. There is a collet
chuck at the end of the motor shaft
that can hold many types of cutting
tools. Some of the common router
bits and cutters are shown in Fig.
349. To install the cutter bit, loosen
the nut on the chuck and slip the bit
in place. Then tighten the nut or
nuts. To adjust for depth of cut, the
base is raised or lowered. In some
types the base screws onto the
motor housing. In others it slides up
and down. Common uses are:

1. *Freehand routing*. This is
done when the operator moves the
router about without guides. Fig.
350A. A good example of this
would be routing out a name plate
or numbers of an address. In freehand routing, the letters or numbers
are sometimes formed by the cutter
bit. In other cases, the background
around the letters and numbers is
routed so the numbers stand out.

2. *Shaping an edge or making
a molding*. By using a bit with a
pilot on the end, the edge of a table
top or molding for picture frames
can be made. Fig. 350B. The pilot
on the bit does no cutting, so the
edge can be shaped without a guide.
Select the right bit shape and fasten
it in the chuck. Move the base up
and down until the bit is out the
correct distance. Select a piece of
scrap wood of the same thickness as
the finished article. Try the bit on
the scrap stock.

3. *Routing with a guide*. For
making such cuts as a groove or a
dado, a guide is attached. Fig. 351.
The width of the cut is determined
by the bit. Of course, a wider cut
can be made with a narrower bit by
making two or more passes. The
depth of cut is determined by adjusting the base to the motor housing.

## Can You Answer These Questions on the Router?

1. Name the major parts of the router.
2. What is freehand routing?
3. Is a guide necessary in shaping an
edge?
4. Name some of the common router
bits.

348. PORTABLE ROUTER. This model is open on one side and has a light under the motor. This makes it easy to see the cutting being done.

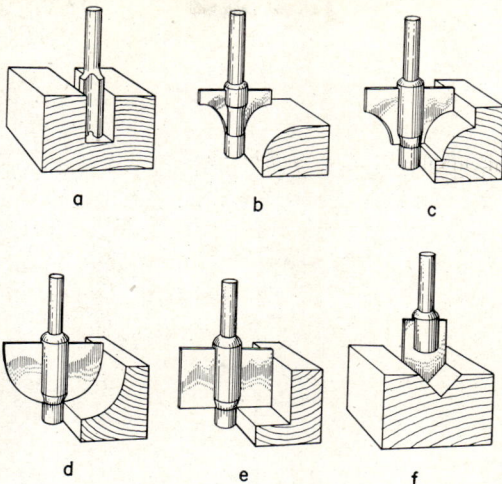

349. A FEW OF THE COMMON ROUTER BITS: A. Straight bit. B. Rounding-over bit. C. Beading bit. D. Cove bit. E. Rabetting bit. F. V-grooving bit.

350A. FREEHAND ROUTING. The router is moved and controlled by the operator.

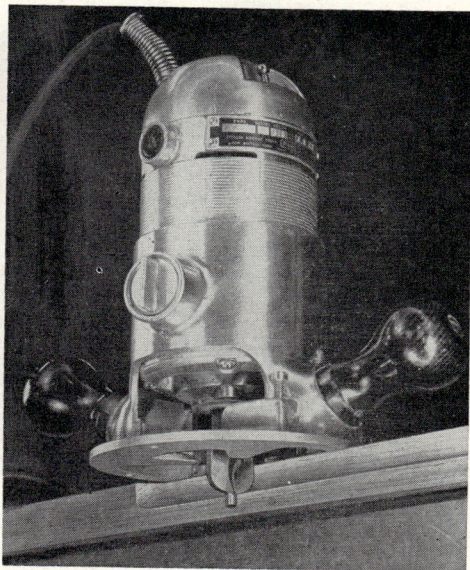

350B. THE PILOT ON THE END OF THE CUTTER controls the amount of cut. It rides on the edge and does no cutting.

219

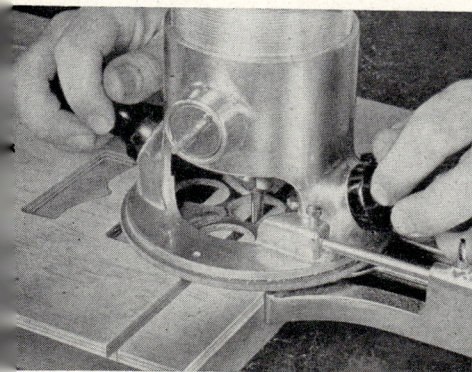

351. USING A GUIDE ATTACHMENT for cutting a dado.

past the cutter. If end grain must be cut, make several passes across the cutter until the desired depth is reached.

The shaper can also be used as a spindle sander. Fig. 351.

## Can You Answer These Questions on the Shaper?

1. At what speed does the shaper operate?
2. What are the two methods of controlling the depth of cut on the shaper?

3. What are the common uses of the shaper in the woodshop?
4. In what way is the shaper a dangerous machine for the beginner?

## WOOD LATHE

The wood lathe is one machine that will perform many basic operations that cannot be done by hand. You will find a variety of uses for it in making turned parts for your projects. The machine consists of a bed, the headstock assembly that is permanently fastened to the bed, a tailstock that slides along and can be locked in any position on the bed, and a tool rest. Fig. 352. The headstock spindle has a hollow-ground taper into which is fastened the spur or live center. The outside of the spindle is threaded to receive the faceplate. The speed of the lathe is controlled by changing the belts to the various positions. Fig. 353. The tailstock is also taper ground and a dead or cup center is inserted in the spindle.

The common cutting tools include a 1-inch gouge, a ½-inch gouge, a 1-inch skew, a ½-inch skew, a roundnose, spear and parting tool. Fig. 354. In addition, the operator must have a good bench

352. A WOOD LATHE, SHOWING THE MAJOR PARTS.

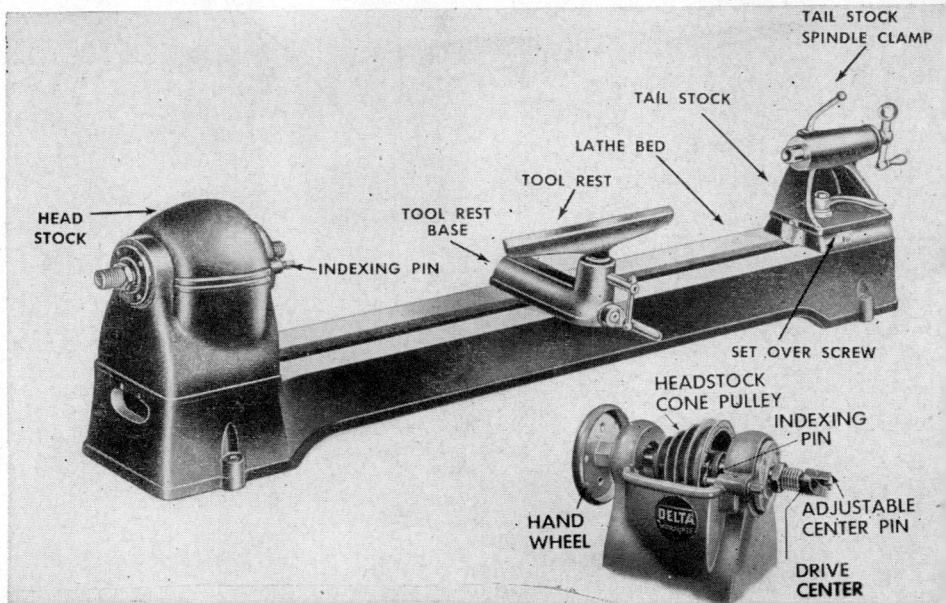

ruie and a pair of outside calipers. To do the most elementary work on a lathe, a satisfactory job can be done by scraping the surface of the wood. Real wood turning, however, is done by using the tools for cutting action.

## Preparing stock to be turned

Select a piece of correct kind of wood that has a rectangular measurement larger than the diameter to be turned and is about an inch longer than the finished piece should be. Mark a line across the corners of either end to locate the center of the stock. Fig. 355. Place the live center over the stock and tap it with a wooden mallet to force the spurs into the wood. Figs. 356 and 357. If it is hardwood, it may be necessary to make two saw kerfs across the corners so that the wood will hold. If the stock is over 3 inches in thickness, the corners should be trimmed off to form an octagon shape before inserting the wood in

353. THE HEADSTOCK ASSEMBLY, illustrating the threaded headstock spindle. The inner end has a right-hand thread and the outer end has a left-hand thread. Note the V pulley and also the indexing mechanism. The mechanism is for dividing faceplate work and for doing such jobs as fluting and reeding.

354. THE COMMON TURNING TOOLS INCLUDE: A. A large gouge for roughing cuts and a smaller gouge for smaller concave curves. B. A large skew for smoothing and a smaller skew for squaring ends; cutting shoulders, V-grooves, and beads. C. A roundnose for cutting out concave curves. D. A spear point for finishing V-grooves and beads. E. A parting tool for cutting off, and for cutting to specific diameters.

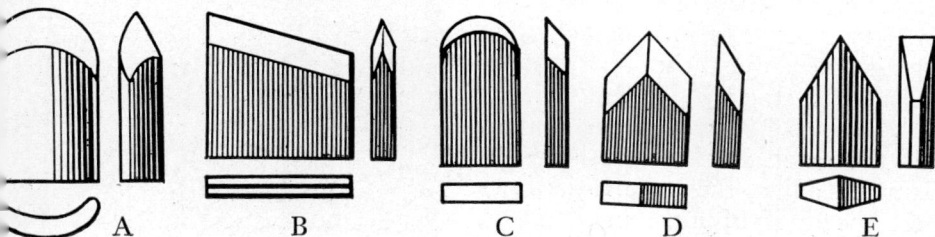

A     B     C     D     E

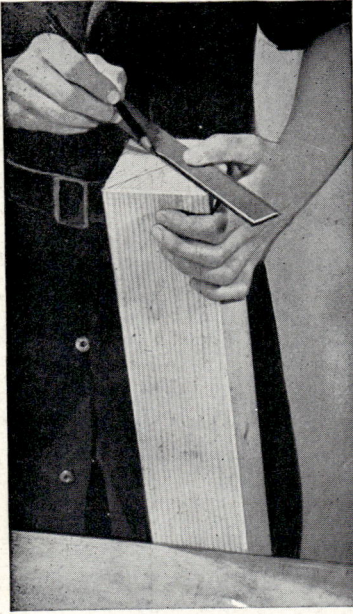

**355. HERE A LINE IS BEING DRAWN** across the corners to locate the center of the stock.

**356. ONE METHOD OF SETTING THE SPUR** or live center is to drive it into the wood with a mallet.

**357. NEVER USE THIS METHOD of** fastening stock to the live center, especially on a light lathe, as it places too much strain on the headstock assembly.

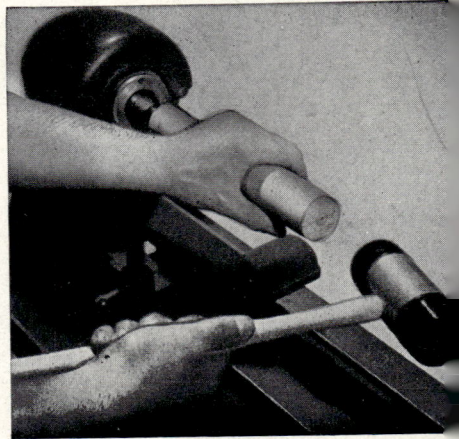

the lathe. Hold the wood against the live center and bring the tailstock to within about 1½ inches of the end of the stock. Lock the tailstock to the bed and then turn up the tailstock handle, forcing the cup center into the wood about 1/32 inch. Back off the cup center and use a little oil or wax to lubricate the end of the stock. Then tighten up the tailstock handle and lock it in position. Adjust the tool rest to clear the stock by about ⅛ inch and about ⅛ inch above center. If the stock is of rather large diameter, adjust the lathe to its lowest speed; if of medium diameter, at medium speed; and if of small diameter, at the highest speed.

Rotate the stock by hand to see if it has sufficient clearance.

## Rough turning using a gouge

The large gouge can be held in two ways in the left hand. It can be grasped close to the cutting point with the hand underneath and the thumb over it, with the forefinger serving as a stop against the tool rest, as shown in Fig. 358; or you can place your hand over the tool with the wrist bent at an angle to form the stop, as shown in Fig. 359. Grasp the handle of the gouge in

359. THE SECOND METHOD OF HOLDING A GOUGE. Here the hand is placed over the tool, with the wrist bent, and against the tool rest.

358. THE FIRST METHOD OF HOLD-ING A GOUGE. The thumb is placed over the tool and the other fingers under it, using the forefinger as a guide against the rest.

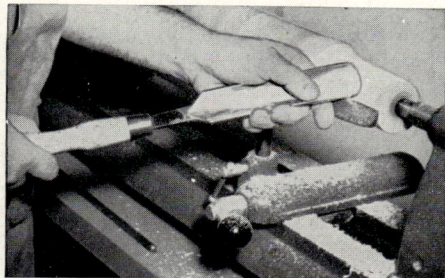

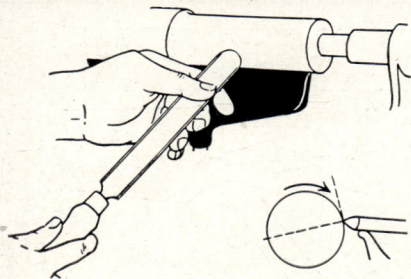

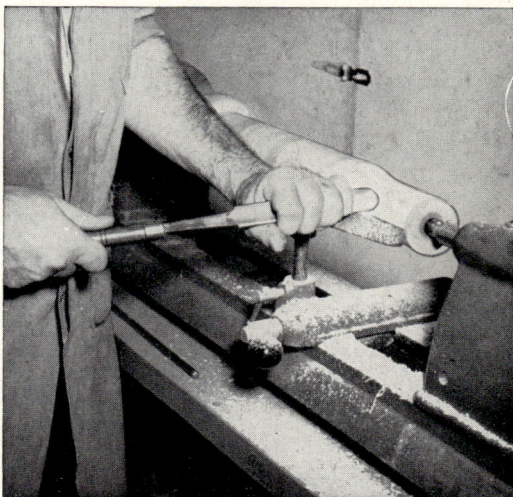

your right hand, tilting it down and away from the direction in which the cut is to be made. Be sure to hold the tool securely against the tool rest. Begin about one third of the way in from the tailstock. Twist the gouge to the right so that a shearing cut will be taken. Then move the cutting edge toward the dead center. Make certain that you grasp the tool firmly during this operation, since the revolving corners will tend to throw the tool out of your hand. After each cut, begin about 2 inches closer to the live center.

To finish the rough turning, tip the cutting edge to the left and work toward the live center. Turn off the lathe and check the diameter

360. USING THE SKEW AS A SCRAP-
ING TOOL. This is the simplest
method of using the turning tools, but
is satisfactory only for the most elementary operations.

of the stock with an outside caliper.
Continue to use the large gouge to
rough-turn until the stock is about
⅛ inch over the finished size. The
beginner frequently forces only the
point of the gouge into the work,
thus producing a scraping action.
This practice will dull the cutting
edge of the gouge rapidly.

## Finish turning with a skew

The skew is a more difficult tool
to handle. Fig. 360. The cutting
edge is tapered, the uppermost point
being called the toe and the lower
point the heel. Grasp the tool, holding it firmly against the tool rest
with the cutting edge well above
and beyond the work. Then slowly
draw the skew back, turning it at a
slight angle until the center of the
cutting edge comes in contact with
the wood. Fig. 361. Lift the handle
slightly and force the cutting edge
into the wood. Work from the cen-

ter toward the live and dead centers,
taking a shearing cut. Never attempt to start at the ends of the
stock to do the cutting. Make sure
that the toe does not catch in the
revolving stock, since this could
easily throw the tool out of your
hands. A little practice will indicate when you are getting a desirable cut. If the skew is properly
sharpened, the surface will be so
smooth and true that it will need no
sanding.

## Squaring off the ends

When the stock is turned to the
proper diameter, use a pencil and
rule to lay out the length needed.
Force a parting tool into the revolving wood about ⅛ inch from the
measured length. Fig. 362. Make
the groove slightly wider than the
width of the tool so that the cutting
edge will not burn as it is forced
into the wood. Reduce the stock

361. USING THE SKEW AS A CUT-
TING TOOL.

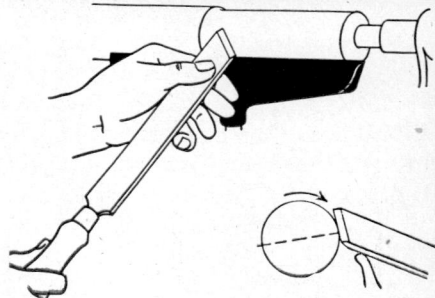

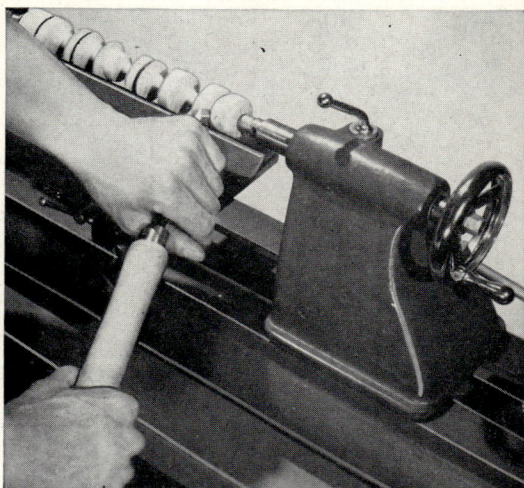

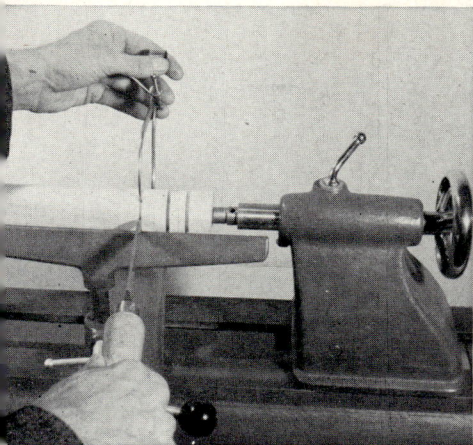

362. USING A PARTING TOOL. The parting tool is held with the narrow edge against the rest and is being forced into the wood. At the same time, the diameter is being checked with an outside caliper. In using the caliper on revolving stock, be careful not to apply any pressure, as this will cause it to spring over the stock.

363. USING A SMALL SKEW TO SQUARE OFF THE END OF STOCK. The toe of the skew is doing the cutting, with the bevel or ground edge parallel to the end of the stock. This is accomplished by tipping the handle to the right.

364. USING THE SKEW TO MAKE THE HORIZONTAL CUT OF A SHOULDER. The heel of the skew is doing most of the cutting.

at this point to a diameter of about ⅜ inch. Use a small skew to finish off the end. Hold it with the toe edge against the tool rest. Turn the handle until the bevel or ground edge of the tool is parallel with the surface to be cut. Fig. 363. Use the toe of the tool to do the cutting and remove about 1/32 inch with each cut. As the cut becomes deeper, it will be necessary to secure clearance for the tool. This can be done by turning the handle away from the cuts being made and then making some tapered cuts to form a half V.

## Cutting a shoulder

The procedure for cutting a shoulder is similar to that for squaring off the end. First use a parting tool to cut a groove, reducing the diameter at this point to slightly more than the smaller size. Then,

365. FORMING A SHOULDER BY THE SCRAPING METHOD.

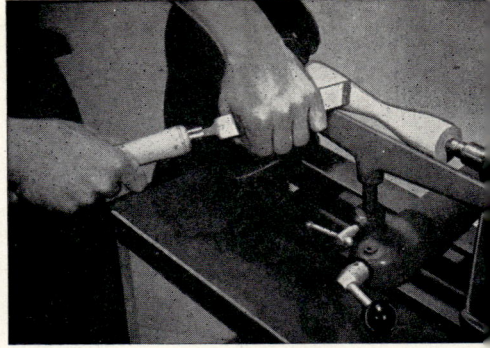

366. CUTTING A TAPERED SURFACE. Here the taper has been roughed out with a gouge and the skew used to finish the tapered surface. The cutting should be done from the large diameter to the small diameter.

367. CUTTING V's. The V is being cut with the heel of the skew. The tool is forced into the stock at the angle of the V.

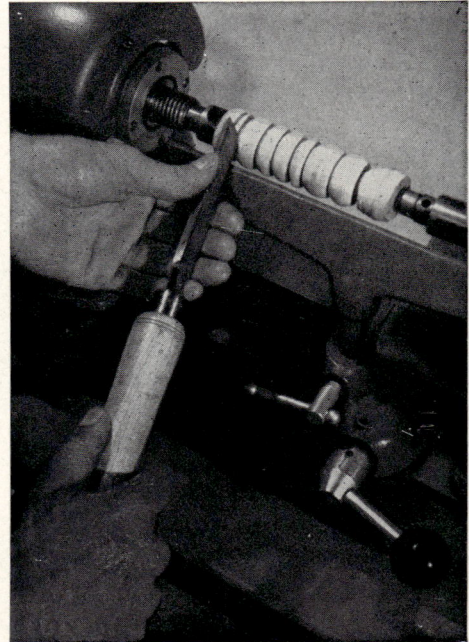

with a small gouge, remove most of the stock from the smaller diameter. Cut the vertical part of the shoulder, using the toe of the skew. Cut the horizontal part of the shoulder with the heel of the skew in a manner similar to finish turning. Fig. 364. It is possible to form a shoulder or square an end by the scraping method, but this is not so satisfactory. Fig. 365.

## Cutting a tapered surface

Turn the stock to the largest diameter. Then use a parting tool to mark the smallest diameter. Make several grooves each of lesser depths as guides for the turning. Rough out the taper with a gouge. Then finish-turn the taper with a skew, using the heel to do most of the cutting. Fig. 366.

## Cutting V's

Use a small skew to do the cutting. Force the heel into the stock a small amount and then work in at an angle as shown in Fig. 367 to cut

368. CUTTING BEADS. Here again the skew is being used. The cut is started with the tool held fairly high and, as the bead is formed, the tool is drawn back and turned simultaneously.

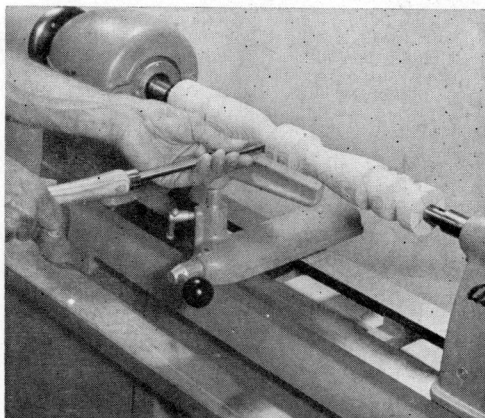

369. USING A SMALL GOUGE TO TURN A CONCAVE SURFACE. The tool should be rolled to form the desired curvature.

one side of the V. Continue to cut one side of the V to the correct depth and then turn the skew in the opposite direction to finish the V.

## Cutting beads

Cutting accurate beads is a rather difficult operation. With the toe of a small skew, mark the point at which the beads are to join. Continue to cut a V shape in the stock with the toe of the skew. Now turn the skew around and use the heel to cut the bead. Hold the tool high on the stock to start the bead and then slowly draw the handle back, at the same time turning the cutting edge to form the arc. Fig. 368. Repeat in the opposite way to form the other half of the bead.

## Turning concave surfaces

Concave surfaces can be turned either by scraping with a round-nosed tool or by cutting with a small gouge. The simplest way is to force a round-nose tool into the wood and work the handle back and forth to form the concave surface. If a small gouge is used, tip it on edge and begin the concave cut by rolling the gouge as pressure is applied. Continue to take shearing cuts, first from one side then the other, until the desired concave surface is formed. Fig. 369.

## Turning convex designs

Most pieces that need to be turned are combinations of straight turning, beads, V's, and long concave or convex surfaces. The usual procedure is to turn the stock to the largest diameter to be finished, then, with a parting tool, mark points along the stock where material is to be removed. In many cases, the parting tool is used at intermittent points to show where stock is to be removed and to what depth. Then the gouge, skew, and round-nosed tool are used to form the design. If necessary, a file and sandpaper may be used to smooth the surface.

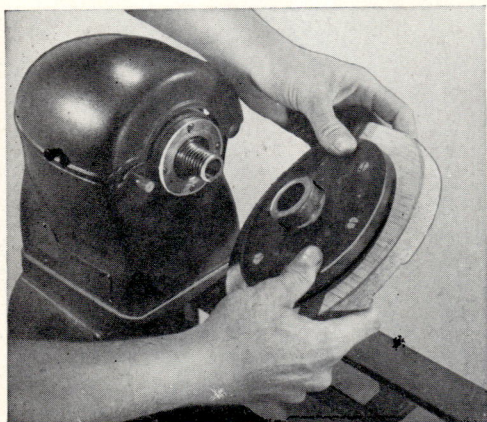

370. FASTENING STOCK TO THE HEADSTOCK SPINDLE. The work has been fastened to the faceplate with short wood screws. The faceplate is being attached to the headstock spindle.

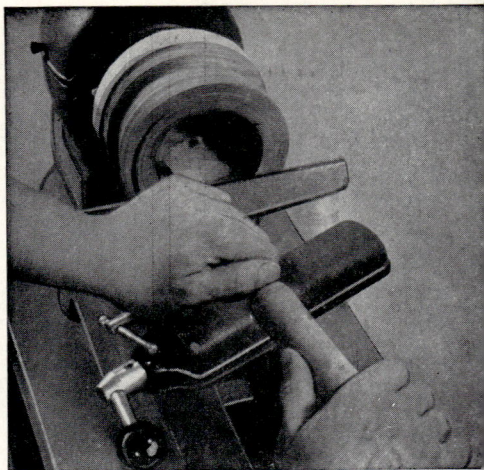

372. TURNING A TRINKET BOX WITH A SMALL GOUGE doing the internal work. The box has been glued to a piece of scrap stock and that piece then attached to the faceplate with short screws.

371. TURNING A JEWEL BOX, using a roundnosed tool to do the scraping.

## Turning on a faceplate

To turn many articles, such as small bowls, the stock must be fastened on the faceplate. Stock of the proper thickness is cut out on the band or scroll saw to a large enough circle to complete the project. Attach the wood to the faceplate with short wood screws. Fig. 370. Remove the live center and fasten the faceplate on the headstock spindle. Set the lathe to low speed and dress the outside edge of the stock with the gouge or skew to true it up. Then use a small gouge or round-nosed tool to do the forming as shown in Fig. 371. If the back of the stock will be damaged unduly from the screws, a piece of scrap stock can be glued to the wood to be turned with a piece of paper between them. Fig. 372. Then, after the turning has taken place, this scrap stock can be split apart from the finished project. To do turning in which both surfaces must be formed, a wood chuck, Fig. 373, is used to hold the stock while it is being turned.

# Can You Answer These Questions on the Wood Lathe?

1. Describe a wood lathe and name its parts.

2. What are the tools needed for wood turning?

3. Describe the two methods of turning.

4. What are the two methods of fastening a live center to the stock?

5. What is the largest size stock that can be turned from a square without first trimming the corners?

6. Cup centers need what lubricants?

7. What is the relation between the diameter of the stock and the speed of the lathe?

8. What tool is selected for rough turning?

9. Holding a gouge can be done in two ways. What are these?

10. How can the cutting action of a gouge be controlled?

11. What makes the skew a difficult tool to use?

12. What is the major danger involved in using the skew?

13. Tell how you can square off the ends of stock in the lathe.

14. What tools are used for cutting a shoulder?

15. When a tapered surface is to be produced, what part of the skew should do most of the cutting?

16. Cutting V's is done with what tool?

17. What kind of work is turned on a faceplate?

373. TURNING A SHALLOW TRAY with the piece held in a wood chuck. Whenever it is necessary to turn both the front and back of a piece, make a chuck to hold the stock for turning the second side.

18. Is it good practice to use a file and sandpaper on the lathe? Explain.

# Section XII

# Woods and Wood Products

## TREES AND LUMBER

SINCE WOODS are the raw material of woodworking, it might be well to learn a little about their structure, names of their parts, classification, and identification.

### How a tree grows

The tree is one of the most interesting of Nature's plant life. As you will see in Fig. 374, the basic structure consists of long, narrow tubes or cells. These narrow tubes, which are about as fine as human hairs, are lined with still finer, spiral-wound strands of cellulose. The tubes themselves are held together with a substance called lignin. These tubes provide the passageway for water and other growth-giving materials from the earth into the tree. During the spring and early summer, when there is much moisture, the tree grows rapidly, while in the summer and fall the tree develops much slower. If you look at the cross section of a tree, you will observe the dark or summer rings, called annular rings. Fig. 375. Some idea of the age of the tree can be obtained by counting these rings.

### Parts of a tree

Fig. 376 shows a cross section of a tree trunk. Beginning at the center is a porous material called the pith. This sometimes becomes rotten, leaving a hollow center in the tree. Around the pith is the mature wood or the heartwood. This is generally darker in color because of

374. AN ENLARGED VIEW OF WOOD, SHOWING THE TUBE STRUCTURE. Here you can see why it is easier to cut with the grain than across it.

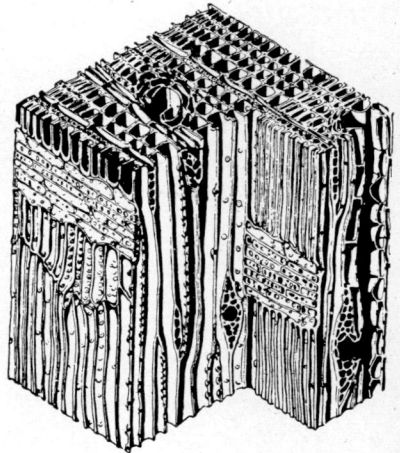

the presence of resin and other materials during the many years of growth. Beyond the outside of the heartwood is the newer growth of sapwood which is usually lighter in color. Between the sapwood and the inner bark is a pitchlike material called cambium in which the cell formation takes place to form more sapwood. Radiating out from the center of the tree are pith rays or medullar rays. These are cell-like structures that form passageways for food in feeding the tree for growth and development.

## Hard and soft woods

There are several ways of classifying woods into hard and soft. One of the most common is to divide all trees into those that shed their leaves annually, such as oak, walnut, maple, ash, basswood, birch, cherry, gumwood, etc., called hardwood (deciduous) trees and those

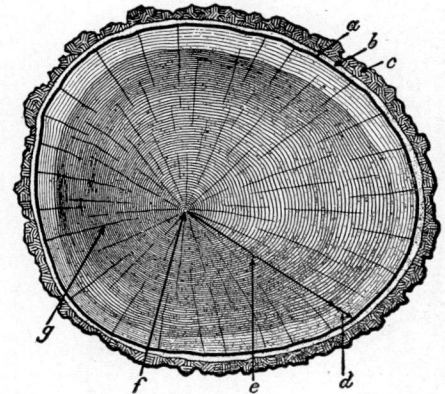

376. CROSS-SECTION OF A TREE TRUNK, SHOWING: a, cambium, b, phloem, c, bark, d, sapwood, e, heartwood, f, pith, g, wood ray.

375. A SECTION OF A LOG SHOWING THE ANNULAR RINGS.

that are evergreen or produce cones (conifers) such as fir, pine, cedar, cypress, and spruce, which are called "softwoods." However, in this method of classification, many of the so-called softwoods are harder than some of the hardwoods.

For purposes of use, woods are classified according to their actual hardness or ability to resist wear, and this method, which is most practical for the woodworker to follow, would reveal the following classifications:

| Hard | Med. Hard | Soft |
|---|---|---|
| Oak | Gum | Cedar |
| Maple | Butternut | White Pine |
| Yellow Pine | Chestnut | Spruce |
| Birch | Walnut | Beech |
| Georgia Pine | Mahogany | Cypress |
| Elm | | Poplar |
| Ash | | Bass |
| Southern Pine | | Fir |
| Rosewood | | Redwood |
| | | Sycamore |

Another important method of classification, especially for the woodworker and wood finisher, is based on whether or not the wood has open or closed grain. The wood finisher especially is concerned with this problem because the open-grained woods provide greater opportunity for finishes and contrasting filler colors.

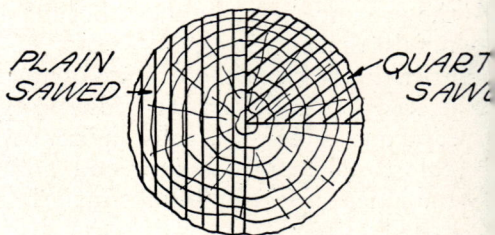

377. THE TWO METHODS OF CUTTING LUMBER longitudinally — plain-sawed and quarter-sawed.

| Open-Grained | Closed-Grained | |
|---|---|---|
| Mahogany | Birch | Poplar |
| Oak | Redwood | Fir |
| Ash | White Pine | Spruce |
| Walnut | Yellow Pine | Maple |
| Elm | Cypress | Bass |
| Butternut | Holly | Georgia Pine |
| Chestnut | Gum | Cherry |
| Rosewood | Beech | Cedar |
| | Southern Pine | Sycamore |

## Methods of cutting trees

There are two common ways of cutting trees longitudinally, the one

method called plain-sawed or flat grained and the other called quarter-sawed. Most lumber that is used for ordinary work is plain-sawed, but some lumber, especially oak, is quarter-sawed to reveal the flake-like substance of the rays. In quarter-sawing, the wood is cut as shown in Fig. 377, or parallel to the medullar rays. Wood is quarter-sawed also to prevent warpage and to provide a better wearing surface.

## Can You Answer These Questions on Trees and Lumber?

1. Name the substance that holds the tubes or cells of a tree together.
2. At what time does most of the growth take place in trees?
3. How can you determine the age of a tree?
4. Name the parts of a tree.

5. What are the three classifications of wood.
6. Which of the following woods are hardwoods: oak, maple, white pine, fir, poplar, ash, hickory?
7. What is the advantage of quarter sawing lumber?

## THE STORY OF LUMBERING

Lumbering has always been one of the most fascinating and romantic of all occupations. It has been glorified in song and story in our history as no other occupation has

been. While some of the practices of lumbering have not changed in the last 100 years, most of lumbering has become mechanized and modernized into a highly efficient process. The actual methods of lumbering vary with the geogra-

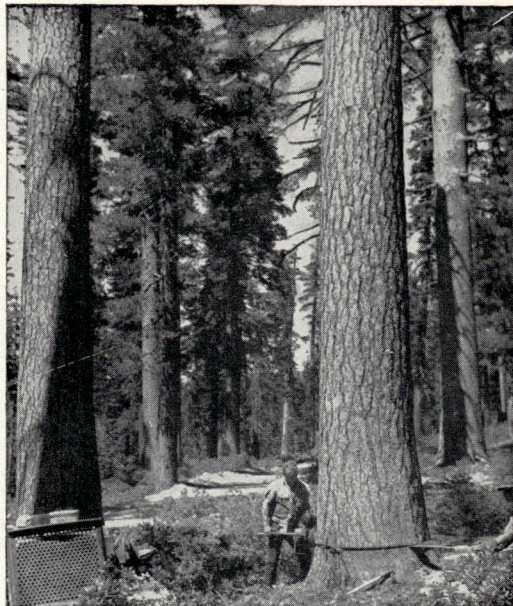

378. CUTTING A NOTCH IN A LARGE PINE TREE. A team of fallers are undercutting a pine tree. Note the X mark on the tree, which indicates that it has been selected for cutting. By cutting a notch in the tree, it will fall within inches of its planned position. The cutting begins on the opposite side from the notch.

379. THE MODERN METHOD OF FELLING TIMBER, USING A POWER SAW. A wedge is driven into the saw kerf to direct the fall of the tree.

phic location and the size of the company, but generally speaking the procedure includes cutting the trees, transporting them to the mill, cutting the logs into lumber, and then seasoning the lumber.

## Cutting trees

The first step is to locate and lay out the site for the logging camp. After this, the necessary roads and camps are built to provide working and living facilities for the men. The mature trees are marked for cutting. The first step

in cutting the trees is to cut a notch in the side of the tree toward which the tree is to fall. Fig. 378. Then, with a hand crosscut saw or, with more modern methods, a power saw, the tree is cut from the opposite side of the notch. Fig. 379. As the cut is made, a wedge is driven into the saw kerf to force the tree to fall in the proper direction. After the tree is felled, the small branches are trimmed off. The logs are then dragged or pushed to a loading site where they are stacked. Fig. 380.

## Transporting the logs to the mill

In years past, logs were moved to the nearest river or stream, accumulated there during the winter,

**380. HAULING LOGS TO A LOADING SITE.** Here the logs are being dragged by a Caterpillar to a truck or train landing where they will be loaded and hauled to the mill.

**381. LOADING LOGS ON A RAILROAD CAR.** This shows the method by which logs are handled in loading them on large trucks or on railroad flat cars.

and in the spring, as the water rose, the logs were floated down the river to the mill. While this still continues in some places, it is not nearly so common. Today, most of the lumber is loaded on trucks or railroad flatcars by means of a crane and taken directly to the mill. Fig. 381. At the mill, they are placed in a millpond to prevent them from drying out before cutting. Fig. 382.

## Cutting the logs

From the millpond, the logs are carried up to the mill on a conveyor. As they rise to the mill, they are sprayed with water to clean off the dirt. Inside the mill, a log is loaded on a conveyor or carriage which holds it as it is being cut. Today the log is sawed into timbers, planks, and boards by means of large band saws, many of which have cutting edges on both edges of the blade so that the log is cut com-

**382. UNLOADING LOGS INTO THE MILLPOND.** Here the trucks are unloaded and the logs splash. See on the left the log entering the sawmill on the conveyor.

**383. CUTTING THE LOGS INTO PLANKS.** The large band saw is cutting the logs into green lumber, the first step in the actual manufacture of lumber. Notice the huge band saw that is doing the cutting.

**384. STACKING LUMBER FOR AIR DRYING.** Here the lumber is stacked with spacers between to permit the air to circulate freely on all four sides. The tops of these stacks will be covered to protect the lumber.

ing and going. Fig. 383. In some mills, gang saws or multiple band saws are used, which speeds the cutting.

After the log is cut to proper size, it is carried by conveyors to other saws that trim the bark off the edges and cut the stock into standard sizes. All soft lumber is cut into standard dimensions in thickness, width, and length, but hardwoods are cut in standard thickness only, since they are much more expensive and too much waste would result otherwise. Then, too, the very nature of the use of hardwoods does not require standard lengths.

## Seasoning the lumber

After cutting, lumber is sorted and graded as to its size and quality, then stacked in uniform piles with small blocks between each piece to permit air to circulate around the wood. Since wood that comes from the mill is green and contains a great deal of moisture, it is necessary to dry out or season lumber before it is fit for use.

There are two common methods of doing this. The first, called *air drying*, is to leave the stacks of lumber out in the open in sheds where it can dry naturally over a period of several months. Much of our soft lumber is air-dried.

A more efficient way of controlling the moisture content of lumber is to dry the lumber artificially in a controlled moisture-temperature room called a kiln. In this procedure, woods are allowed to dry for several months, then are placed in a building made usually of cement brick or hollow tile where the stacks are first sprayed with steam, then the steam turned off, the building closed, and warm air circulated through the lumber. This is continued during a period of from two to eight weeks until the moisture content of the lumber is down to 6 to 12 per cent. Kiln-dried lumber is the only satisfactory lumber to use in furniture making and for all types of better construction.

## Can You Answer These Questions on the Story of Lumbering?

1. Name the many ways in which lumbering has become mechanized.

2. What is the first step in cutting trees?

3. Why is a notch cut in the tree on the side toward which it is to fall?

4. Are most of the logs moved to the mill by floating them downstream?

5. Why are logs kept in a millpond for a time?

6. Describe the sawing of logs into planks, timbers, and boards.

7. Why is soft lumber cut into standard dimensions?

8. What are the two common methods of drying lumber? Which kind is better for furniture wood?

### PRODUCTS OF OUR AMERICAN FORESTS

The forests of our country provide a storehouse of wealth for our use. Woods and lumbers and their by-products are such an important part of our life that it is impractical to list here all of the uses to which they are put. Fig. 385. There are at least 4,500 specific uses for wood and wood products: from the lowly toothpick to the thousands of telephone and telegraph poles, from the woods used in novelties and trinkets to the woods used in home and industrial construction, and from the

385. ALL THESE ARTICLES ARE MADE FROM WOOD. They include paper, laminated wood, impregnated wood, plastics, and just plain wood. It is hard to believe that so many different items are all products of American forests.

by-products that make paper to those that are used for making rayon, plastics, and other chemical materials.

## Saw logs

Each year, well over 30 billion board feet of lumber are needed for construction and industrial use, not to mention the uncounted amounts of unsawed wood and fuel wood used. The main use of construction lumber is, of course, in the building of homes, public buildings, commercial buildings, and other large frame structures. Each year $3\frac{1}{2}$ million poles are purchased by telephone and utility companies. Our railroads make use of about 50-million railroad ties a year and our farmers 400 to 600 million fence posts.

Most hardwoods go into industrial lumber and are used primarily for furniture making and vehicle construction such as boats and trucks, for machinery and equipment, and for such manufactured products as amusement devices, athletic equipment, and children's toys.

## Veneers and Plywood

*Veneer* is a very thin sheet of wood that is sawed, peeled or sliced from a log. Several sheets of veneer may be glued (laminated) to lumber, to make *lumber-core plywood* or they may be bonded to other sheets of veneer to make *veneer-core plywood*. Veneer plywood is built-up veneer sheets with the

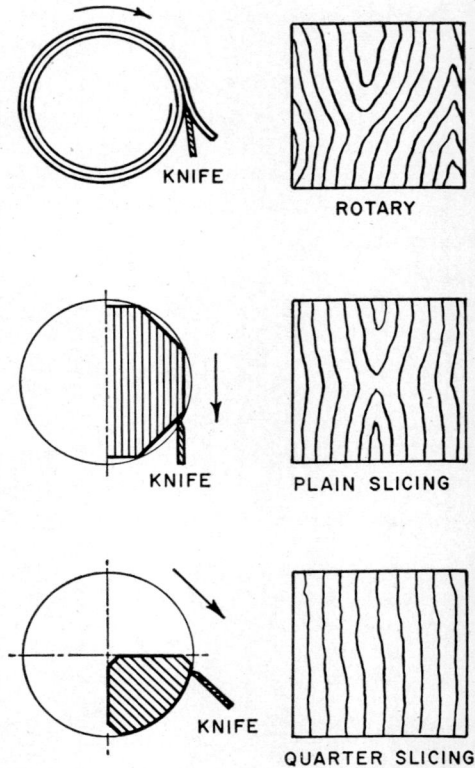

386. THE THREE WAYS OF CUTTING VENEER: rotary, plain or flat and quarter.

grain of adjacent sheets (or plies) running at right angles to the sheets above and below. This change in direction gives relatively thin plywood great strength and rigidity. Veneer is cut on giant lathes or on slicers in three ways: *rotary cut, flat sliced,* or *quarter sliced.* Fig. 386. Fir plywood is rotary cut. The veneer logs are cut into blocks 8, 10, or 12 feet long after the bark is removed. These veneer logs are placed in gigantic lathes which turn them against a razor-sharp knife.

The thin, continuous sheet of wood that is peeled off the log looks very much like thick wrapping paper being peeled off a roll. The veneer is cut to specific widths, eliminating any defects. It is then sorted as to grade. These sheets of green veneer are put through driers that remove much of the moisture content. Glue is applied to the veneer and the sheets are stacked with the grain of each at right angles to the sheet above and below it. The glued sheets are placed in huge hydraulic presses where the glue is set under

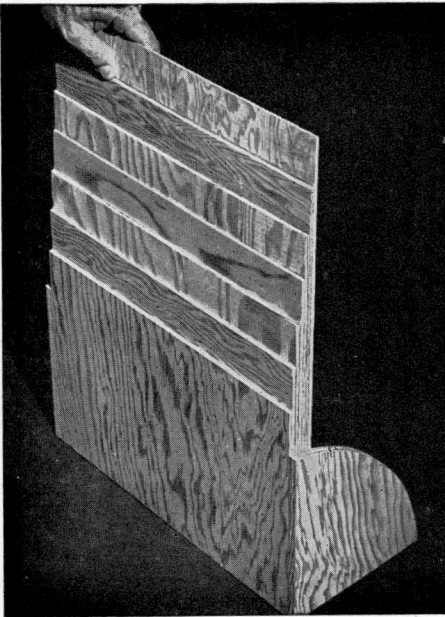

388. GLUING UP PLYWOOD. The veneer has been coated with glue and arranged with the grain of each ply at right angles to the one above and below it. They are then placed in a hot press, in which the combination of heat and pressure welds the plies together.

387. PLYWOOD CONSTRUCTION. A piece of 1-inch, 7-ply wood is cut away to show the direction in the grain of the alternate pieces. Plywood, pound for pound, is stronger than steel.

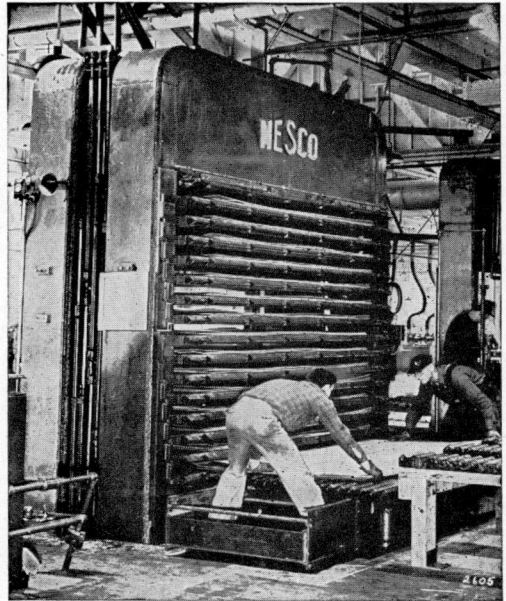

heat and pressure. Fig. 388. When dry, the panels are sanded to specified thickness and cut to certain lengths and widths.

*Plywood* is usually made in an odd number of plies (layers), such as 3-ply, 5-ply, or 7-ply. Fig. 387. Plywood is held together with either moisture-resistant glue or moisture-proof glue. The former is used on interior plywoods; the latter is for exterior use. Plywood provides great strength and, at the same

389. THIS LAMP BASE IS MADE FROM PLYWOOD. The surface has been striated.

time, surprising lightness. In addition to the soft and hard plywoods, there are many specialty types. These include those with special or decorative surfaces. The face of plywood may have a striated surface to give it a combed look. Figs. 389-390. Others have a brushed face to accent the grain. Another has a sandblasted surface. Plywoods are also available in many special grades for specific purposes. There is a cabinet-grade plywood designed especially for making the doors of kitchen cabinets and built-ins. See page 26.

390. THIS DESK IS MADE FROM "WELDTEX" PLYWOOD. The grooved surface gives it an unusual texture.

## Wood chemistry

While the commercial uses of wood in which chemistry is involved are not of direct concern to the woodworker, it is important to have an appreciation of woods in this respect. Much of the paper made is a product of wood pulp. Each year about 15 ½ million cords of pulpwood are made into paper and paperboard. A more recent development in the use of pulpwood flour and sawdust is that which has gone into the making of cellulose products such as rayon cloth, plastics, dyes, paints, explosives, linoleum, turpentine, and resins. Wood is also a source of sugar, alcohol, and feed for cattle. With many new chemical developments, wood provides the raw material that is being developed into thousands of commercial products.

## Miscellaneous uses

In addition to all of the previous uses, many of the by-products of wood that in years gone by were considered waste materials have become valuable wood products. Sawdust is used, for example, for insulation, for packing, and other commercial uses. The bark is made into flavorings, drugs, and chemicals. The roots are made into oils, tea, and as wood for making smoking pipes and trinkets. Pine needles and "Spanish" moss, the latter a parasite growing on trees in the South, are very good as upholstery padding.

## Can You Answer These Questions on Products of Our American Forests?

1. Make a list of the uses of wood and wood products. There are hundreds, of course, but name as many as you can, using your study of other subjects to help you.
2. How many board feet of lumber are needed annually for construction and industrial use?
3. Which needs the most lumber, the railroad or the telephone and utility companies?
4. What is veneer? Describe and tell how it is used.
5. What advantage has plywood over solid wood?

6. How is the grade of plywoods indicated?
7. Name the common sizes of plywood as to thickness, width, and length.
8. What kind of plywood has a grain-like surface?
9. Boat construction requires what kind of plywood?
10. From what is most of our newspaper "newsprint" made?
11. List some of the products of wood chemistry.
12. What by-products of wood are common today?

## OPPORTUNITIES IN WOODWORKING

While many products that in years past were made of wood are now being produced of metal, plastics, and synthetic materials, wood and wood products are still the source of employment for over one million individuals. Indirectly, over two million in the United States alone depend for their livelihood on the products of the American forests. Over 20,000 concerns produce lumber and lumber products and make up the fifth largest manufacturing industry. There are many and varied opportunities for anyone interested in this field. The jobs or occupations range from the professional types, such as the research worker or furniture designer who

must have years of training, to routine factory workmen. The opportunities in woodworking closely parallel the flow of lumber and lumber products, as follows:
1. Many men work in and around sawmills where the logs are converted into rough lumber.
2. Others are employed in the processes of grading and seasoning lumber.
3. Still other thousands earn a living moving the lumber from forest to mill and from mill to factory.
4. At the factory there are many machine operators who use all types of woodworking machines, such as the planer, jointer, circular saw, tenoner, dovetailer, and many other machines.
5. There are many jobs in as-

sembling and finishing products in furniture factories and manufacturing concerns, such as sash-and-door and box companies.

6. There are many others who do maintenance work around woodworking machines, such as saw filing and other repair jobs.

7. A more select group of individuals earn a living on the craft level of woodworking. These will be discussed a little more completely, because your background in the woodworking shop will give you a good start in the craft occupations.

8. Of utmost importance to the field of woodworking are the thousands of people who earn a good living teaching woodworking in industrial arts programs, in vocational education apprentice training, and in other educational areas. Of the over 30,000 industrial arts teachers alone, a large majority teach woodworking either as a fulltime subject or as part of a general shop. Industrial teaching as a career offers the added opportunity of being largely a man's occupation and is therefore not so competitive as some other types of teaching.

Those who teach in other areas of industrial arts and vocational education have urgent need for a thorough knowledge of woodworking. Some idea of the popularity of woodworking both as a school subject and as a later-years activity for laymen is indicated by the fact that woodworking is the second most popular creative hobby in the United States. Most of the adults who enjoy this hobby learned the fundamentals in the school shop under some industrial arts instructor.

## The craft occupations

For you who have a real interest in woodworking, the craft careers are the ones that provide a real future. These include the cabinetmaker, the carpenter, furniture finisher, patternmaker, wood carver, boat builder, aircraft woodworker, ship carpenter, wood lather, and millman. Each of these jobs requires trade school training and/or an apprenticeship. The individual entering any of these must be skilled in the use of all hand tools and common woodworking machines. In addition, one must possess special talents that fit him for the particular kind of work.

The cabinetmaker, for example, must be qualified to make fine furniture and to do fine interior work. The carpenter must have a knowledge of commercial and home construction and be able to read all types of architectural drawings. The patternmaker must know and understand foundry work and how castings are made, and be able to use special tools. The wood carver must have special talents in design and must be skilled in doing detailed work. The boat builder and aircraft worker must understand the special problems in those kinds of transportation and be able to use the different woods and methods of construction needed in the solution of these problems. The millman must have a thorough knowledge of the construction and operation of all woodworking machines and must be able to check the correct setups.

In considering a job in woodworking, you must realize that many of these jobs require that you work in somewhat noisy and dusty surroundings or, at times, exposed to the elements. There is also some danger of accidents to the hands and fingers. On the other hand, all of the craft jobs provide worth-while satisfaction to the individual as well as an opportunity to construct and build. An expert in any of the craft occupations will earn a good living, and he is doing a real man's job.

There is also an opportunity for advancement in the woodworking field. The carpenter, for example, can work toward becoming a contractor or the patternmaker to becoming a foreman or supervisor.

For anyone interested in a particular woodworking occupation, details as to what training you will need, how you can get experience, what you will earn, and what promotions are in prospect, can be secured from: "Job Descriptions for the Lumber and Lumber Products Industries," a bulletin published by the United States Department of Labor, Washington, D. C.

## WOODS: KINDS, QUALITIES, AND USES

Here is a brief description of some of the woods that you will commonly use. The selection of the wood for each project should be made with care. Each kind of wood has its own peculiar color, working qualities, and properties. If you become particularly interested in one furniture wood, you can find many books and government bulletins devoted entirely to that kind of wood. There are also national associations that will supply all the information an individual desires concerning a particular kind of wood. Some of these associations are: American Walnut Manufacturer's Association, Mahogany Association, Western Pine Association, National Oak Flooring Manufacturer's Association.

The U. S. Forest Products Laboratory at Madison, Wisconsin, will supply technical and scientific information about wood and wood products.

## Ash

The three most common types of ash are white, green, and black. White ash is very common in furniture construction; it has a wide use in sports equipment such as skis, baseball bats, and toboggans. It is well suited to these uses because of its strength and hardness but par-

ticularly because it holds its shape well after it has been formed.

## Basswood

Softest of commercial hardwoods, basswood is white with a few black streaks, fuzzy because of long fibers, fairly strong for bending, nonwarping, with little or no grain marking. Basswood is the best wood for drawing boards, for small moldings, for burned designs, and for thin lumber for jigsaw work. It is not durable for outside uses. It makes a very strong glue joint and is easy to plane or sand but does not scrape well because of its long fibers and yielding surface. It is usually painted but may be stained to imitate other woods.

## Birch

Birch is a hardwood of fine texture and close grain, coming primarily from the north central states and Canada. Yellow birch is the most common.

Curly birch is found only in occasional trees, the result of a rare grain development. It has a delicate, wavy figure and is sought for fine furniture and panels. It is difficult to work and must be finished by scraping. The heartwood is red in color and the sapwood is white and therefore a single board may be either red or white or red with white edges. It is a good wood for table tops, doors, rails, and any furniture parts which require extra

strength. Birch will take practically any desired color of stain and is one of the finest woods for enamel finishes. It is sometimes finished to resemble mahogany, walnut, or maple.

## Red cedar

There are many kinds of cedar that vary in color from white to deep red. The red cedar most commonly used for making chests and lining drawers and closets comes from Tennessee. Cedar is a softwood with a very distinctive odor. It is one of the simplest woods to identify. Because of its odor, which makes it moth-repellent, it is a good liner for closets in which woolens are stored.

## Cherry

Black cherry, which is found generally in most parts of the United States, is not abundant enough to be a common furniture wood, even though it is a very desirable wood for that purpose. The heartwood is a reddish brown in color, while the sapwood is white. Cherry resembles unfinished mahogany. It is a very durable wood, does not dent easily, and warps very little. There are many heirlooms of genuine cherry, indicating that it was more common many years ago. Cherry darkens with age. It is best finished with shellac or lacquer and because of this has a natural suitability to modern as well as period furniture.

## Cypress

Red cypress, which comes from Louisiana swamps, is softer grained, darker colored, and more durable than the upland or yellow cypress. For boats, lawn furniture, and outdoor use, it has always been durable and popular. The grain is rather hard, making the wood splinter easily.

## Gumwood

Gumwood is a native of the deltas of the rivers throughout the south. Because of its tendency to warp in seasoning, gumwood was not commonly used for many years as a distinctive commercial wood. Only recently has it become popular. Previously, when it was used at all, it was finished to imitate some other type of wood. At the present time, it is recognized as a wood of great beauty and a wide range of usefulness. The heartwood, which is called red gum, ranges from a light to a deep reddish brown. The sapwood is light colored and is referred to as a sap gum. While gumwood is considered by its producers a hardwood, it really is a medium hardwood, not so hard as maple and harder than many pines.

Fine furniture and trim are made from gumwood. It is one of our most decorative woods. One of its unusual features is that no two long boards produce the same figure in the wood. The wood is close grained and has a very fine texture. Gumwood is either plain-sawed, quarter-sawed, or veneered. Selected gumwood finishes very well in the natural color, but best results are produced when it is given a light brown stain. Where light streaks appear next to the dark, it is good practice to give the light wood a thin preparatory coat, wipe it off, and then give the entire surface a separate coat.

Water stains should always be chosen for gumwood, though these have a tendency to raise the grain. This means that a light sanding is required before the succeeding finishing can be done. The beauty of gumwood is better preserved by a dull treatment than by a gloss or polished finish. Dull lacquer, dull varnish, or hand-rubbed varnish produces the best effect on either interior trim or furniture. Because of its coarse grain, gumwood makes an excellent foundation for an enameled finish.

## Mahogany

Mahogany, a medium hard, open-grained wood, is considered one of the finest furniture woods we have. It is often preferred because of its pleasing figure, its density or weight, its low shrinkage characteristics, and its ease of working. Mahogany comes from many countries and is frequently identified by the name of the country—for example, Honduras Mahogany. The color of mahogany varies from white to light brown. It is a very beautiful wood in its natural state and can be finished either as a darker wood for traditional furniture or bleached for modern pieces.

## Maple

Maple is a hard, tough, strong wood that has good resistance to shock and wears very well. The grain is usually straight and fine in texture. The heartwood of maple is light reddish brown and its sapwood is white. Because of its wear-resisting qualities, maple is ideal for fine flooring. It is found very extensively in Colonial furniture and also in modern design. A white, clear grade of maple, which comes from the sapwood, is especially light. It is the white wood which can be made into furniture and for the finer floors on which natural finish is to be used. The heartwood is brown and makes a good base for a brown, mahogany, or dark stain. Curly maple is the result of a twisted growth and the manner in which the lumber is sawed. Bird's-eye maple is cut from sugar maple trees and the texture is a result probably of thwarted bud growth.

## Oak

Oak has always been one of the most popular cabinet woods. Now and then one or more woods come into vogue for a few years but there is always a sure return to oak. The reason for this is the lasting quali-ties, the durability, permanence, and the appearance of strength and solidity that oak possesses. Oak is very beautiful in its natural state and this beauty is intensified by a greater variety of finishes that can be applied to it than to any other wood.

It is an international wood, found in many countries, and is the leading hardwood of North America. There are nearly 300 kinds of oak in the United States, but from the woodworker's standpoint there are only two, white and red. White oak has a better color, finer texture, and more prominent figure. It is considered a superior wood for fine furniture. Red oak, however, because of its slightly reddish tinge and because it is coarser in grain, can be used very successfully to secure desired decorative effects.

Oak is cut in two ways, plane-sawed and quarter-sawed. Quarter sawing reveals the distinctive characteristics of oak, the pronounced flakes that result from the medullary ray of the tree formation. Because of its open grain, oak offers a greater opportunity for the use of fillers which contrast with stains than is offered by any other wood.

## White Pine

There are many kinds of white pines, but the ones most commonly selected for work in the woodshop are the northern white, ponderosa, sugar or California, and western white or Idaho pine. All have the same general characteristics, although they differ slightly in color, texture, hardness, and working qualities. White pine has a soft, uniform texture that makes it an ideal building material. The sapwood is white and the heartwood ranges from cream to light reddish brown. White pine is used for millwork, building construction, window frames, doors, and interior trim. Pine does not swell or shrink with the change in moisture, which makes it ideal for patterns. It is the equal of any wood and superior to most of them as a foundation for paint or enamel finishes. White pine is not a desirable wood for most stain finishes, although selected boards having markings more pronounced than average can be stained with light mahogany or light brown stains.

## Yellow Poplar

Poplar is a durable, soft, medium strong hardwood. It is one of the largest native trees supplying lumber. The sapwood, which is frequently several inches thick, is white, while the heartwood is yellowish brown with a green tinge. The wood is moderately light in weight, straight grained, uniform in texture, easy to nail because it does not split readily, easy to glue, stays in place well, holds paint and enamels well, is easily worked, and finishes smoothly. Because of all these qualities, it is very satisfactory for inexpensive furniture that is to be painted and enameled. It is also a very suitable wood for beginners to choose.

## Walnut

Walnut, a medium hardwood that is one of the most beautiful native woods, is found in the eastern half of the United States. The heartwood is brown, while the sapwood is nearly white. Walnut is a strong, durable, and stiff wood. It is used chiefly for cabinetwork, furniture, veneers, and gunstocks. The veneer is cut from the best grade walnut and is made into panel stock and plywood. Walnut is excellent for cabinetwork because it works well, glues up very satisfactorily, and takes a good finish. Walnut is usually finished in the natural wood. It is an open-grained wood and requires a filler. Usually the filler is very dark, but at times a lighter filler is applied for constrast. The wood is finished with a high-gloss varnish that is frequently rubbed to a high polish.

## Can You Answer These Questions on Woods: Kinds, Qualities, and Uses?

**1.** Where can you obtain information of a technical and scientific nature about wood and wood products?

**2.** Name the three common types of

ash. What are among the chief uses of ash?

3. Why is basswood a good choice for beginning projects?

4. What is the color range of birch? Why is birch chosen for making bed rails?

5. What is cedar's chief characteristic?

6. Cherry resembles what other kind of wood?

7. Is cherry as common today as it was many years ago? Why?

8. Where does cypress come from?

9. Has gumwood increased or decreased in popularity in recent years? Why?

10. What kind of stain should be put on gumwood?

11. What are the characteristics of mahogany that make it a desirable furniture wood?

12. Would you consider mahogany a rather common wood? What are the chief sources of this wood?

13. Why is maple considered a very desirable material for flooring?

14. What style of furniture is usually made from maple?

15. What is bird's-eye maple?

16. How many kinds of oak are there? Why is oak consistently popular as a cabinet wood?

17. Name the two large classifications of oak. Why is oak quarter-sawed?

18. Name some common types of white pine. What are the principal uses of white pine?

19. Is white pine usually finished by staining? Explain in detail.

20. Yellow poplar is a very good selection for beginning woodworking projects. What are the reasons for this?

21. Give the color range for yellow poplar.

22. Name the chief uses for walnut. Why is walnut so often chosen for gunstocks and other articles that must be formed?

23. Describe the grain of walnut.

## WOODS FOR PROJECTS

| Kind | Color | Working Qualities | Weight | Strength | Lasting Qualities (Outside Use) |
|---|---|---|---|---|---|
| *Hardwoods* | | | | | |
| Basswood | Lt. Cream | Easy | Light | Weak | Poor |
| Birch | Lt. Brown | Hard | Heavy | Strong | Fair |
| Cherry | Dk. Red | Hard | Medium | Strong | Fair |
| Gum (Red) | Red-Brown | Medium | Medium | Medium | Medium |
| *Mahogany (Honduras) | Gold-Brown | Easy | Medium | Medium | Good |
| *Mahogany (Philippine) | Med. Red | Easy | Medium | Medium | Good |
| Maple, hard | Red-Cream | Hard | Heavy | Strong | Poor |
| Maple, soft | Red-Brown | Hard | Medium | Strong | Poor |
| *Oak, red | Flesh-Brown | Hard | Heavy | Strong | Fair |
| *Oak, white | Grey-Brown | Hard | Heavy | Strong | Fair |
| Poplar | Yellow | Easy | Medium | Weak | Fair |
| *Walnut | Dk. Brown | Medium | Heavy | Strong | Good |
| *Softwoods* | | | | | |
| Cedar | Red | Medium | Medium | Medium | Good |
| Fir, Douglas | Orange-Brown | Medium | Medium | Medium | Medium |
| Pine, Ponderosa | Orange to Red-Brown | Easy | Light | Weak | Poor |
| Redwood | Dk. Red-Brown | Easy | Light | Medium | Good |

Woods marked with (*) are open grain woods and require a paste filler.

# Section XIII

# Projects—The Finished Product

## SOME SUGGESTIONS BEFORE BEGINNING YOUR PROJECT

YOUR EXPERIENCES in woodworking and the fun you get out of it depend largely on how much enthusiasm you have and the kind of projects that you decide to make. To make any project and to get the most out of it, you must carefully do four things:

1. Make a good selection.
2. Plan wisely.
3. Construct well.
4. Rate your work.

### Selecting

What should I make? That's the question you will be asking yourself as soon as you get started. Well, what can you use? Do you need a new lamp for your room at home or can your home use a new set of house numbers? Perhaps your dad will have a birthday soon and would be able to use a pipe rack or pants holder. How about a shoeshine box for yourself or for the entire family to use? These are cues to what to select.

Of course, you should start on something that you can complete and that isn't too difficult. It's usually a good idea to select the first project, at least, from a plan that has already been drawn. With this in mind, the projects that appear on the following pages have been grouped so that you can tell about how difficult they are to build. See list, page 252. If this is your first experience in the woodshop, you ought to select a project from Group 1 of the beginning projects and progress from there. Your instructor may also have some ideas for your first project.

Whatever you decide upon, you will find that there is a lot of fun in making such things as the dachsund tie rack or the bird feeder.

### Planning

Ask anyone who builds things and he will tell you to plan well, for in so doing you will save time, eliminate errors, and do a better and more enjoyable job. It is a good idea for anyone in woodworking to make a written plan of procedure or planning sheet in which h tells what tools he is going to use, what materials he will need, and exactly how he is going to proceed to make the project. In addition, it is an excellent idea to make a picture sketch of the article and a working drawing, if one is not available.

The exact way in which you build the project will differ with its size and difficulty, but in general you will proceed about the same and in the approximate order described below.

## Building

If you have looked through the ten sections on hand woodworking in Part I of this book, you will note an order of arrangement. These are in approximately the order in which projects should be built. As you make out your plan of procedure, look over these sections and decide exactly what you must do to make your own project. In general, you will be doing the following:

1. Getting out the stock.
2. Planing the surfaces.
3. Making curved parts.
4. Shaping and forming parts.
5. Cutting holes.
6. Making joints.
7. Assembling with nails, screws, and glue.
8. Finishing.

The larger the project, the more steps there will be to carry out and the more pieces there will be to make. When you qualify to use the machines, many of the steps that you first did with hand tools can be accomplished faster and with greater efficiency. Remember, however, that you must know how to use hand tools before you can expect to go on to machine work.

## Rating

When you have finished your project you should take a few minutes to rate your own work, because in doing this you will improve as you go along. Don't be one of those fellows who say, "I could have done it better, but I was in a hurry."

Some of the things you should ask yourself are:

1. Is the project as good as I expected it to be?
2. What could I have done better?
3. How could I have completed it sooner?
4. What have I learned how to do that I didn't know before?
5. Have I improved in any of the skills I learned before?
6. What have I learned about materials that I have used?
7. How have I become a better and more coöperative worker?
8. Have I applied anything I have learned in other subjects to the making of this project?

# YOUR GUIDE FOR SELECTING THE PROJECT TO MAKE

## Beginning Projects

(All the work can be done by hand. Only the butt joint is used.)

### Group 1
Cutting Board
Note Box
Match-Box Holder
Candelabra
House Numbers
Dachshund Tie Rack
Mailing List Cover

### Group 2
Pants Holder
My Shine Box
Bird Feeder
Flowerpot Holder
Pennsylvania Wall Box

### Group 3
Handy Pen Holder
Elephant Lamp
Storage Hassock
Plant Base
Wastepaper Basket
Pilgrim Footstool
Pilgrim Cradle

## Intermediate Projects

(First use of machines. Use of all types of joints.)

### Group 1
Watch Stand
Treasure Chest

Circular Tie Rack
Pipe Rack
Salt Shaker and Pepper Mill
Courting Mirror
Ring Game
Book Ends

### Group 2
Tile Hot-Dish Holder
Cribbage Board
Pin-Up Board
Weldtex Lamp
Weldtex Flower Holder
Flat Bow
Small Turnings
Knife Box
File Case

### Group 3
Lazy Susan
Shelf-All
Glass Brick Lamp
Hanging Wall Shelf
Book Trough

## Advanced Projects

(For those with experience in woodworking.)

### Group 1
Coffee Table
Jewel Box

### Group 2
Desk
End Table
Breakfast Table
Skis

## Hot Dish Holder

## Candelabra

391. HOT DISH HOLDER. Combines the best in wood and ceramics. The soft appearance of the oak frame makes a pleasing contrast to the bright tile pattern. Makes a good base for hot dishes, but four or six of them grouped on the wall over the mantel or bookcase would add a highly decorative note. Assemble by gluing the frame to the base and then inserting the tile. A square of felt has been glued to the base.

392. CANDELABRA. Combines wood and plastic. The plastic top provides a drip shield and also makes an unusual contrast to the dull wood, both in texture and color. Very simple to make. The wood used here was walnut.

## Lazy Susan

393. LAZY SUSAN. Can be turned on a lathe. Walnut. Finish by rubbing mineral oil in.

394. PLANT BASE. This three-legged plant base is made of walnut and two kinds of metal. Two circles are cut, one of wood and the other of a water-repellent material, and glued together. The legs are fastened to the wood with screws and the metal wrapped around the circle and held with escutcheon pins.

## Plant Base

## CANDELABRA

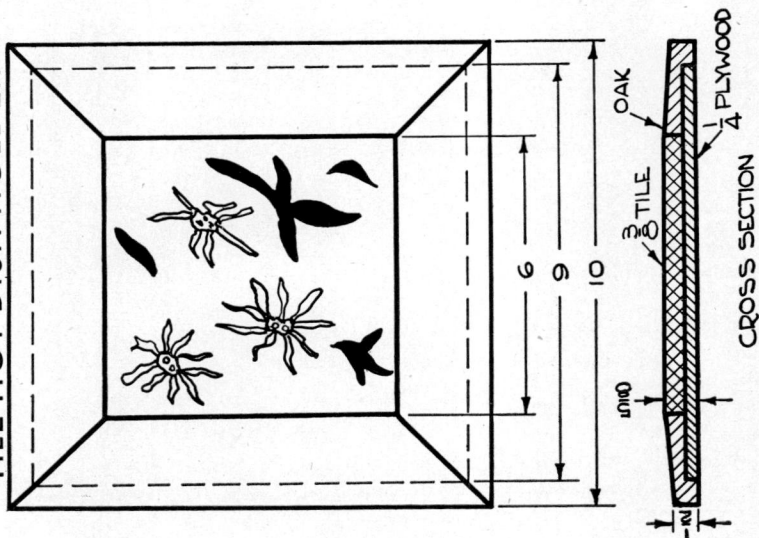

## TILE HOT DISH HOLDER

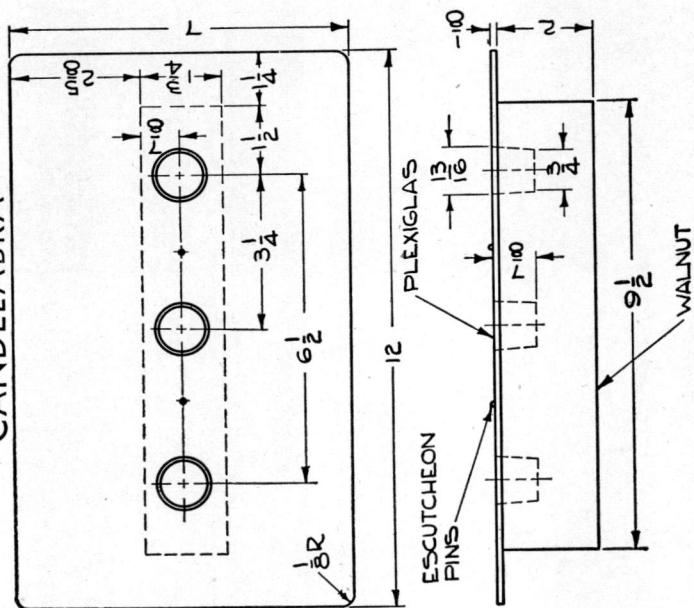

CROSS SECTION

254

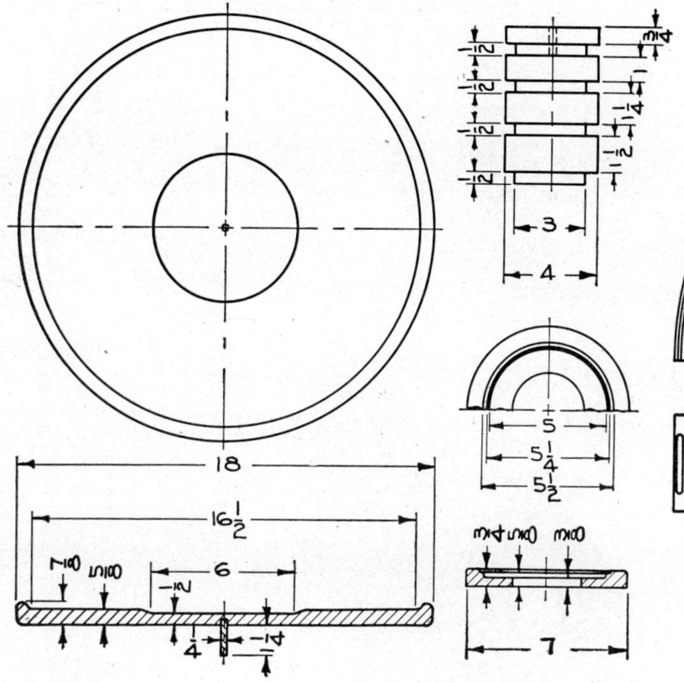

# PLANT BASE

32 EQUALLY
SPACED BRASS
ESCUTCHEON
NAILS

ALUMINUM
COPPER
PRESS BOARD

SOFT
WOOD

$3\frac{3}{4}$ R

$3\frac{1}{4}$ R

THREE EQUALLY
SPACED LEGS

$\frac{3}{4}$ WALNUT
3 - NO. 4 R.H.
SCREWS

$\frac{3}{4}$

$\frac{1}{2}$

$\frac{5}{8}$

1

$\frac{3}{8}$

$\frac{5}{8}$

$\frac{5}{8}$

1

# LAZY SUSAN

$\frac{3}{4}$

1

$\frac{1}{4}$

$1\frac{1}{2}$

$\frac{1}{2}$

$\frac{1}{2}$

$\frac{1}{2}$

$\frac{1}{2}$

3

4

5

$5\frac{1}{4}$

$5\frac{1}{2}$

7

18

$16\frac{1}{2}$

6

$\frac{1}{2}$

$\frac{1}{4}$

$\frac{1}{4}$

255

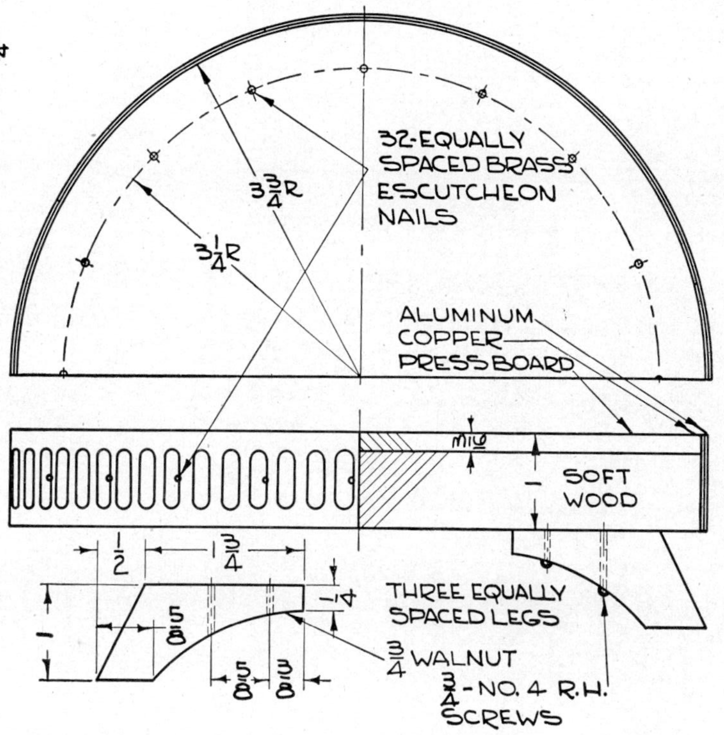

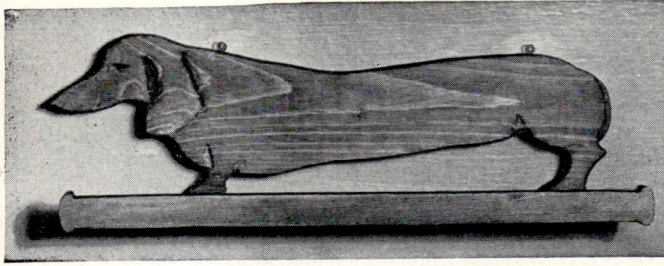

**Dachshund Tie Rack**

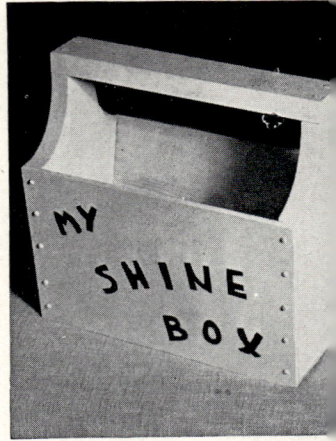

**My Shine Box**

395. DACHSHUND TIE RACK. Here is a project that anyone will like and yet it is very simple to make. It can
be cut out with a coping saw or jig saw and the rack
itself made in the shape of a long bone. To give char-
acter to your dog, you can shape the eyes, ears, and
tail with a gouge, although these marks can be painted
on also. This one was made of pine.

396. MY SHINE BOX. Keeping shoeshining equipment together all in one place is always
a problem unless you have a compact container for the purpose. Then, too, when you
are actually shining your shoes, the handle becomes an excellent footrest. This one
is built of poplar and ⅛-inch fir plywood. It is another good beginner's project. You
and everyone else in the house will enjoy using it.

**Watch Stand**

**Treasure Chest**

397. WATCH STAND. For use as a small clock around the house, this little watch stand
is ideal. The arms and back can be cut out with a coping or jig saw and, if a decorative base is desired, it can be cut on a shaper. This one is made of red cedar, but
almost any wood could be chosen.

398. TREASURE CHEST. A miniature version of the good old pirate chest! The pine
surface is gouged and burned to give it the appearance of age, and the brass trim
is patterned after the Captain's Sea Chest of old. This one, however, is just the right
size for jewelry, trinkets, a boy's marbles or small change.

# DACHSHUND TIE RACK

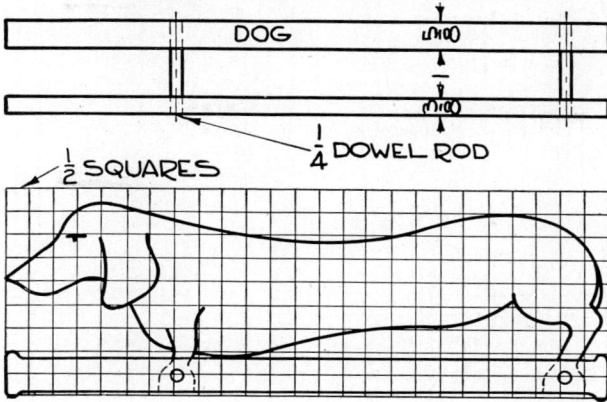

DOG

1 3/8

2 3/8

1/4 DOWEL ROD

1/2 SQUARES

# MY SHINE BOX

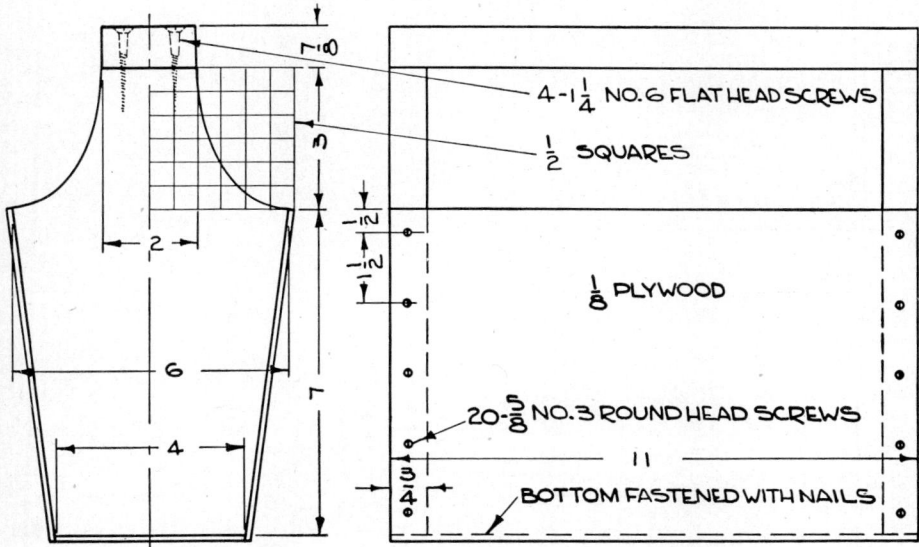

4-1 1/4 NO. 6 FLAT HEAD SCREWS

1/2 SQUARES

1/8 PLYWOOD

20-5/8 NO. 3 ROUND HEAD SCREWS

11

BOTTOM FASTENED WITH NAILS

# WATCH STAND

$\frac{1}{2}$ SQUARES

2-$\frac{5}{8}$ NO. 2 R.H. SCREWS

2-$\frac{3}{4}$ NO. 3-R.H. SCREWS

$\frac{1}{4}$

$\frac{5}{8}$

$\frac{4}{16}$

$\frac{1}{2}$

2

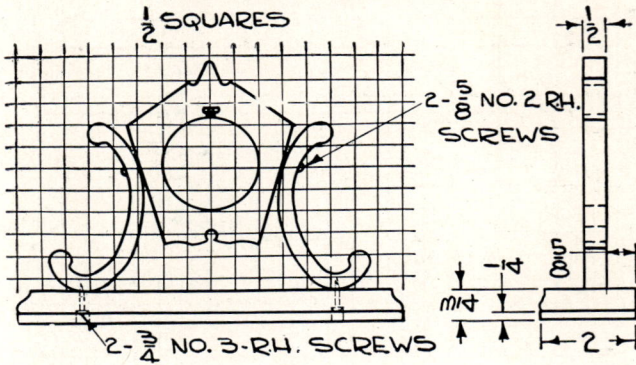

# TREASURE CHEST

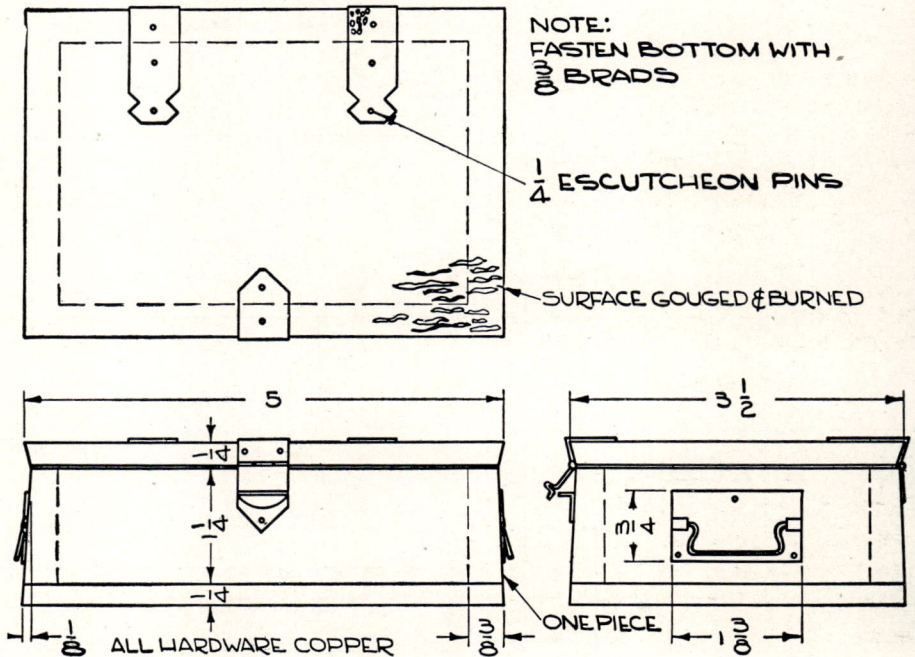

NOTE:
FASTEN BOTTOM WITH
$\frac{3}{8}$ BRADS

$\frac{1}{4}$ ESCUTCHEON PINS

SURFACE GOUGED & BURNED

5

$\frac{1}{4}$

$\frac{1}{4}$

$\frac{1}{4}$

$\frac{1}{8}$   ALL HARDWARE COPPER

$\frac{3}{8}$

ONE PIECE

$3\frac{1}{2}$

$\frac{4}{16}$

$1\frac{3}{8}$

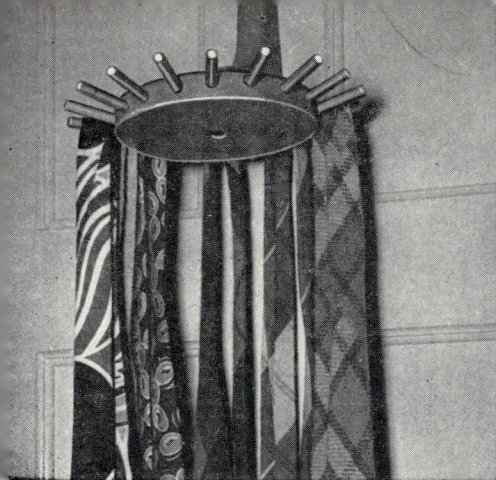

Circular Tie Rack

Pants Holder

**399. CIRCULAR TIE RACK.** The rack can be flicked around with your finger to bring forward any tie for easy choice. The rack has plenty of room for all of your ties and none of them is hidden from view. Can be made of almost any kind of wood. While it is not quite so simple as some kinds of tie racks to build, it will provide a real challenge to the fledgling woodworker.

**400. PANTS HOLDER.** This is a real convenience. No more wrinkles in your trousers when you use this holder. This one holds 9 pairs of trousers at one time, and each can be removed without disturbing the others. Another useful feature is that the holder hangs from the closet rod like a hanger, thus conserving closet space.

Pipe Rack

**401. PIPE RACK.** This design can be made longer or shorter to suit your needs. Has places for four pipes but could easily be enlarged to accommodate any number. The pipe rests in the base have been gouged out by hand. Walnut is therefore the ideal wood to choose for it. The uprights are attached to the base with rabbet joints and the cross piece is fastened with two dado joints. The edge of the base can be rounded or decorated in a more complicated design if shaper cutters are available.

House Numbers

**402. HOUSE NUMBERS.** An idea that you can apply to many different projects. You might make a set of house numbers, room identification numbers, or you could design cut-out letters for a nameplate for a desk or for your room. By fastening these numbers or letters to a simple background, you will obtain squaring-up experience and still have an article that you will be proud to take home.

# PANTS HOLDER

## CIRCULAR TIE RACK

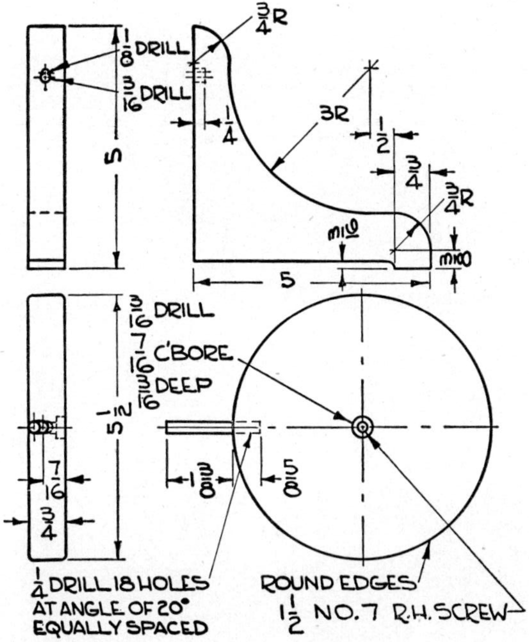

PANTS HOLDER drawing labels:
- 12
- 4½
- 4
- 1½
- ³⁄₁₆ SLOTS FOR SUMMER PANTS
- ¼ DRILL
- ³⁄₈ R
- 1½ R
- ¾ R
- 2
- 6
- 4½
- ¾
- 6¾
- ¼¼
- 4 NO. 4-1¼ F.H. SCREWS

CIRCULAR TIE RACK drawing labels:
- ¾ R
- ¾ R
- 3 R
- 1½
- ⁹⁄₁₆
- ⁹⁄₁₆
- 5
- ¼
- ¹¹⁄₁₆ DRILL
- ³⁄₁₆ DRILL
- ³⁄₁₆ DRILL
- ⁷⁄₁₆ CBORE
- ³⁄₁₆ DEEP
- 5
- 5½
- ⁵⁄₈
- ³⁄₈
- ⁷⁄₁₆
- ¾
- ⁵⁄₈
- ³⁄₈
- ROUND EDGES
- 1½ NO. 7 R.H. SCREW
- ¼ DRILL 18 HOLES AT ANGLE OF 20° EQUALLY SPACED

260

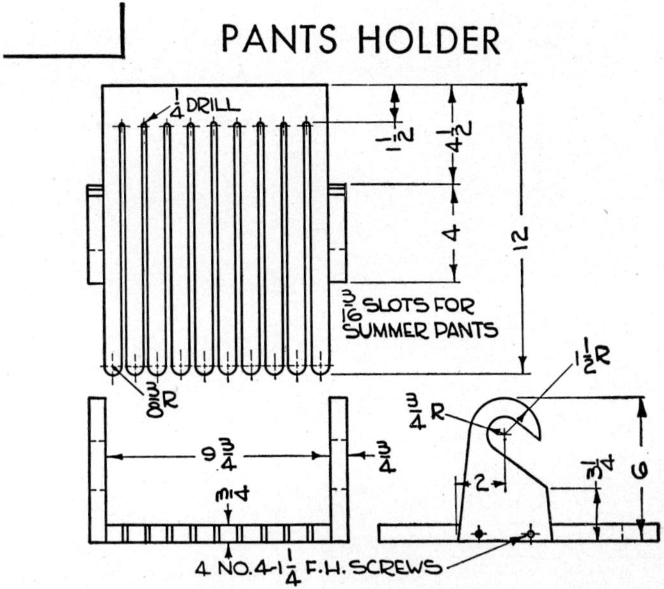

# HOUSE NUMBERS

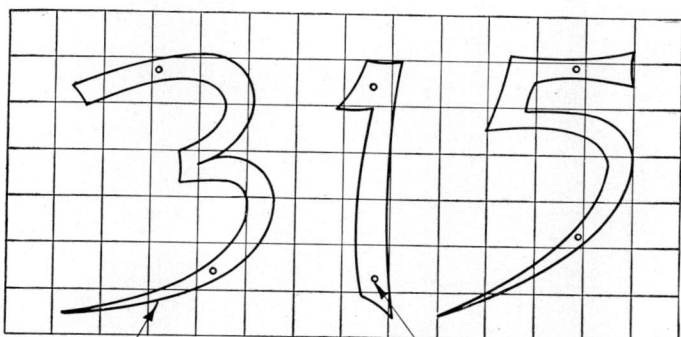

$\frac{3}{32}$ PLYWOOD    $\frac{1}{2}$ SQUARES    $\frac{1}{2}$ ESCUTCHEON PINS

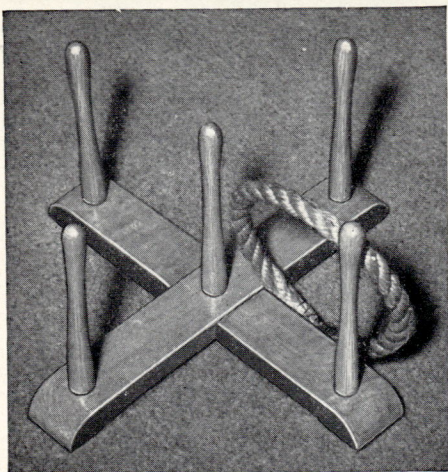

**Ring Game**

**Cribbage Board**

**403. RING GAME.** A project that will make a favorite indoor game is this one for tossing the rings. It is a good choice for beginning, as it will give you a chance to learn to make a lap joint and still make something desirable and usable.

**404. CRIBBAGE BOARD.** Anyone who plays cribbage or who would like to own a good board would certainly want to make one of these folding boards. It is ideal for traveling because it folds into a small, compact box shape. Inside are compartments for both the cards and pegs. Because it has to be formed, the ideal wood is walnut. When drilling the holes, it is a great help to use a little metal jig. Hinge sizes can vary.

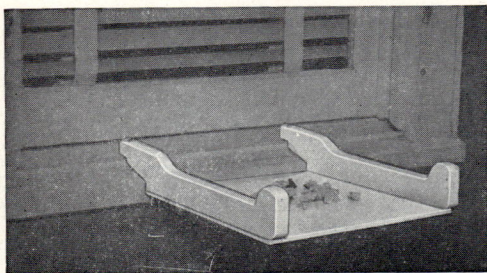

**Bird Feeder**

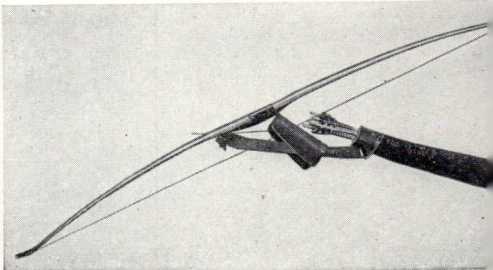

**Flat Bow**

**405. BIRD FEEDER.** Here is a little device that will bring the birds right to your window sill. Can be fastened to any sill and stocked with bread crumbs conveniently from the inside. The feeder can be attached either above or below the sill. If necessary, the tapered portion can be made longer or shorter to fit the particular window for which it is intended.

**406. FLAT BOW.** Archery is still a favorite outdoor pastime, and making the bow is a very fascinating part of the game. You can buy the wood for making a bow in the rough and then shape your own bow in the manner illustrated in the unit on the use of the homemade hand scraper, or you can begin by splitting up a piece of timber to make the rough bow yourself. Use lemonwood, osage orange, hickory, or ash

262

# PIPE RACK

# RING GAME

263

# CRIBBAGE BOARD

DRILL HOLES IN BOTTOM SAME AS
TOP EXCEPT FOR STARTING HOLES

# BIRD FEEDER

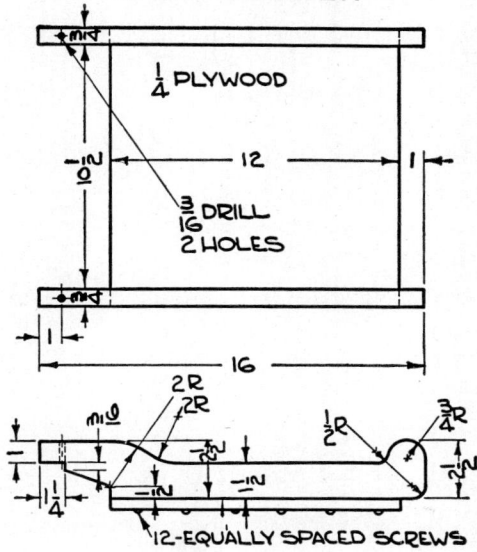

$\frac{1}{4}$ PLYWOOD

12

1

$\frac{10}{2}$

$\frac{3}{16}$ DRILL
2 HOLES

1

16

2R
2R

$\frac{1}{2}$R
$\frac{3}{4}$R

$2\frac{1}{2}$

1
$1\frac{1}{4}$

12-EQUALLY SPACED SCREWS

# FLAT BOW

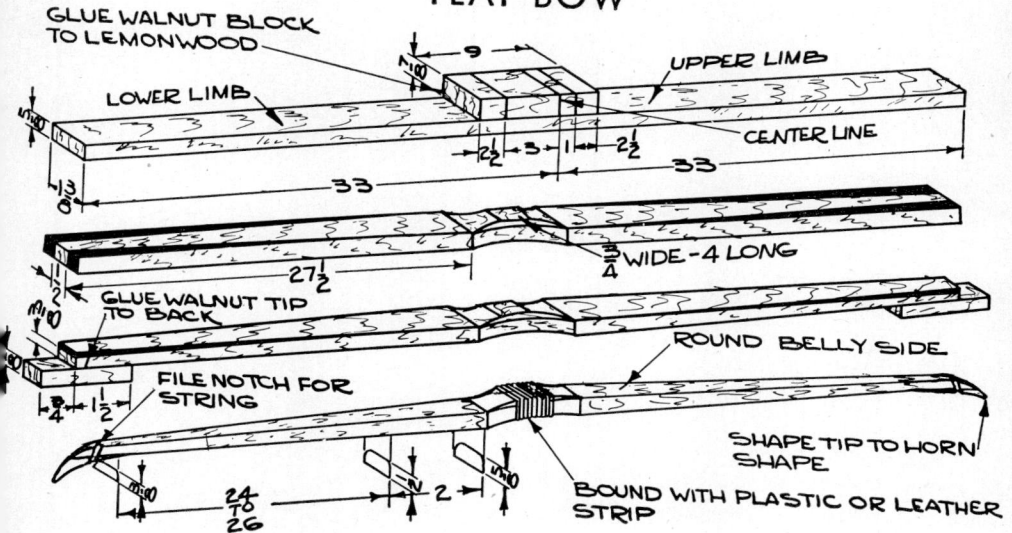

GLUE WALNUT BLOCK
TO LEMONWOOD

9

UPPER LIMB

LOWER LIMB

CENTER LINE

$2\frac{1}{2}$   3   1   $2\frac{1}{2}$

33

33

$\frac{3}{8}$

$27\frac{1}{2}$

$\frac{3}{4}$ WIDE - 4 LONG

GLUE WALNUT TIP
TO BACK

ROUND BELLY SIDE

FILE NOTCH FOR
STRING

$\frac{3}{4}$   $1\frac{1}{2}$

$\frac{24}{TO}$
$\frac{}{26}$

$\frac{1}{2}$   2

SHAPE TIP TO HORN
SHAPE

BOUND WITH PLASTIC OR LEATHER
STRIP

**Small Turnings**

**Jewel Box**

407. SMALL TURNINGS. These are only a very few samples of small turnings that can be made on a wood lathe. There are many uses for turnings, such as for salad bowls, pin boxes, cheese boxes, table and chair legs, and countless others.

408. JEWEL BOX. The beauty of this box is in its simple lines, the unusual grain, and the hand-rubbed finish. It is made of curly maple giving it fine grain formation. Assemble with dowels and glue. An imitation pearl piece is set in the top with glue.

**Salt Shaker and Pepper Mill**

409. SALT SHAKER AND PEPPER MILL. The outside shape can be varied in many ways to express your own design ideas. Suggested plans are on page 268. See source C, page 311.

410. GLASS-BRICK LAMP. Glass, metal, and wood combined. Glass brick can be purchased in various sizes and designs. Around it you can build a frame of any type. This one has an oak base finished with a black pigment, rubbed down, and then a white filler added. Joined with flathead screws.

**Glass-Brick Lamp**

# SMALL TURNINGS

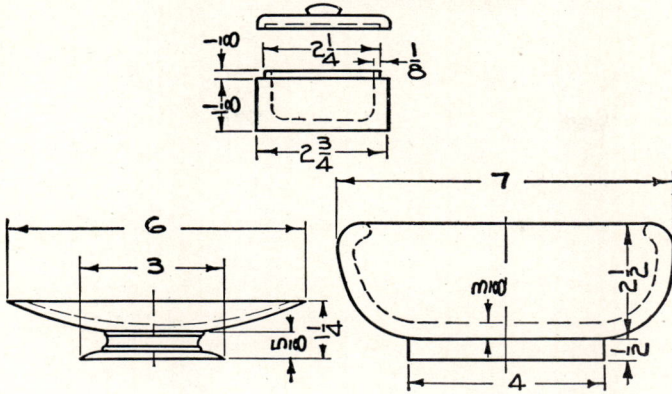

# JEWEL BOX

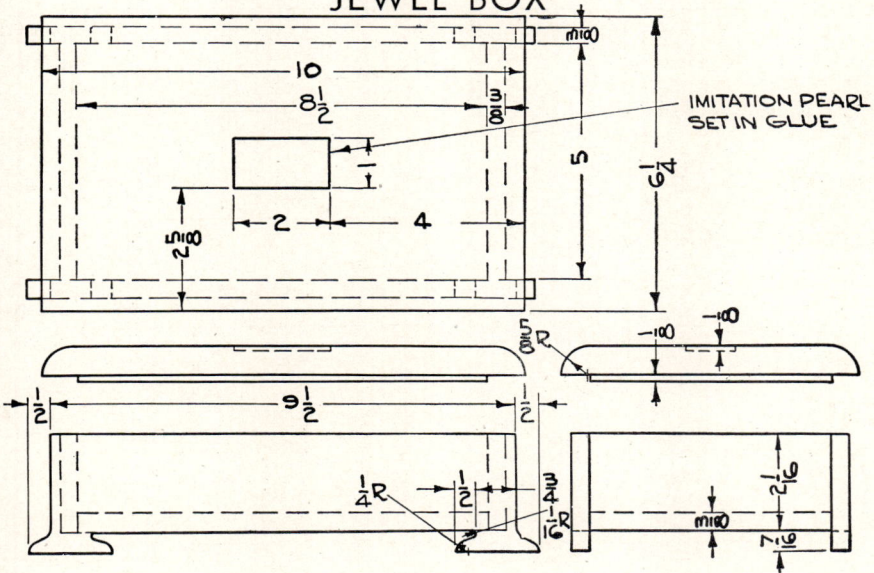

IMITATION PEARL
SET IN GLUE

SPIDER
(LID REMOVED)

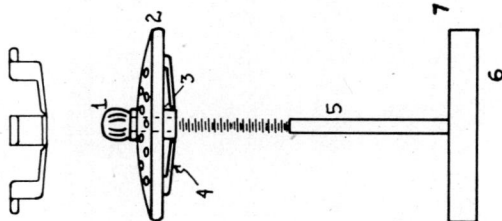

## SALT HARDWARE

1. Knurled Knob
2. Lid
3. Spider Nut (Hidden)
4. Spider
5. Threaded Shaft
6. Base
7. Plastic Liner (Hidden)

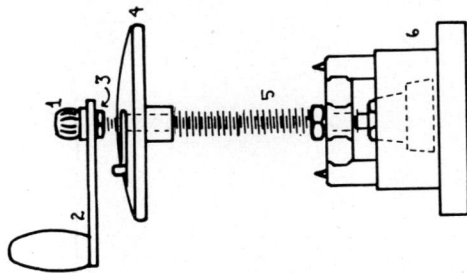

## MILL MECHANISM

1. Knurled Knob
2. Handle
3. Under-Handle Nut
4. Lid
5. Threaded Sleeve
6. Base-Stator Assy.

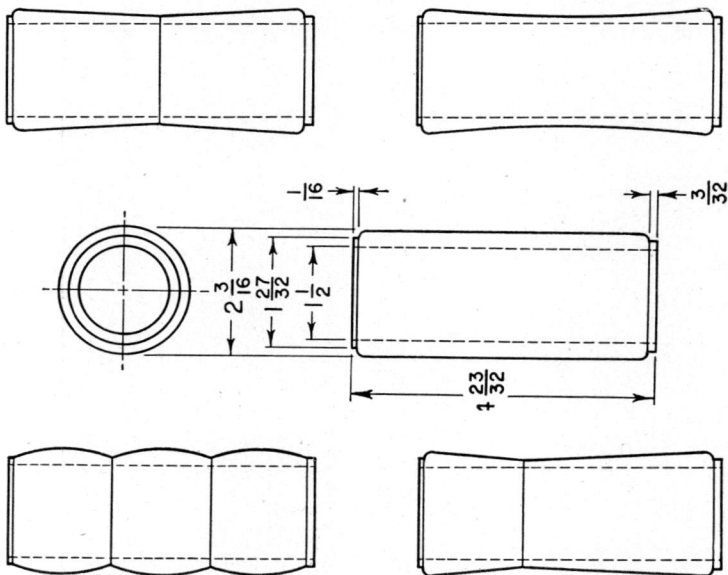

$\frac{1}{16}$

$\frac{3}{32}$

$2\frac{3}{16}$
$\frac{27}{32}$
$1\frac{1}{2}$

$4\frac{23}{32}$

# GLASS BRICK LAMP

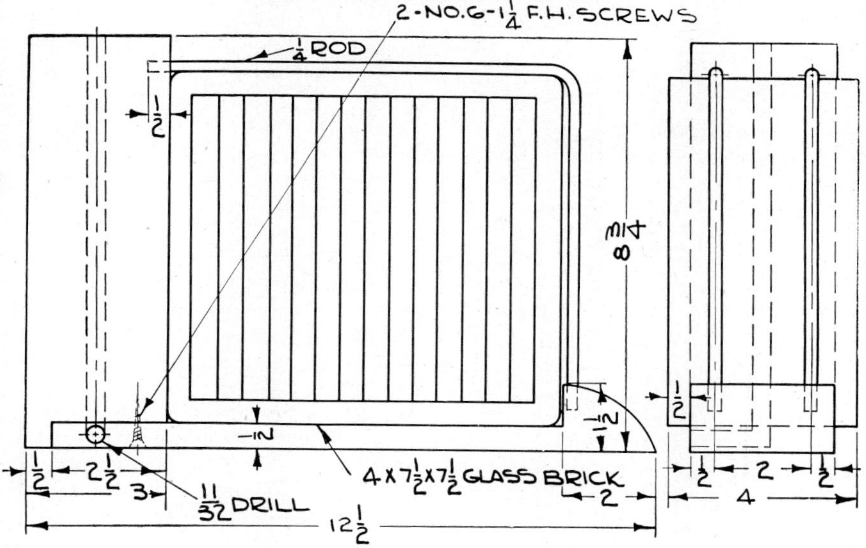

2-NO.6-1¼ F.H. SCREWS

¼ ROD

½

8¾

½

½ 2½ 3

11/32 DRILL

─2─

4 X 7½ X 7½ GLASS BRICK

½

½

2

12½

2

2

4

# CUTTING BOARD

¾ THICKNESS

1-SQUARES

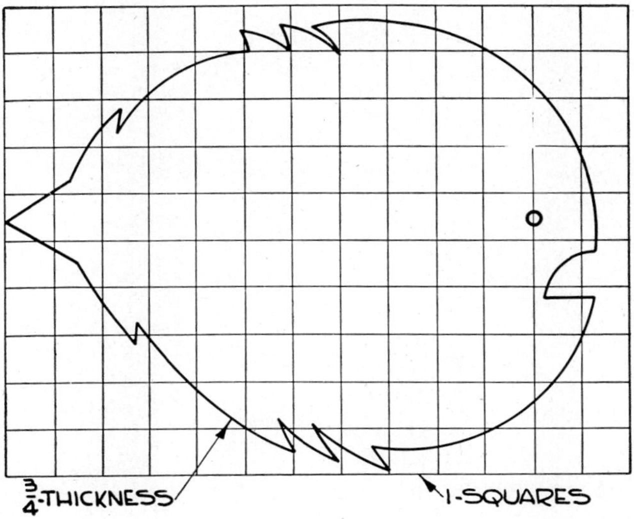

**Cutting Board**

**Note Box**

411. **CUTTING BOARD.** This cutting board shows only one of many different designs that could be cut out. Simple to construct, requires no squaring up of the stock, and can be completed in a relatively short time. Can be made of white pine, birch, maple, or almost any wood. It helps you learn to glue up stock, or it can be made of a piece of plywood

412. **NOTE BOX.** Early American style. Just right to hold kitchen grocery lists, telephone notations, and the like. It could also be used as a tiny knicknack shelf held on end and hung on the wall. Made of ¼-inch pine, it is assembled with ¾-inch escutcheon nails and given a maple finish.

**Match Box Holder**

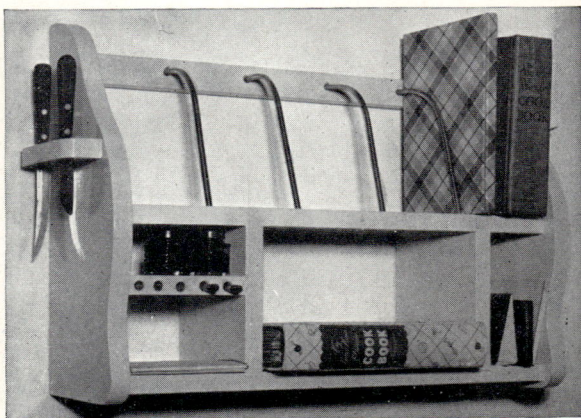

**Shelf-All**

413. **MATCH BOX HOLDER.** Exactly the right size for a full box of kitchen matches, Early American style. Made of pine with a big knot exposed, assembled with 1-inch escutcheon nails or pins and finished with maple coloring. You could glue a piece of sandpaper to the bottom for scratching the matches.

414. **SHELF-ALL.** An all-purpose shelf for the kitchen. The top shelf is built for cookbooks and reference materials; the left part of the bottom shelf is just right for 3x5-inch cards and, with the places for pencils, it is immensely helpful for taking notes and making lists. The right opening is made for note pads. A hook for bills is on the right side. Joints are glued.

ROUND ALL EDGES

$\frac{1}{4}$
$1\frac{1}{2}$
$\frac{1}{4}$
$5\frac{1}{4}$
$5\frac{5}{8}$
$\frac{1}{4}$
$\frac{1}{4}$

# NOTE BOX

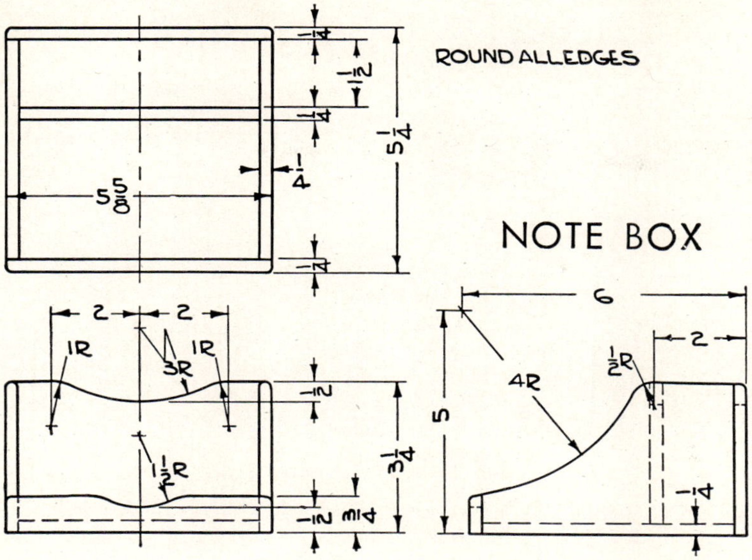

2   2
1R   3R   1R
$1\frac{1}{2}$R
$\frac{1}{2}$
$3\frac{1}{4}$
$\frac{1}{2}$   $3\frac{3}{4}$

6
$1\frac{1}{2}$R
2
4R
5
$\frac{1}{4}$

# MATCH BOX HOLDER

$\frac{3}{16}$ DRILL
$\frac{1}{2}$
$3\frac{7}{8}$
$3\frac{3}{4}$
$4\frac{1}{4}$
$7\frac{1}{2}$
$\frac{3}{8}$
$2\frac{5}{8}$
$1\frac{1}{8}$
1
$\frac{3}{4}$
$\frac{3}{8}$

ESCUTCHEON PINS

$\frac{3}{8}$   $2\frac{3}{4}$   $\frac{3}{8}$

$\frac{1}{2}$ SQUARES

271

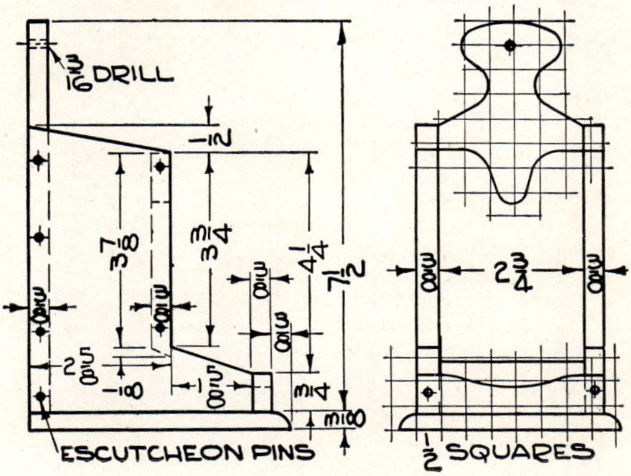

## Breakfast Table

**415. BREAKFAST TABLE.** A breakfast table big enough for six, with a design as modern as the present-day kitchen. The frame is bulit of 2″ x 4″ and the outside covered with ¾″ x 4″ baseboard. All parts are assembled with screws and nails. Linoleum top.

## Handy Pen Holder

**416. HANDY PEN HOLDER.** Many interesting things can be made from a piece of hard wood, and here is one of them. Fastening a desk calendar to it, drilling holes for the pen and pencil, and cutting out a square for the ink bottle, make a practical item for a desk.

**417. ELEPHANT LAMP.** Here is a real lamp for a boy's room. Attractive enough to win anyone's heart. This one represents a circus pole with the elephant doing the pushing. Other animals are as good. Almost any combination of woods can be chosen for the lamp. For boring the long, electric cord hole, a twist drill or auger bit of this diameter can be made longer by welding a piece of rod to the shank. Animal may be thinner.

## Elephant Lamp

# SHELF-ALL

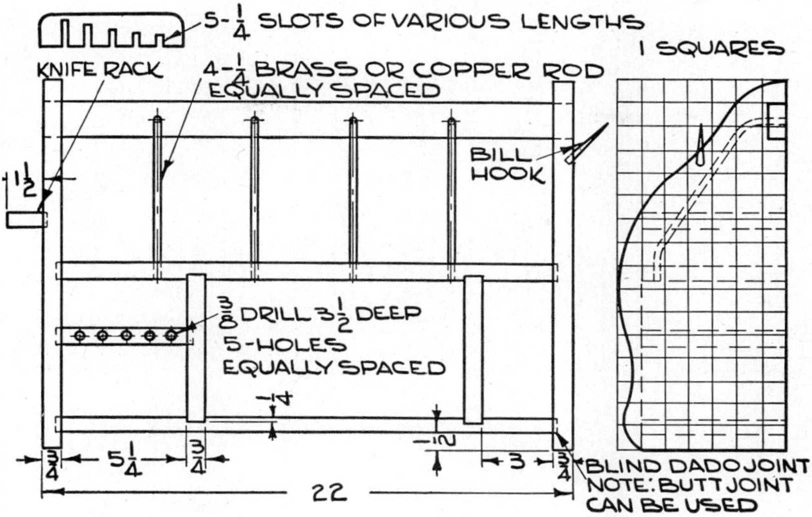

KNIFE RACK

5-$\frac{1}{4}$ SLOTS OF VARIOUS LENGTHS

4-$\frac{1}{4}$ BRASS OR COPPER ROD EQUALLY SPACED

1 SQUARES

BILL HOOK

$1\frac{1}{2}$

$\frac{3}{8}$ DRILL $3\frac{1}{2}$ DEEP
5-HOLES
EQUALLY SPACED

$-\frac{1}{4}$

$\frac{3}{4}$   $5\frac{1}{4}$   $\frac{3}{4}$

$-\frac{1}{2}$

3   $\frac{3}{4}$

22

BLIND DADO JOINT
NOTE: BUTT JOINT
CAN BE USED

BASE BOARD
MOLDING
($\frac{3}{4}$x4)

TOP REMOVED

2x4

52

# BREAKFAST TABLE

RINGS MADE OF
#12 WIRE

$\frac{3}{4}$ PLYWOOD COVERED WITH
LINOLEUM & METAL TRIM

$\frac{3}{16}$x$\frac{3}{16}$ GROOVE

30

$-\frac{1}{8}$

27

$\frac{3}{16}$

$\frac{1}{8}$

$9\frac{3}{4}$

273

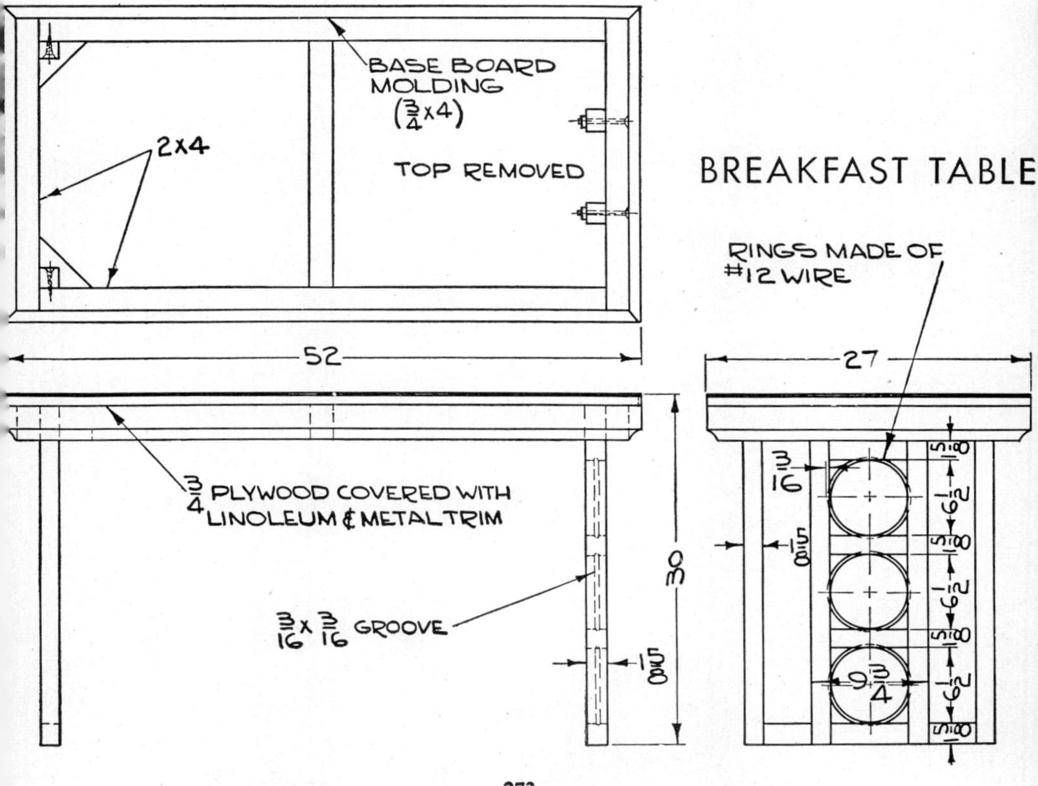

## ELEPHANT LAMP

$4\frac{1}{4}$

$1\frac{1}{2}$

$\frac{10}{16}$

$9\frac{1}{6}$

$\frac{3}{8}$ BORE

BACKSAW KERFS $\frac{1}{8}$ DEEP

STAINED

$\frac{1}{2}$ SQUARES

$\frac{1}{2}$

$2\frac{1}{4}$

$12\frac{1}{2}$

$1\frac{1}{4}$

$1\frac{3}{4}$

$1$

$1$

$1$

$\frac{1}{16}$

$4 - 1\frac{1}{2}$ NO.5 F.H.SCREWS

## HANDY PEN HOLDER

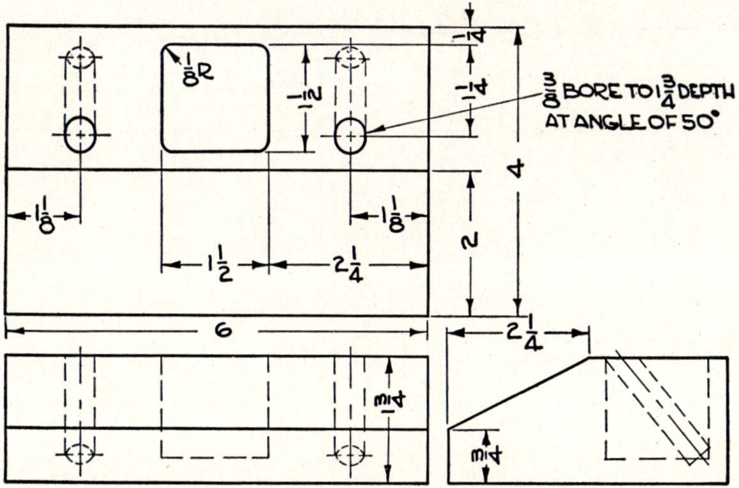

$\frac{3}{8}$ BORE TO $1\frac{3}{4}$ DEPTH AT ANGLE OF 50°

$\frac{1}{2}$

$1\frac{1}{4}$

$4$

$2$

$2\frac{1}{4}$

$\frac{1}{4}$

$\frac{3}{8}$

$1\frac{1}{8}$

$2\frac{1}{4}$

$1\frac{1}{2}$

$6$

$\frac{1}{2}$

$1\frac{1}{8}$

$\frac{1}{8}R$

$\frac{1}{8}$

$1\frac{1}{4}$

274

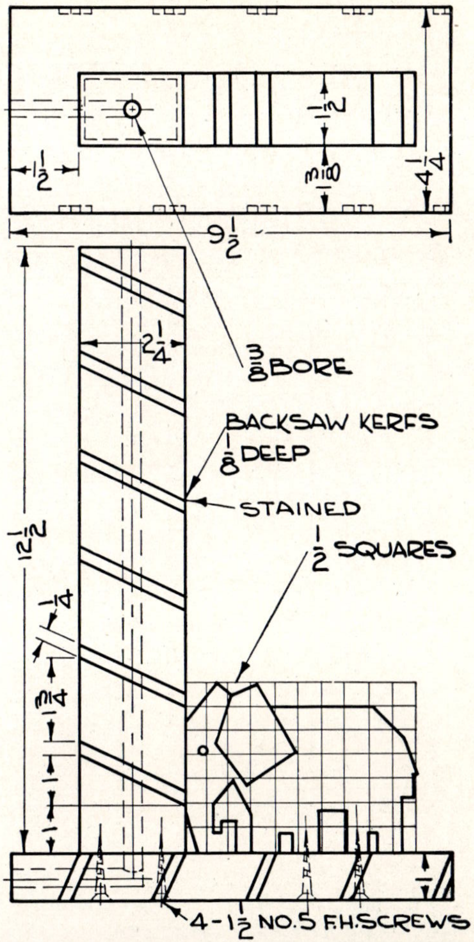

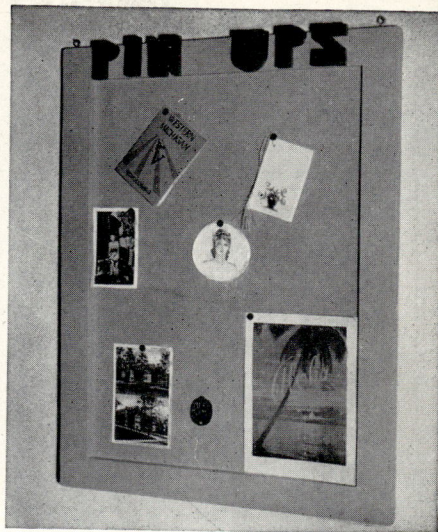

## File Case and Pin-Up Board

**418. FILE CASE.** A filing case is practical for storage whether you are a student or not. This one, made of ¾-inch plywood with a hinged top, will hold a considerable number of paper folders. It would be excellent for shipping back and forth from home to school, or for an extra case at home. Assemble with 1¼" flathead screws.

**419. PIN-UP BOARD.** Just the thing for a young boy's or girl's room is this board which will keep pin-ups, pictures, and clippings where they belong and also provide a convenient place to jot down important dates and appointments. It is an excellent example of the use of the miter joint.

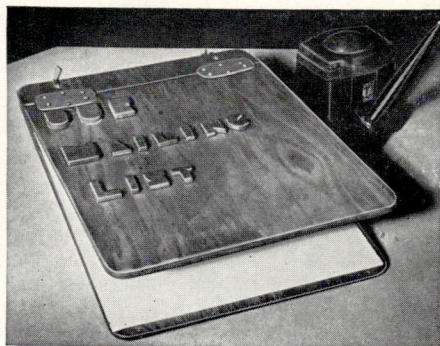

## Knife-and-Fork Box                 Mailing List Cover

**420. KNIFE-AND-FORK BOX.** An attractive Early American design that could be put to many different uses. It can be made of pine, cherry or birch. (Courtesy of Woman's Day) See Source B, page 311.

**421. MAILING LIST COVER.** There is always a need for a convenient place to keep Christmas mailing lists, addresses, or other reminders. Here is one made with plywood covers, with the letters cut out of a darker colored ⅛" plywood. The same idea would be good for a photograph album or scrapbook.

# FILE CASE

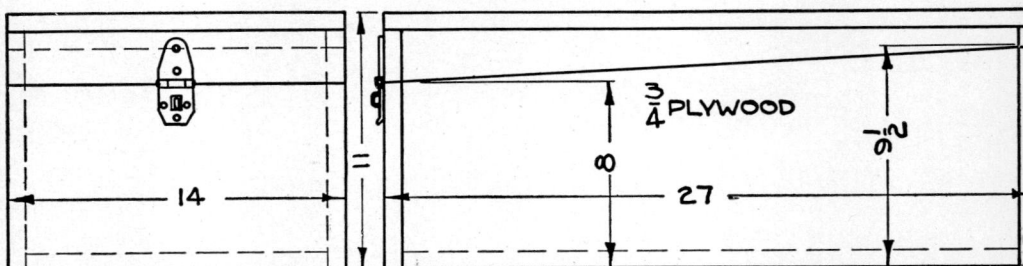

14     11     $\frac{3}{4}$ PLYWOOD     8     27     $9\frac{1}{2}$

# PIN-UP BOARD

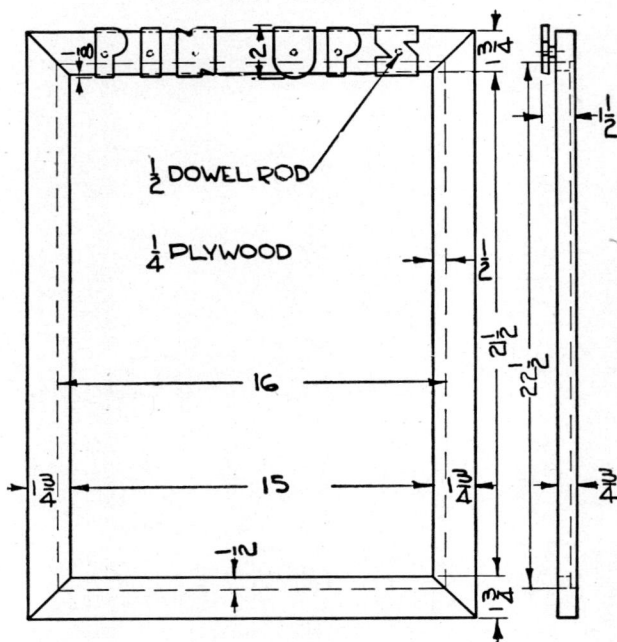

$\frac{1}{2}$ DOWEL ROD

$\frac{1}{4}$ PLYWOOD

16     15     $21\frac{1}{2}$     $22\frac{1}{2}$

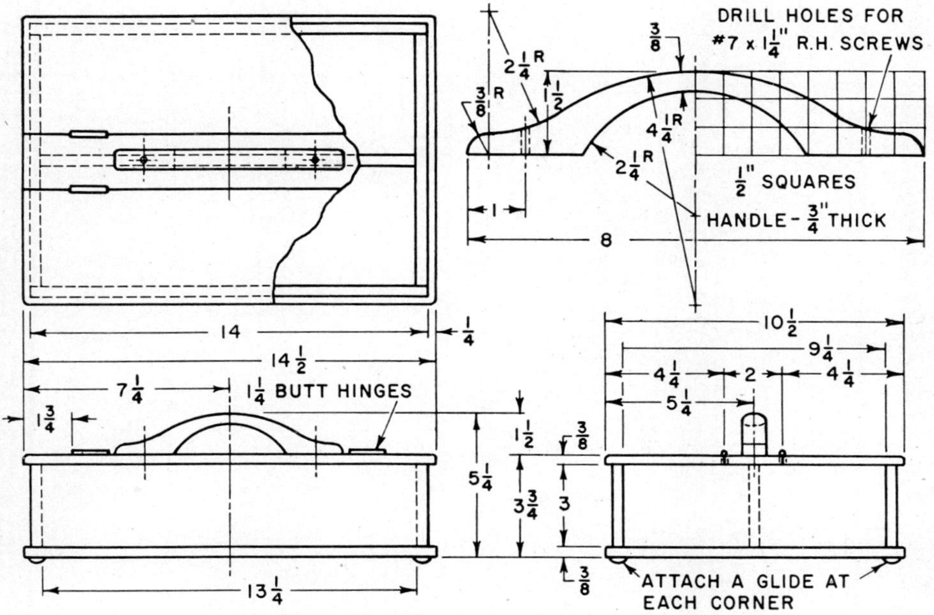
DRILL HOLES FOR
#7 x 1 1/4" R.H. SCREWS
1/2" SQUARES
HANDLE - 3/4" THICK
1 1/4 BUTT HINGES
ATTACH A GLIDE AT
EACH CORNER

KNIFE-AND-FORK BOX

MAILING LIST COVER

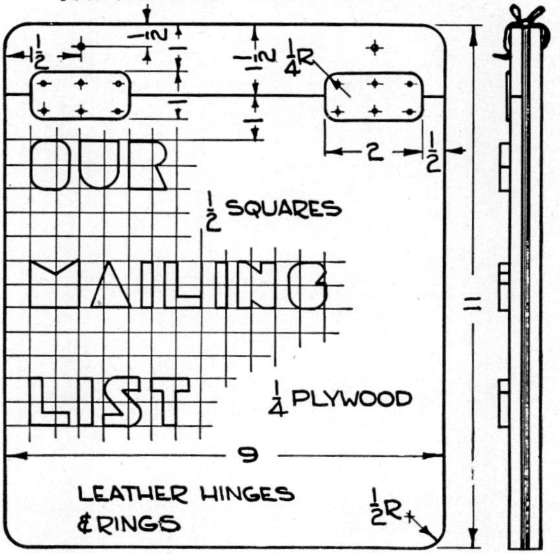
OUR
MAILING
LIST
1/2 SQUARES
1/4 PLYWOOD
LEATHER HINGES
& RINGS

Book Trough

Storage Hassock

Student's Desk

422. BOOK TROUGH. Traditional in design, this book trough is made of cherry. Its construction is different from most of the other projects here in that a pinned mortise-and-tenon joint holds the parts together. The stock is shaped to simulate age.

423. STUDENT'S DESK. This is a simple, practical desk for your room which can be made in a short time of fir plywood. The whole desk can be cut from one 4- by 8-foot panel ¾ inch thick. There are roomy pigeon holes for small items and shelf space. Under the drop-leaf writing surface are two drawers. See Source A, page 311.

424. STORAGE HASSOCK. Here is an excellent beginning project which includes some simple upholstery. It is a handy seat as well as a storage unit.

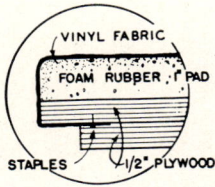

VINYL FABRIC

FOAM RUBBER 1" PAD

STAPLES 1/2" PLYWOOD

LID DETAIL

METAL ANGLE
CORNER CLIPS

VINYL FABRIC
ON 1/2" PLYWOOD

1"x1" LEDGER
ALL AROUND

15"

2-1/8"     13-1/2"     2-1/8"

17-3/4"

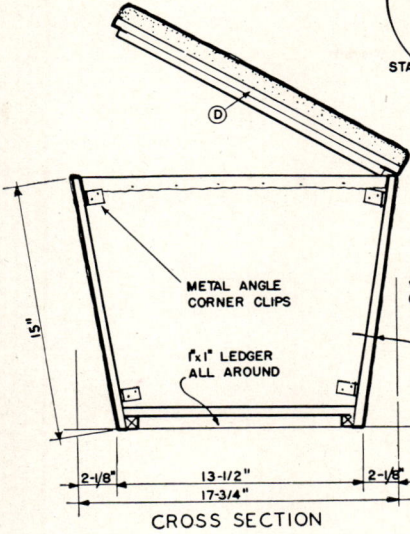

CROSS SECTION

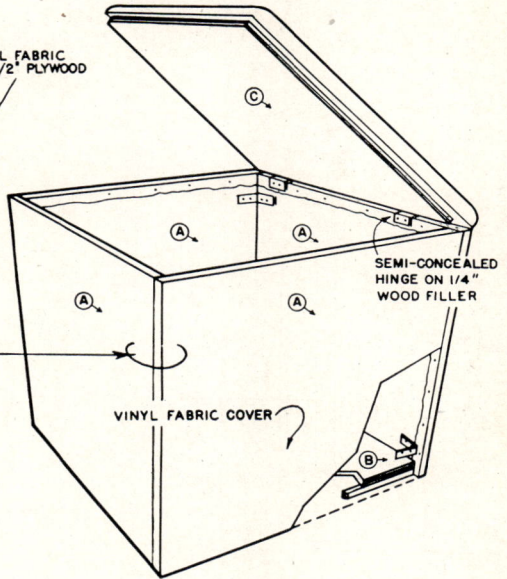

SEMI-CONCEALED
HINGE ON 1/4"
WOOD FILLER

CORNER
DETAIL

VINYL FABRIC COVER

# STORAGE
# HASSOCK

## PARTS SCHEDULE

| CODE | NO. REQ'D | SIZE | PART IDENTIFICATION |
|------|-----------|------|---------------------|
| A | 4 | 15"x17¼" | Sides |
| B | 1 | 12½"x12½" | Bottom |
| C | 1 | 16¼"x16¼" | Underside of Lid |
| D | 1 | 17¾"x17¾" | Lid |
| | 1 Pc. | 17¾"x17¾" | 1" Foam Rubber |
| | 1 Pc. | 3'x5' | Vinyl Fabric |
| | 5 Lin. Ft. | 1"x1" | Ledger Strip |
| | 8 Ea. | — | Clip Angles |
| | 1 Pr. | — | Semi-Concealed Hinges |

Miscellaneous—4d Finish Nails, Staples and Glue

# STUDENT'S DESK

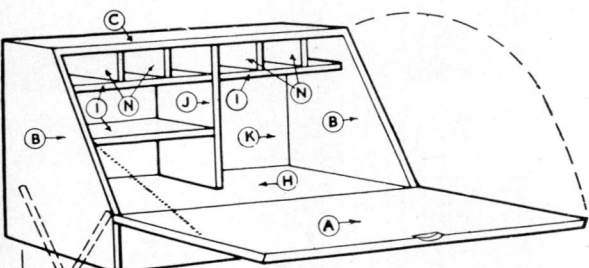

PROVIDE LID-SUPPORT, CHAIN, OR REST LID ON PARTLY-OPEN DRAWERS.

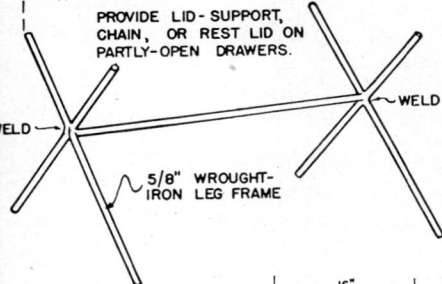

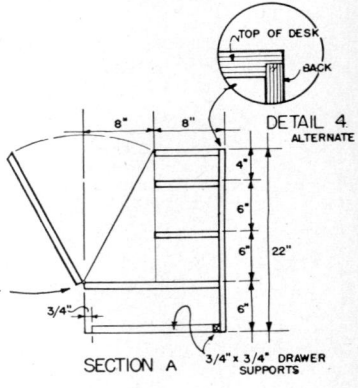

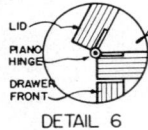

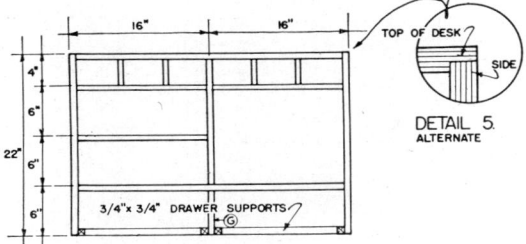

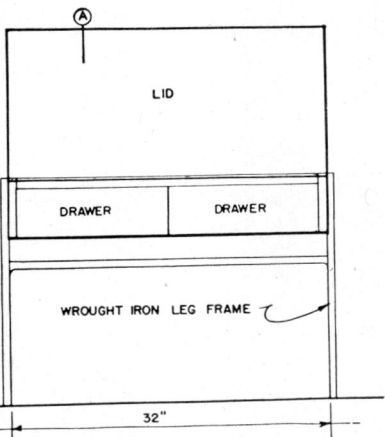

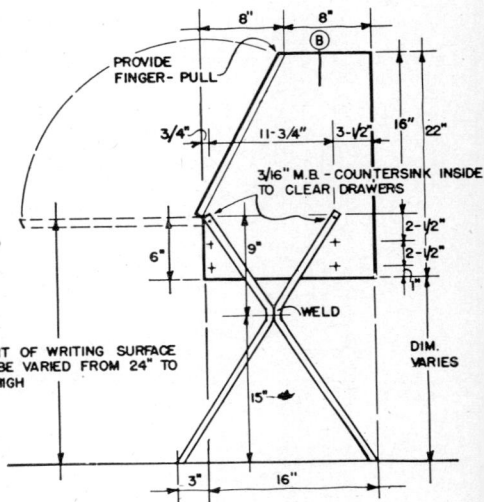

WELD

WELD

5/8" WROUGHT-IRON LEG FRAME

TOP OF DESK

BACK

DETAIL 4
ALTERNATE

8"    8"

4"

6"

6"    22"

6"

3/4"

SECTION A

3/4" x 3/4" DRAWER SUPPORTS

LID

PIANO HINGE

DRAWER FRONT

DETAIL 6

TOP OF DESK

SIDE

DETAIL 5.
ALTERNATE

16"    16"

4"

6"

22"

6"

6"

3/4" x 3/4" DRAWER SUPPORTS

SECTION B

LID

DRAWER        DRAWER

WROUGHT IRON LEG FRAME

32"

FRONT ELEVATION

PROVIDE FINGER-PULL

8"    8"

3/4"    11-3/4"    3-1/2"    16"    22"

3/16" M.B. - COUNTERSINK INSIDE TO CLEAR DRAWERS

6"    9"    2-1/2"

2-1/2"

1"

WELD

HEIGHT OF WRITING SURFACE CAN BE VARIED FROM 24" TO 29" HIGH

DIM. VARIES

15"

3"    16"

SIDE ELEVATION

280

# FLOWERPOT HOLDER

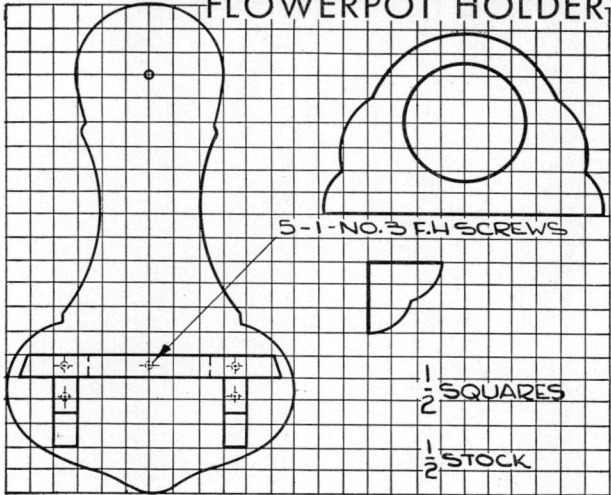

5 - 1 - NO.3 F.H SCREWS

$\frac{1}{2}$ SQUARES

$\frac{1}{2}$ STOCK

# BOOK TROUGH

1 - SQUARES

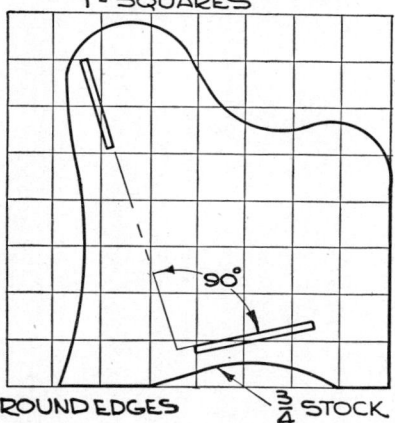

90°

ROUND EDGES          $\frac{3}{4}$ STOCK

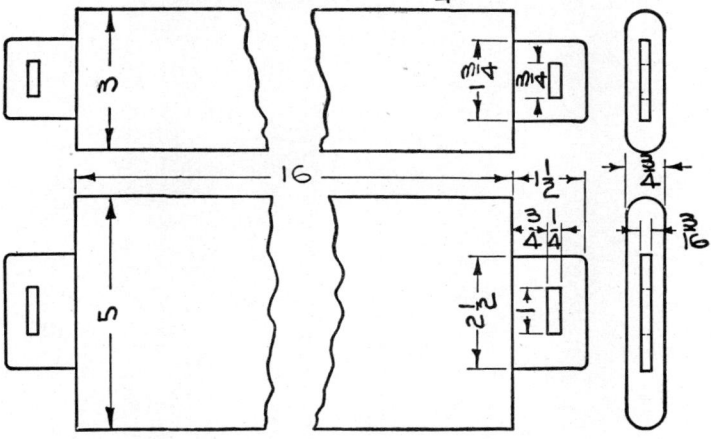

3

$\frac{1}{4}$   $\frac{1}{4}$

16          $1\frac{1}{2}$

$\frac{3}{4}$   $1\frac{1}{4}$

5          $2\frac{1}{2}$   $\frac{1}{4}$

$\frac{3}{4}$

$\frac{9}{16}$

**425. FLOWERPOT HOLDER.** This holder is so simple in design that any wood or finish could be chosen for it, depending on where in the home it is to be hung. It holds a small flowerpot, or the opening could be eliminated and the piece used as a shelf for miniatures. Make hole to fit pot.

**Flowerpot Holder**

**Wastepaper Basket**

**426. WASTEPAPER BASKET.** The wood part is plywood, good on one side; the metal is copper; and the stain is dark, followed by varnish. Gives lots of opportunity for designing to suit yourself. The sides of the basket are attached to the base with escutcheon nails, and the sides themselves are joined with copper bands or clips.

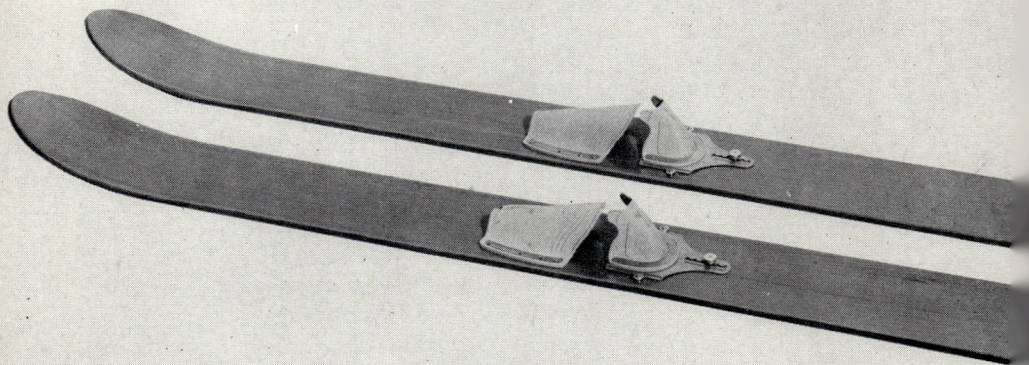

**427. WATER SKIS.** Here's an excellent sports-equipment project that doesn't take too long to make. The blanks are obtained pre-bent. All that remains is the shaping and finishing. See Source D, page 311.

# HANGING WALL SHELF

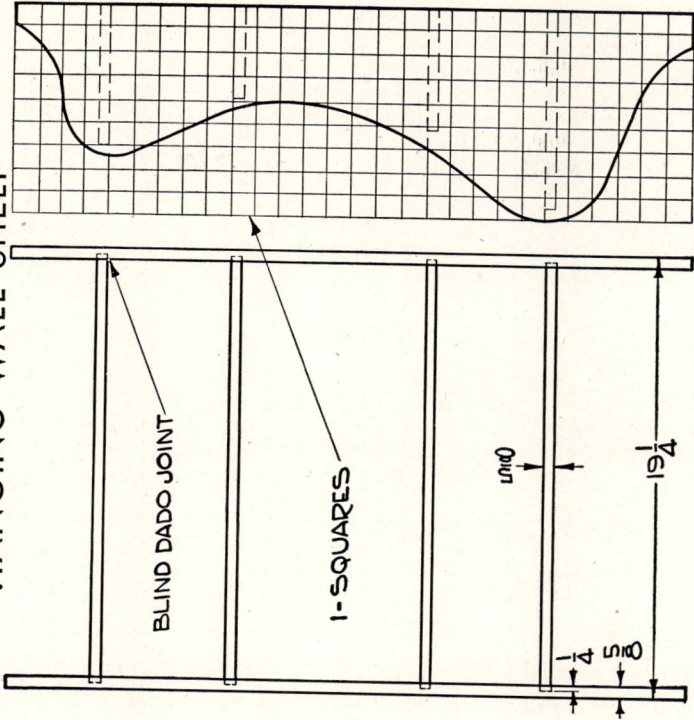

BLIND DADO JOINT

1" SQUARES

$9\frac{5}{16}$

$\frac{1}{4}$

$19\frac{1}{4}$

$\frac{1}{4}$

$\frac{5}{8}$

# WASTEPAPER BASKET

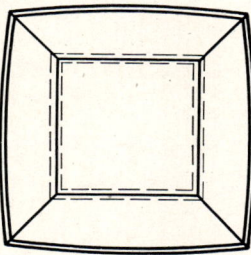

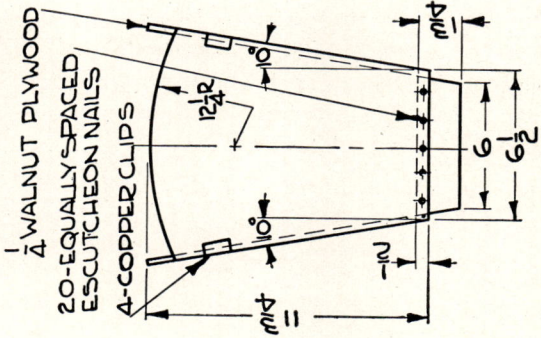

$\frac{1}{4}$" WALNUT PLYWOOD

20-EQUALLY SPACED
ESCUTCHEON NAILS

4-COPPER CLIPS

$12\frac{1}{4}$R

$10°$

$10°$

$11\frac{3}{4}$

$6\frac{1}{2}$

$6$

$1\frac{1}{4}$

$2$

283

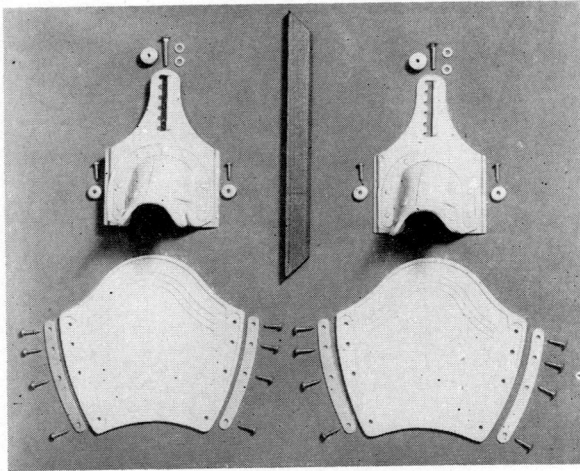

## SKI SIZE CHART FOR SKIER WEIGHTS

### Straight Pairs

5'-11" x 6¾"........175 pounds or over
5'-9" x 6¾"..........130 to 175 pounds
5'-6" x 6¾"..........100 to 130 pounds
5' x 6¾"............75 to 100 pounds

Width may be narrowed to 6½" or 6" depending on ability and experience of skier.

### Banana Shape Pairs

5'-11" x 6¾"........130 pounds or over
5'-8" x 6¾"..........75 to 130 pounds

## LOCATION OF FITTINGS

Figure A shows the location of fittings for the 5'-11" x 6¾" blanks. For other length skis locate as follows, keeping in mind that relationship between toe and heel pieces remains same as shown in Figure A:

5'-11" length, screw hole "X" 34" from heel
5'-9" length, screw hole "X" 33" from heel
5'-6" length, screw hole "X" 31½" from heel
5' length, screw hole "X" 29" from heel.

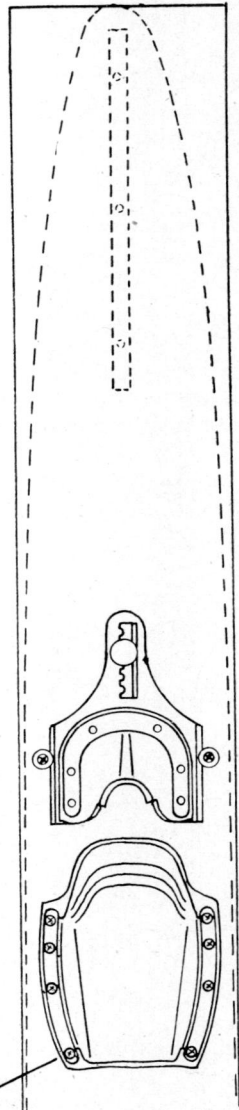

# ASSEMBLING SKI-CRAFT WATER SKIS
## Fig. A

**428. HANGING WALL SHELF.**
Simple to construct, hanging
shelves are always a pleasant
addition to a room and very useful as well. This one was made
of inexpensive stock and painted.
However, it could be greatly
improved by making it of a
better wood and finishing it
with stain.

anging Wall Shelf

Book Ends

**429. BOOK ENDS.** Made of oak, these book ends are heavy enough to be practical and
simple enough to fit into the modern room. Felt has been glued to the base to protect
the surface of furniture. They are finished in a light-wood filler to emphasize the grain.

"Weldtex" Flower Holder

**430. "WELDTEX" LAMP.** Plywood with a
"weldtex" surface on one side forms the
base of the lamp, and its dull texture is en-
hanced by the bands of bright brass above
and below the column of the base. Since
these lamps are rather tall, the core is hollow
to keep them from being top heavy. The
"weldtex" can be attached to the adjoining
pieces with either glue or brads.

"Weldtex" Lamp

**431. "WELDTEX" FLOWER HOLDER.** "Weldtex" plywood is the material in this
flower holder, which was made as a companion piece to the "weldtex" lamp. The top
edging, however, is made of oak, finished with a light stain and filler. A sheetmetal,
waterproof container fits inside it to make it usable for cut flowers or plants. The
metal around the bottom is brass, the same as on the lamp. Join same as lamp.

285

# "WELDTEX" LAMP

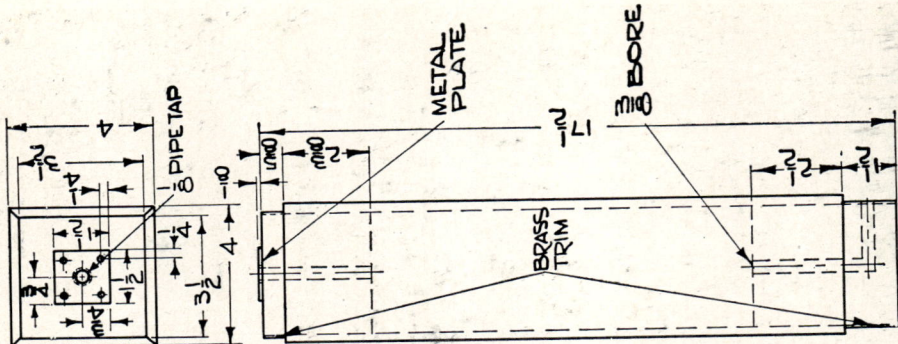

# BOOKENDS

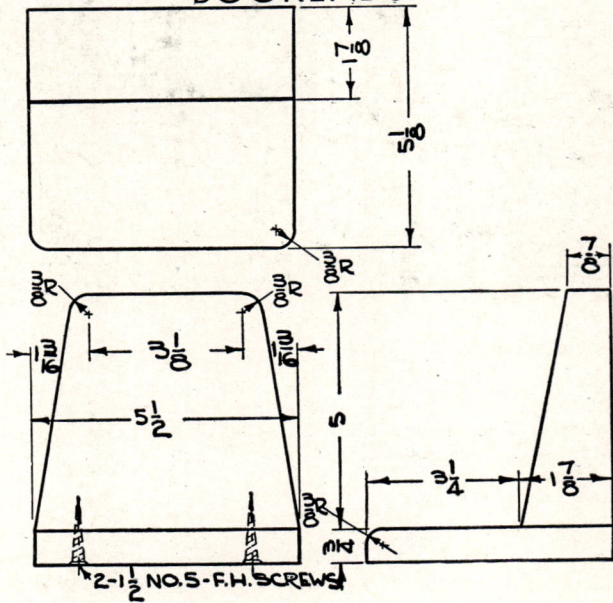

2-1½ NO. 5-F.H. SCREWS

**End Table**

**Courting Mirror**

**432. END TABLE.** The construction of this table could be varied to suit your needs and tastes. This one is high enough to double as both lamp table and magazine storage. As a pair they would be especially effective. It is made of birch but would be equally suited to mahogany or maple.

**433. COURTING MIRROR.** Here's a charming accessory that would fit nicely in a bedroom, living room or study. Use one-inch squares to make an enlarged pattern of the back. The back is made of ¾-inch thick plywood, 12 inches by 16 inches. (B) is made of 4 feet of standard molding ¾ inch wide. (C) is made from a piece of stock ¼ inch by ½ inch by 4 feet. DOUGLAS FIR PLYWOOD ASSOCIATION.

# ENDTABLE

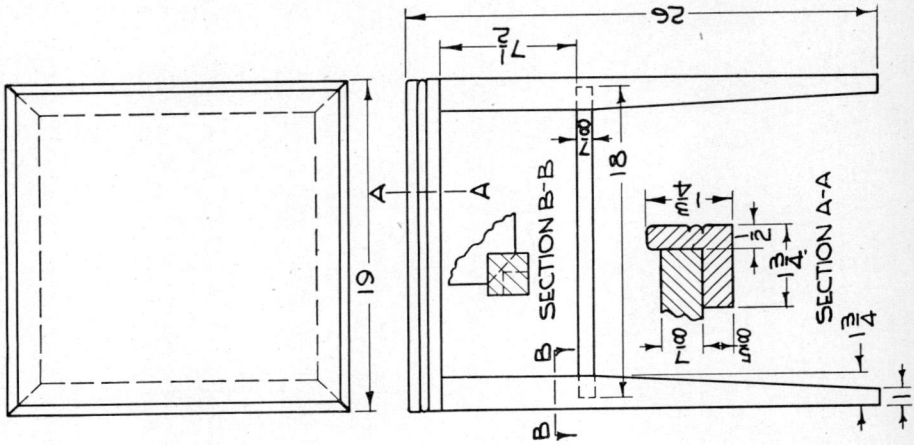

SECTION B-B

SECTION A-A

# "WELDTEX" FLOWER HOLDER

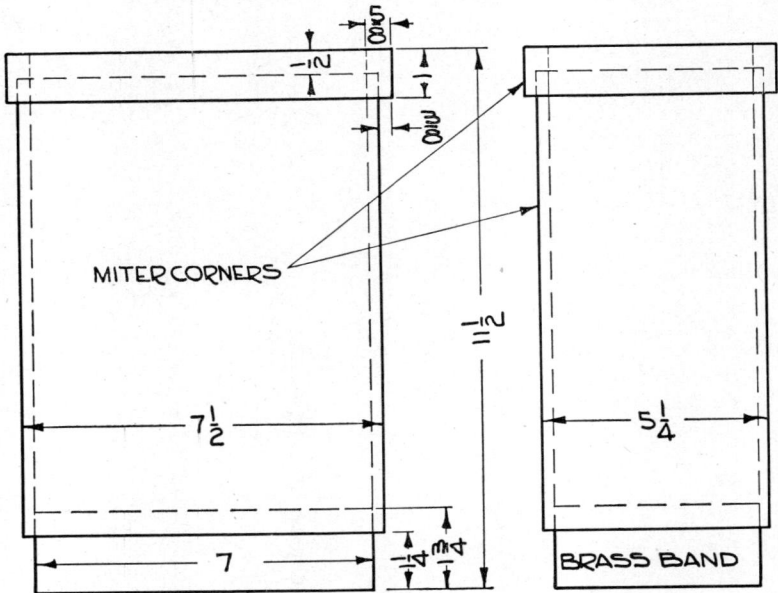

MITER CORNERS

BRASS BAND

## Pennsylvania Wall Box

434. **PENNSYLVANIA WALL BOX.** This is an authentic reproduction of an Early American Pennsylvania wall box. It was used for candles, spices and other household items. Make a full-size pattern of the back and side by using one-inch squares. The other pieces you will need include: (C) 1 piece 5¼ inch by 10½ inch, bottom; (D) 1 piece 2⅞ inch by 9 inch, front, and (E) 1 piece 5 inch by 9 inch, lid. DOUGLAS FIR PLYWOOD ASSOCIATION.

*Courting Mirror*

*Pennsylvania Wall Box*

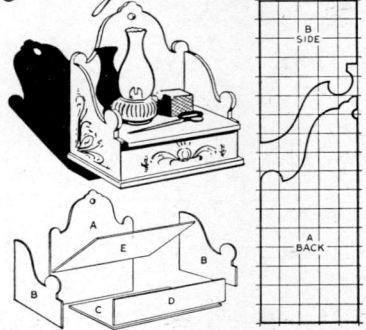

**435. PILGRIM CRADLE.** Here is a pattern for making a striking reproduction of an authentic pilgrim cradle. It can be used as a toy or as a letter holder or planter. Part (A) is a piece 6 inches by 15¼ inches. All other parts are determined by making a full-size pattern using one-inch squares. DOUGLAS FIR PLYWOOD ASSOCIATION.

**436. PILGRIM FOOTSTOOL.** This is a footstool just like the ones made by early craftsmen. You can make one for your own family or as a gift for a friend. Part (A) is a piece ¾ inch by 8 inches by 17 inches. The sides and ends are made by enlarging a pattern to full size using one-inch squares. DOUGLAS FIR PLYWOOD ASSOCIATION.

Pilgrim Cradle

Pilgrim Footstool

D-END    C-END
E-ROCKER-2 PIECES
B-SIDE-2 PIECES

C-END
2-PIECES
B-SIDE-2 PIECES

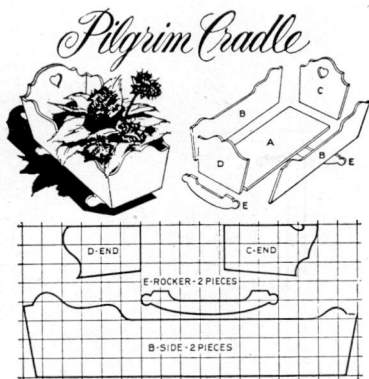

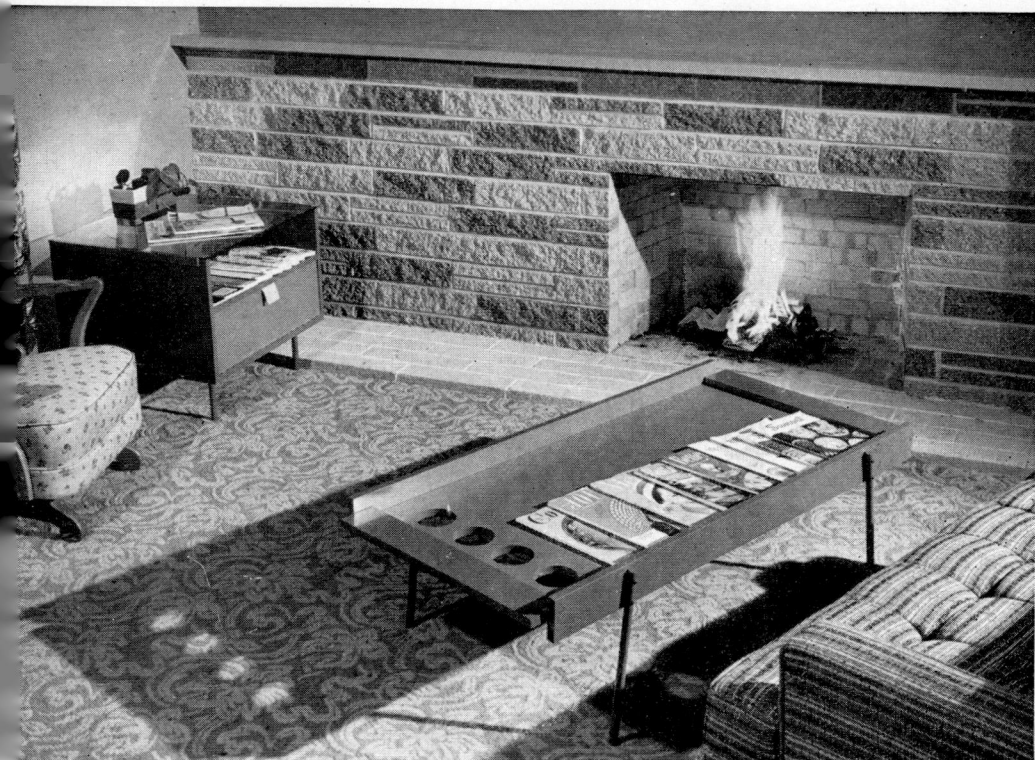

437. COFFEE TABLE. This idea illustrates how a very attractive project can be made by simple construction methods. The design is the most important feature. DOUGLAS FIR PLYWOOD ASSOCIATION.

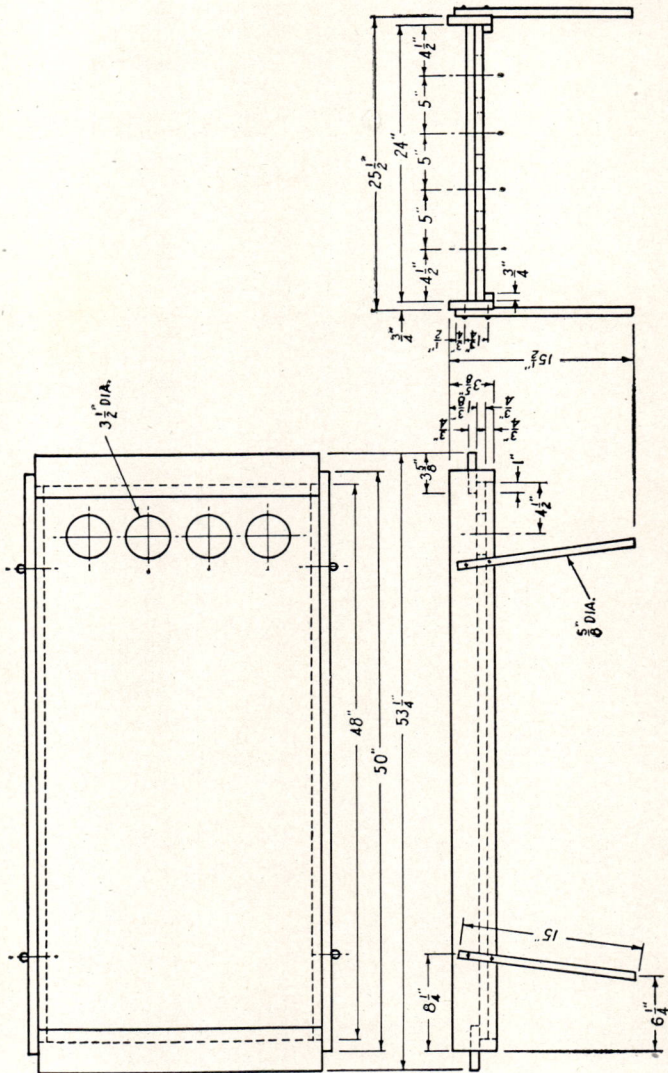

Coffee Table

## Section XIV

# Design—an Important Part of Woodworking

Every day you see and use things that have been designed. Your home, the furniture in it, cars and parts of cars, appliances, and even lead pencils and bars of soap have been developed from a design on paper. Some of these things are pleasing in design, some are not. Fig. 438.

*A design is the outline, shape, or plan* of something. There is no one who will agree completely with everyone else as to what is good or bad design. Everyone looks at things in a slightly different way and sees in them things he likes or dislikes. Here, for example, are designs of some modern chairs. Fig. 439. Not

438. DO YOU THINK THESE CANDLESTICKS are well designed? How about the salt and pepper shakers? Study each.

439. THESE CHAIRS LOOK A GOOD DEAL DIFFERENT from those most of us are used to seeing but are very comfortable. If you could try them, you'd know why they are well designed.

everyone will agree that they are *attractive*. They are, however, *well designed*.

The things that are made in woodworking can be divided, as far as design goes, into three groups:

1. *Trinkets or gadgets which are made to satisfy your own inter-ests and desires*. You may make a "dachshund-dog" tie rack or a "bowling-pin" pin-up lamp. You like it because you made it for your-

self or for someone in your family. You may have used your own idea completely in designing it. Oftentimes it will be something you may like for a few years and then discard or redesign and make over. It was fun to design and make this project even though the design might not have been the best. You can learn and improve each time you make something.

2. *Practical objects that must be some standard size if they are to be any good at all.* For instance, a basketball backboard must be 4 x 6 feet. A high hurdle must be a certain size also. These things might not always be ornamental to look at but they are well designed because they serve a certain purpose. *If you were to make these things a different size,* they would be poorly designed!

3. *Artistically designed objects* include furniture, accessories for the home, and the home itself. In furniture there are many different designs and styles. You should become well acquainted with the best designs of today. *One of the great mistakes made in the home and school workshop in building furniture is the making of something with no design or style.* You shouldn't waste your time building furniture that is out-of-date, like the "moderne" of 1930, or the plain, "production-line" kind of furniture often seen in public buildings. You

might say, "Yes, but I see some of these things in furniture stores." It is true that a certain percentage of the furniture made today is what we call "commercial" or "unstyled" furniture. This is the cheapest and poorest kind. You might as well buy it already made.

## What goes to make up design

1. First of all, an object is made up of *lines: straight, wavy, curved,* and *circular* lines. Fig. 440. You can see examples of this in many furniture pieces.

2. Lines make up *shapes,* some of which are square, rectangular, triangular, circular, and oval. Can

440. HOW MANY KINDS OF LINES can you see in this cabinet?

441. MOST OF THE COMMON SHAPES ARE SHOWN HERE. Point them out.

you identify some of these common shapes illustrated in the furniture in this section? Fig. 441.

3. *Mass* is the thickness and width, or bulk, or design, (shapes make up cubes, boxes, spheres, cones, and rods, all of which are part of the mass).

4. *Tone and texture* add to the surface design. In woodworking each different kind of wood has a texture. Wood is given additional texture by many processes. For example, the plywood used in the lamp, Fig. 442, has a grooved surface. Another kind of plywood has the surface sand blasted to bring the grain into high relief. All natural woods have tones and textures of their own. *Finishes* are used to bring them out and protect them.

5. *Color* is another element of design used to add interest. We can add color to any woodworking project by selected woods and using stains, paints and enamels.

## Why does a thing look attractive?

In designing anything there are certain principles that should be followed. This is especially true in

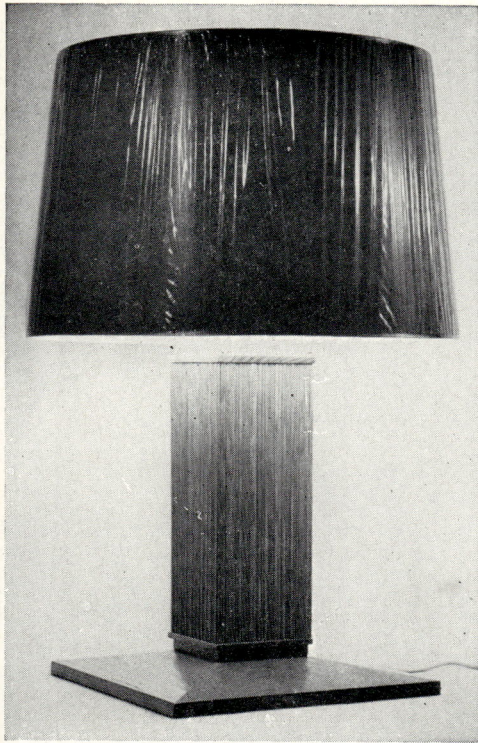

442. THIS LAMP IS MADE with a special kind of plywood. Notice the texture.*

good furniture design. Some of these principles include:

1. *Balance.* Exactly what it sounds like. It makes things look stable. People are balanced. They have an arm on either side, two eyes in balance, etc. We don't like to look at lopsided or unstable things.

There are two kinds of balance, formal and informal. *Formal balance* is present when both sides of

---

* Plans for this and several other project ideas found in this section can be obtained from: Atlas Press Company, N. Pitcher Street, Kalamazoo, Michigan.

443. THERE IS NO DOUBT that this is formal balance.

444. INFORMAL BALANCE is more difficult to recognize and appreciate.

an object are exactly equal. People are examples of formal balance. The lamps shown in Fig. 443 are in formal balance. *Informal balance* gives the impression of things being stable and balanced by the "grouping" of the parts. For instance, two *small* boys on one side of the teeter totter and one *large* boy on the other makes an example of informal balance. Fig. 444 illustrates informal balance by the clever placement of the lamp, flower arrangement, and picture.

2. *Proportion.* A well-proportioned piece is any object that looks well in relation to everything else in life. A dachshund dog doesn't look well proportioned because his legs are so short. We think a clown is funny if he has a great big nose and tremendous feet.

445. THESE PROJECTS ILLUSTRATE the 5-to-8 unit relationship.

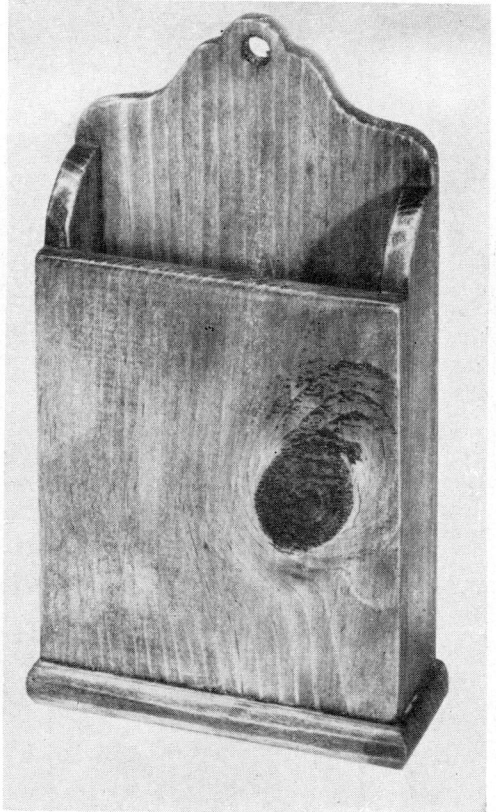

In designing many wood projects, we use a rectangular shape instead of a square one simply because it looks better proportioned to us. Fig. 445. Proportion in design is achieved when the thing is not too fat, not too tall, not too thin, or not too square, but just right to our eyes, and for the use we have for it. That is why large chairs should not have spindly legs. Babe Ruth was often referred to as "piano-legged" because his legs seemed too thin for his powerful body.

3. *Harmony or unity.* When the parts, colors, shapes, and textures of an object seem to get along well together, we say the object has harmony or unity. Fig. 446. Today, *many different materials are used in furniture* but they are blended together to be pleasing. A good example of the *lack of harmony* is putting rough welded legs on a

446. THIS MODERN TABLE is made of metal, wood and chemical composition. Don't they get along well together?

smooth, dainty table top. A piece of furniture with modern lines would not be used with Chippendale "ball-and-claw" legs.

4. *Emphasis.* An "accent" or special point of interest. Oftentimes

in furniture this will be a beautiful piece of hardware on a cabinet or desk, the fine finish itself, or an interesting grain in the wood of a door or drawer.

In deciding whether something is well designed, you should ask yourself the following questions:

1. Does the piece serve the purpose for which it is intended?

2. Does it perform its job efficiently? For example, if it is a chair, is it comfortable to sit in?

3. Is it within your ability to construct and maintain?

4. Is it pleasing to the eye? Fig. 447. (Here everyone won't agree.)

5. Does it satisfy you and other people that you want it to satisfy?

## Designing a woodworking project

After you have had some experience and know what you can

447. YOU CAN DESIGN AND MAKE a small snack container just as attractive as this.

448. A MODEL TRUCK made of wood.

449. THERE ARE STANDARD OPEN-INGS FOR DIFFERENT BIRDS. Here is a point to check in designing a project.

do with tools and machines, you may get a chance to design a project of your own. This is an interesting thing to do. It gives you an opportunity to be creative, which is not easy, but very fascinating.

To design and make a project in wood, follow these steps:

1. *Get the idea for the project you would like to build.* Maybe you have something in mind that you've always wanted to make. If not, popular magazines and books with projects in them are good sources of ideas. Another way to get ideas is to visit different stores selling furniture, hobby, or sporting goods. Some of the things you might like to build would include:

a. Toys, models, games, puzzles and other hobby equipment. Fig. 448.

450. A BEAUTIFUL LAMP you could turn on the wood lathe.

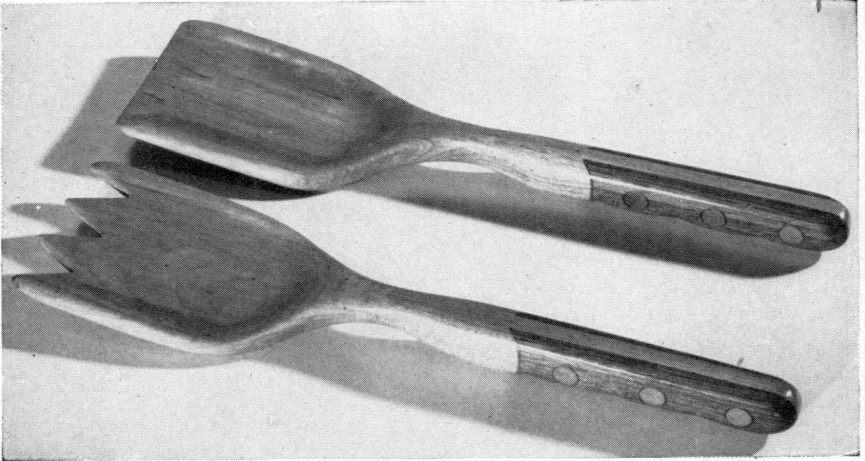

**451. A WOODEN SALAD SET** made by cutting and carving.

**452. A PICNIC TABLE** is a piece of sports equipment you could make.

453. THIS TABLE combines metal and wood.

b. Shelters for birds and pets. Fig. 449.

c. Things for your room or home such as lamps, bookends, shoe racks and tie racks. Fig. 450.

d. Kitchen items such as cutting boards, salt and pepper shakers, shelves. Fig. 451.

e. Sports equipment like boats and skis. Fig. 452.

f. Furniture including chairs, tables, chests, desks. Fig. 453.

2. After you've decided what to make, ask yourself, "What is the purpose of the object?" For example, if it's a book rack or book trough, it is supposed to hold books conveniently. How large are books?

454. REMEMBER, THE LOCATION OF THE DOWEL ROD is an important design feature of this shoe rack.

455. A GOOD EXAMPLE OF THE SAME TYPE OF TABLE in Traditional, Early American, and Modern designs.

What must be the depth of the shelf? If there is to be more than one shelf, what should the distance between the shelves be? If the project is a shoe rack, it must be able to hold shoes efficiently. Fig. 454. It is surprising to find many commercial objects that look nice but don't do the job properly. For instance, there is on the market a fancy shoe rack on which the distance from the wall to the rung that holds the heels of the shoes is too short. The shoes won't stay on it. If you design one, remember that it must be different for men's and women's shoes.

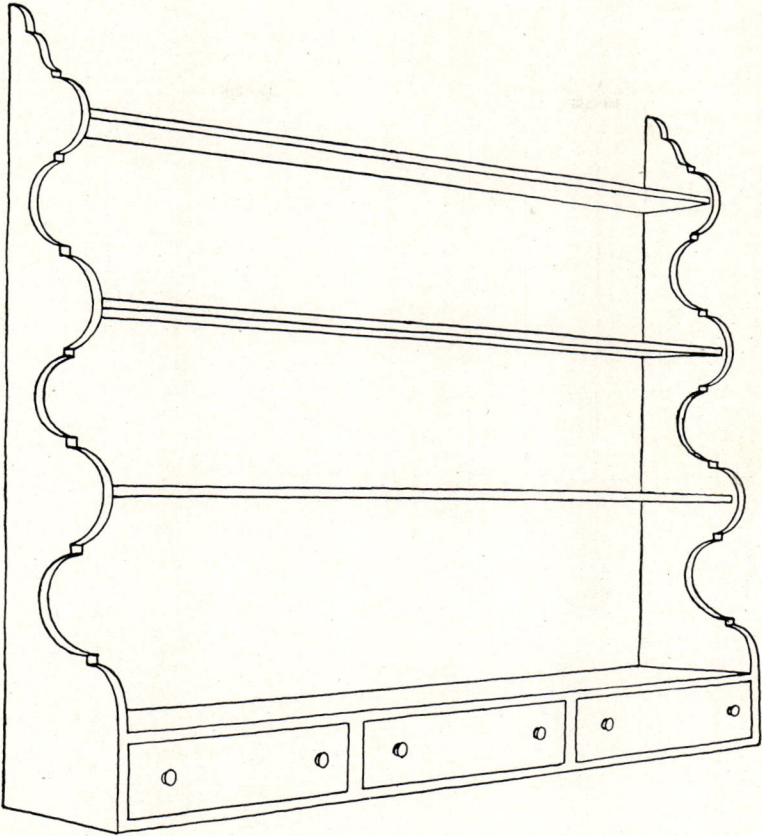

**A**

456. ALL THESE SKETCHES are good examples of Early American design. Any one would be a well-designed project. See pages 306, 307, and 308.

If you are designing a piece of furniture, there are certain standards, especially of height, that must be observed. See the Standard Sizes of Furniture, p. 307. Also, you must decide on the style of furniture that will best fit into your home or your room. Decide if the furniture piece is to be Traditional, Early American, or Modern. Fig. 455.

3. Now make a sketch of the thing you would like to build to see how it will look. Suppose you decide to make a wall rack for your mother. Here are several sketches of possible designs. Fig. 456. Let's suppose you decide on sketch A.

B

4. The next thing is to make a working drawing of the project. Fig. 457. This will be necessary to determine exactly the size of each part and how it is to be made.

5. *Making a model.* It is sometimes difficult to imagine what the finished article will look like with only sketches and drawings. It is helpful to see the three-dimensional appearance of the item by making a small model. This can be made of balsa wood or some other light material that cuts easily with a knife. The model does not have all the small details but will give the general appearance.

6. Now make a bill of materials. Here you need to keep in mind the sizes and kinds of woods and plywoods and the kinds of fasteners to be used. Fig. 458.

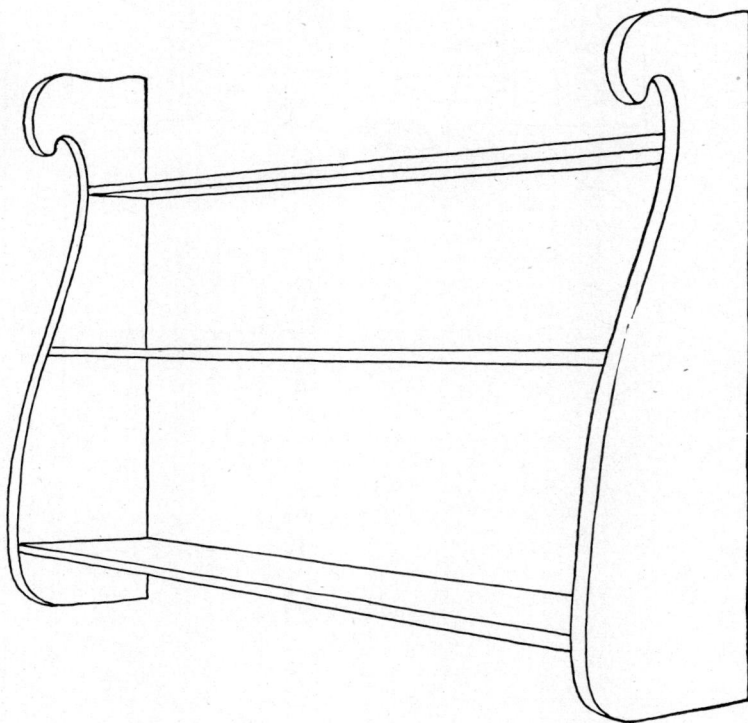

C

## STANDARD SIZES OF FURNITURE

| Item | Height | Item | Height |
|---|---|---|---|
| *Tables* | | *Cabinets* | |
| Coffee | 16″ to 18″ | Sectional | 30″ |
| Card | 29″ | China Storage | 54″ to 60″ |
| Game | 30″ | Kitchen | 30″ to 34″ |
| Writing | 30″ | | |
| Kitchen | 32″ | *Chests* | 32″ to 54″ |
| End | 30″ | *Bookcases* | 32″ to 82″ |
| Dining | 32″ | *Desks* | 30″ |
| | | | |
| *Chairs* | | | |
| Desk | 16½″ | | |
| Dining | 18″ | | |

D

7. You are now ready for the plans for building the project. You will decide on what is to be done first, then second, etc. Fig. 459A. Usually this will include *making a layout, cutting out the pieces and parts, shaping the parts, making the joints, fitting and assembling,* and *finishing.* You have already made a detailed plan of procedure when you planned your work for the first projects you made. See pages 27 and 28.

8. The next thing is to decide on what tools and machines you will need. Your experiences in wood-working will help you decide on how to use the equipment. For example, the jig saw is the ideal tool for cutting out the ends of the wall rack. Fig. 459B.

9. Now the building can be done. Here's the time when you can display your craftsmanship by doing a fine job on each part.

10. The last step in designing is to judge the project in several ways. Fig. 459C. You will decide if the job was done well enough so you could answer "yes" to all the questions found on page 251, "Rating" a project.

5/8 RADIUS

1" SQUARES

5/8"

SHELF
1/2" X 4 X 29 1/4

7/8"R

1 5/16"R

6"

SHELF
1/2" X 5 3/4" X 29 1/4"

1 13/16"R

6 3/4"

SHELF
1/2" X 6 5/8" X 29 1/4"

8"

SHELF
1/2" X 7 3/4" X 29 1/4"

3"

DRAWER
STOP

7"

2 1/2"

9 1/4"

DADO 1/2" WIDE
X 1/4" DEEP

RABBET 1/2" WIDE
X 1/4" DEEP

1 1/8"R

1 3/4"R

1 3/8"R

1 7/8"R

1 3/4"R

1 1/2"R

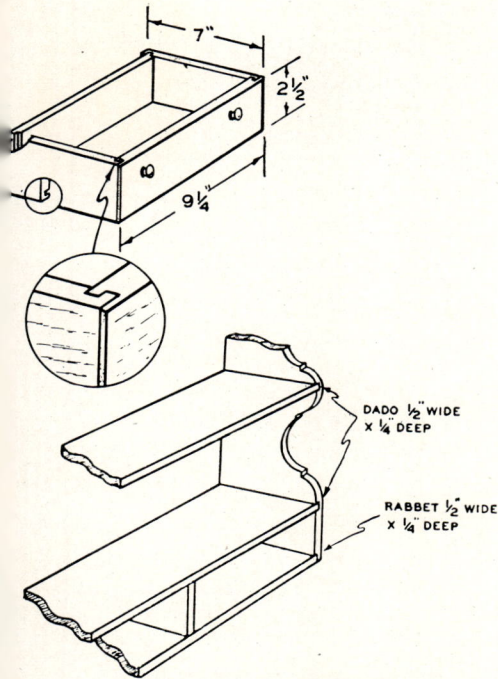

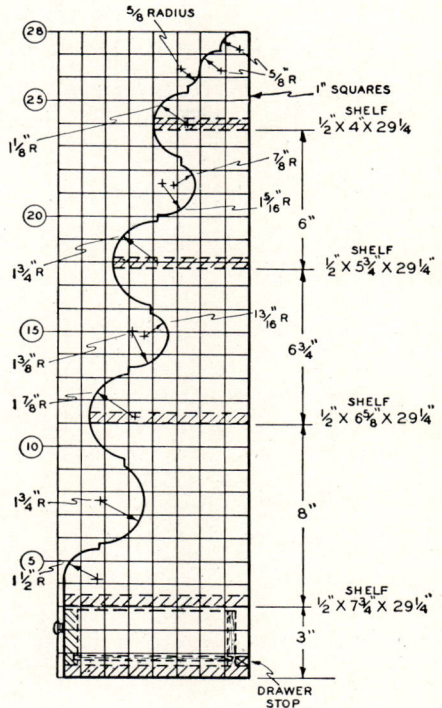

457. A WORKING DRAWING OF
SKETCH A, p. 305.

# BILL OF MATERIALS

| No. of Pieces | Part Name | Thickness | Width | Length | Wood |
|---|---|---|---|---|---|
| 2 | Ends | 1/2″ | 7 3/4″ | 28″ | Knotty Pine |
| 1 | Shelf | 1/2″ | 4″ | 29 1/4″ | Knotty Pine |
| 1 | Shelf | 1/2″ | 5 3/4″ | 29 1/4″ | Knotty Pine |
| 1 | Shelf | 1/2″ | 6 5/8″ | 29 1/4″ | Knotty Pine |
| 2 | Shelves | 1/2″ | 7 3/4″ | 29 1/4″ | Knotty Pine |
| 2 | Drawer Separators | 1/2″ | 2 1/2″ | 7 3/4″ | Knotty Pine |
| 3 | Drawer Fronts | 1/2″ | 2 1/2″ | 9 1/4″ | Knotty Pine |
| 6 | Drawer Sides | 3/8″ | 2 1/2″ | 7″ | Clear Pine |
| 3 | Drawer Backs | 3/8″ | 2 1/2″ | 8 7/8″ | Clear Pine |
| 3 | Drawer Bottoms | 1/4″ | 6 1/4″ | 8 3/4″ | Fir Plywood |
| 6 | Drawer Stops | 1/2″ | 1/2″ | 1″ | |
| 1 | Hardwood Dowel | 1/4″ | | 36″ | |
| 6 | Hardwood Knobs | 3/4″ | | | |

IMPORTANT: All dimensions listed above, except for length of dowel, etc., *finished* size.

458. BILL OF MATERIALS FOR THE WALL RACK.

# WORKING A PLAN

1. Lay out pattern of the ends on paper and trace on wood. Cut out on a jig saw.

2. Cut the dadoes for the shelves and the rabbet for the bottom board.

3. Saw the shelves and bottom board.

4. Dowel and glue the shelves and bottom in place. Before the glue sets be sure the entire structure is square.

5. Make drawer separators; install dowels and glue in place.

6. Cut the drawer fronts and fit into each opening. Then complete the drawers, using the joints suggested in the detailed drawing—or make a simple rabbet joint to fasten the sides and front, and a dado joint to fasten the sides and back. Glue drawer stops in place so the drawer fronts will be flush.

7. Sand edges to give a worn appearance.

8. Apply an antique pine finish, and add knobs.

459A. PLAN OF PROCEDURE FOR THE WALL RACK.

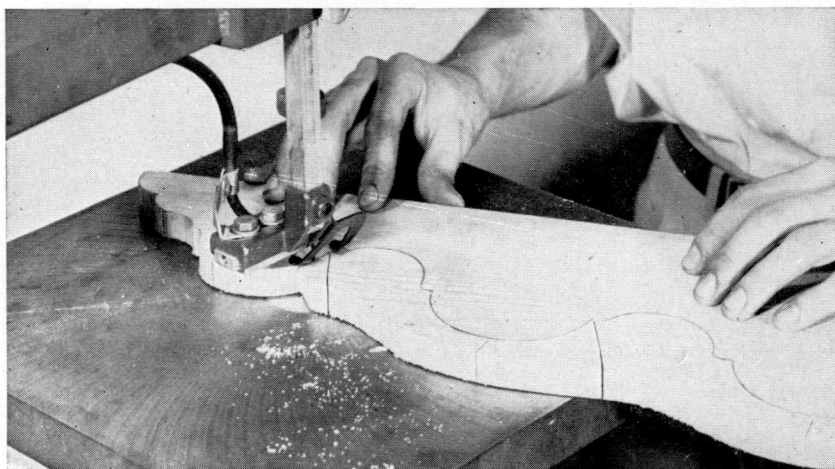

459B. CUTTING OUT AN END on the jig saw.

459C. THE FINISHED PROJECT. Isn't it a beauty?

## Project Plans and Supplies

A. Douglas Fir Plywood Association, Tacoma, Washington.

B. Woman's Day Workshop, 19 West 44th Street, New York 36, New York.

C. The George S. Thompson Corporation, 509 Mission St., South Pasadena, California.

D. Western Wood Manufacturing Company, Portland, Oregon, or regional dealer.

E. Masonite Corporation, 111 West Washington St., Chicago 2, Illinois.

F. Skil Corporation, Chicago 30, Illinois.

# Section XV

# Simple Upholstery

WHILE upholstery can be complicated, there are several simple methods that the beginner can follow. Of the four basic types, the first three are done by older methods. (1) The simplest is a *pad seat* (made without springs) that fits into or on the completed chair. Dining-room chairs may have pad seats. Fig. 460. (2) The next type is the *tight spring seat* found mostly in living-room chairs. A webbing foundation supports the springs. (3) Next is the *overstuffed seat and back* used in large chairs and sofas. In this type there are springs in both the seat and back. (4) The last type is the most modern: *no-sag springs with foam rubber* or rubberized hair.

## MATERIALS

Some upholstery materials must be ordered from a special supply house. Others can be found in hardware and department stores. Before starting a project, it is well to see if needed materials are easy to find in your community.

*Upholstery tacks* are flathead tacks used for holding materials in place. The larger sizes (12 or 14 ounce, about ¾ inch long) are needed for tacking webbing; the smaller (6 or 8 ounce, about ½ inch long) are used for fastening the coverings. The *gimp tack* is a small roundhead used wherever the head is meant to show.

*Webbing* is made from jute fiber; It is used as the foundation. The 3½-inch width is usually specified.

460

312

*Burlap* is used as a covering over webbing, springs, and stuffing. An 8- to 10-ounce (per square foot) weight in 40-inch widths is best.

*Stuffing* means a variety of materials used for filling. Among the most common are *curled animal hair, Spanish moss,* a plant fiber, *tow* made from the stalks of flax plants, and *shredded foam rubber.*

*Rubberized hair* is a light, elastic material made from curled hair and rubber. It comes in pads of standard thickness from ¾ inch to 2½ inches.

*Foam rubber* is made from liquid latex. *Slab stock* comes in thicknesses of ½, ¾, 1 inch, etc. It is possible to buy *cored utility stock* that has molded cylindrical openings in it. You can also buy fully *molded cushions* in many different sizes and shapes. *Rubber cement* is used to fasten tacking tape to foam rubber.

*Tacking tape* is a muslin cloth tape used to fasten the foam rubber to the base.

*Final covers* can be of fabric, plastic material, or leather.

*Other materials* include coil springs and sewing twine, for more extensive work.

## COMMON TOOLS

1. An *upholsterer's hammer* for extensive work in upholstery. One head should be magnetized for holding tacks. For simple jobs, a small claw hammer is satisfactory.

2. A *webbing stretcher* (about 6 inches long) for stretching the webbing before tacking it down.

3. *Trimmer's shears* for cutting foam rubber, rubberized hair, and fabrics.

4. A *stuffing regulator* — a 10-inch metal pin with one sharp and one blunt end. It is used to even out irregularities under temporary coverings. An *ice pick* makes a good substitute.

## MAKING A PAD SEAT

Some of the more common ways of making a pad seat are as follows:

### Making a Pad Seat with a Solid Base and Foam Rubber.

1. Cut a piece of ¼- to ½-inch fir plywood to the required shape for the base. Drill several small holes distributed over the wood for air venting.

2. Select a piece of foam rubber about 1-inch thick.

3. Decide on the kind of edging you want on the seat.

a. *For a cushioned edge.* Cut the foam rubber to shape with shears, allowing about ¼ inch extra all around, plus an extra ½ inch on the cushion edge or edges. Apply rubber cement to about half the width of the tacking tape and 1 inch along the upper edge of the foam rubber. Cement the tape to the smooth top of the stock, about 1 inch from the edge. Tuck the bottom edge of the cushion under

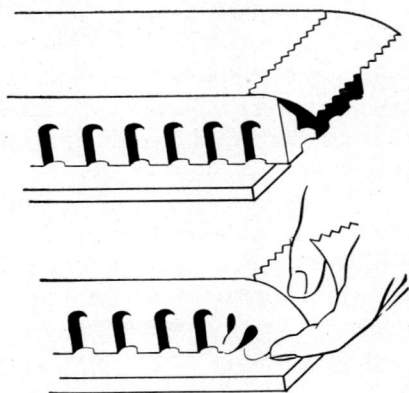

461. CUSHIONED edge.

so that its thickness is held flat against the base. Fig. 461. Keep the tape taut to avoid wrinkling. Tack the tape on the underside with upholstery tacks.

b. *For a feathered edge.* Cut the stock about ¼ inch oversize all around. Cement the tacking tape to the smooth top side about 1 inch from the edge. Bevel the lower edge as shown in Fig. 462. Draw the tape down so that the beveled edge is held flat against the base; tack it in place.

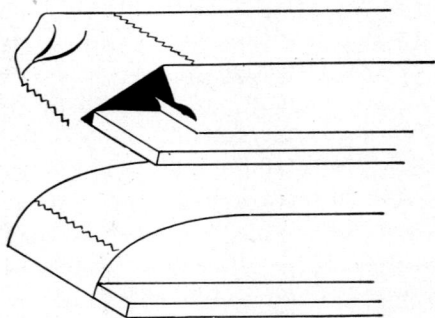

462. FEATHERED edge.

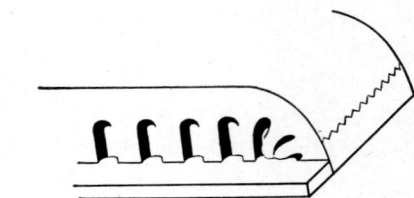

c. *For a square edge.* Cut the rubber, allowing the usual ¼-inch addition all around. Cement the tape flat against the edge of the material and tack the overhang to the base.

4. Cover the foam rubber with a final cover.

## Making a Slip Pad Seat with Webbed Base and Upholstery Cotton.

1. Make an open frame of four pieces of ¾-inch stock that will fit into the main frame of the chair or bench. The corner can be made with dowel joints (Fig. 190), end-lap joints (Fig. 212), or open mortise-and-tenon joints (Fig. 226). Round the upper edge so it won't cut the upholstery fabric.

2. Fold the end of the webbing under about 1¼ inch and tack about ½ inch from the outside of the frame. Fig. 463. The tacks are staggered to keep the wood from splintering. Stretch the webbing tightly over the frame as shown in Fig. 464, and tack it on the other side of the frame. Cut the webbing about 1¼ inch beyond the frame, fold over and tack down again.

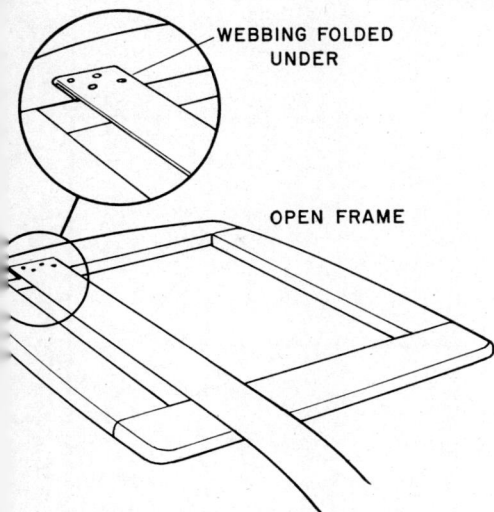

WEBBING FOLDED UNDER

OPEN FRAME

463. TURN THE LOOSE END OF the webbing under and tack in place.

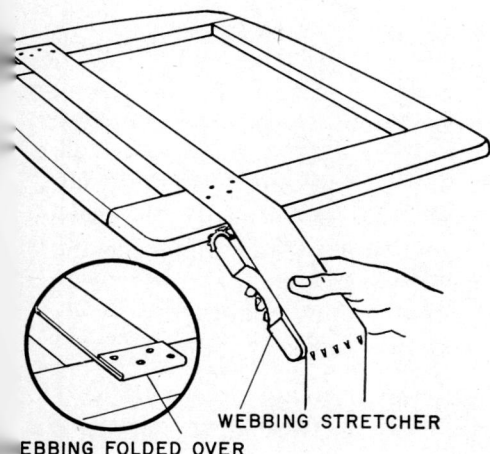

WEBBING STRETCHER

EBBING FOLDED OVER

464. STRETCH THE WEBBING and tack to the other side.

465. WEBBING COMPLETED. Burlap must be fastened over the webbing.

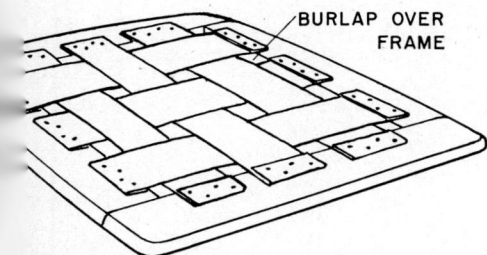

BURLAP OVER FRAME

Fig. 465. Place the next piece of webbing about 1½ to 2 inches away. Space the webbing so the piece will cover the opening. Then weave the other pieces through in the other direction.

3. Tack a piece of burlap over the webbing, making sure that it is not drawn tightly. If tacked too tightly, the cloth will tear when in use.

4. Cut a piece of upholstery cotton about 2 inches smaller in all directions than the frame. Center this over the burlap.

5. Cut another piece of cotton about ½ inch larger in all directions than the frame. Center this over the first piece.

6. Cut a piece of final covering that is about 2 inches larger in all directions than the frame. Place the cover material with the good side down on the bench. Lay the seat face down and start tacking at the center of each side. Fig. 466. Work toward the corners. Tack the corners as shown in Fig 467.

## Making a Slip Pad Seat with a Webbed Base and Stuffing.

1. Make an open frame and cover with webbing and burlap.

2. Place stuffing of hair or moss over the burlap. Make sure the material is well separated and free of foreign matter such as sticks. Distribute handfuls of the stuffing over the base, working it together with your fingers. Cover to a depth

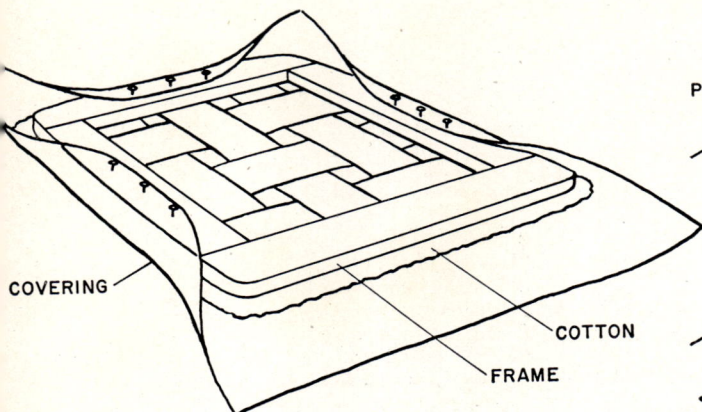

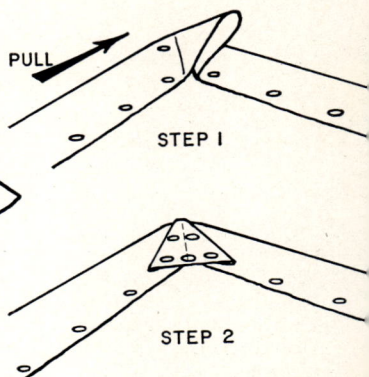

466. TWO LAYERS OF COTTON are in place and the cover is then tacked on.

467. TACK THE SHARP CORNERS carefully.

of about 2 inches. (A rubberized hair pad 1-inch thick, cut to size, can be used instead of the stuffing.)

3. Cut a piece of burlap or muslin about 2 inches larger in all directions than the frame. Lay the cloth over the stuffing and hold it in place as you turn the entire unit over.

468. A CHAIR FRAME with a foundation of no-sag springs.

4. Start tacking at the center of each side and work toward the corners. Drive the tacks only a little way into the wood so you can remove them if necessary to tighten the cover. Check to see that the stuffing is distributed evenly. If not, poke a *regulator* through the cloth to move some of the stuffing around.

5. Place a layer of cotton over the cloth and then apply final cover material.

## Making a Spring Seat with No-Sag Springs and Foam Rubber.

An excellent upholstered spring seat or back can be made quite easily with no-sag springs. Fig. 468. Complete directions for ordering and installing these springs are available from the manufacturer, along with complete kits.*

---

* No-Sag Spring Company, Detroit, Michigan.

# Index